Occupational Health and Safety

Occupational Health and Safety

James Montgomery

Humber College

—

Monica Belcourt, Series Editor

Nelson Canada

I(T)P An International Thomson Publishing Company

Toronto • Albany • Bonn • Boston • Cincinnati • Detroit • London • Madrid • Melbourne
Mexico City • New York • Pacific Grove • Paris • San Francisco • Singapore • Tokyo • Washington

I(T)P™
International Thomson Publishing
The ITP logo is a trademark under licence

Published in 1996 by
Nelson Canada
A division of Thomson Canada Limited
1120 Birchmount Road
Scarborough, Ontario M1K 5G4

Canadian Cataloguing in Publication Data
Montgomery, James, date
   Occupational health and safety

(Nelson Canada series in human resources management)
Includes bibliographical references and index.
ISBN 0-17-604264-4

1. Industrial hygiene. 2. Industrial safety.
I. Title. II. Series.

HD7261.M65 1996   363.11   C96-930308-4

Publisher	Jacqueline Wood
Senior Editor	Rosalyn Steiner
Project Coordinator	Edward Ikeda
Senior Production Coordinator	Carol Tong
Art Director	Liz Harasymczuk
Interior Design	Holly Fisher
Cover Design	Liz Harasymczuk
Lead Composition Analyst	Zenaida Diores
Input Operator	June Reynolds

Printed and bound in Canada

   3 4 (BBM) 99 98

This book is dedicated to three
generous people,
Monica Belcourt, my mentor,
Edward Ikeda, my editor, and
Marion Montgomery, ma femme,
for their patience, understanding,
assistance, and encouragement.

Brief Contents

Contents

About the Series

There is one asset within organizations that provides the competitive advantage for many organizations: human resources. While the purchase of facilities and the adoption of technology are considered major long-term decisions, and accorded the appropriate time and money, senior executives do not give the same consideration to the investment in human resources. Yet, many studies in human capital suggest that investments in human resources do provide a good return, and unlike other resources, are renewable. Because knowledge about the effective management of an organization's employees is critical, Nelson Canada is publishing a series of texts dedicated to those managers and human resource professionals who are responsible for the productivity and satisfaction of employees.

The texts in the *Nelson Canada Series in Human Resources Management* include *Managing Performance Through Training and Development, Occupational Health and Safety, Human Resources Management Systems, Staffing, Compensation Management,* and *Human Resources Planning.*

The *Nelson Canada Series in Human Resources Management* represents a significant development in the field of HR for many reasons. Each book in the series (except for *Compensation Management*) is the first Canadian text in the functional area. Human resource practitioners in Canada must work with Canadian laws, Canadian statistics, Canadian policies, and, Canadian values. This series serves their needs. It also represents the first time that students and practitioners have access to a standardized guide to the management of many HR functional areas. This one-stop resource will prove useful to anyone involved with the effective management of people.

The publication of this series signals that the HR field has advanced to the stage where theory and applied research guide practice. Because the field is still emerging, and new tools and methods are being invented, theory and research are discussed along with common practices used by Canadian HR professionals. The books in the series present the best and most current research in the functional areas of HR. This research is supplemented with examples of successful practices used by Canadian companies who are leaders in the HR area. Each text identifies the process of managing and implementing effective strategies, thus serving as an introduction to the functional area for the new student of HR and as a validation manual for the more experienced HR practitioner. Cases, exercises, discussion questions, and references contained at the end of each chapter provide opportunities for further discussion and analysis.

As you read these texts, I hope you share my excitement at being involved in the development of an important profession, one that affects daily interactions with our own employees as well as those in organizations with whom we conduct business.

Monica Belcourt
SERIES EDITOR
MARCH 1996

Preface

The field of occupational health and safety (OHS) is becoming increasingly important because of the rising costs associated with injuries and illnesses, and, more important, the public's decreasing tolerance for work-related hazards. As employees increasingly ask for, and receive, compensation for disorders such as repetitive-strain injury, the costs to organizations and society escalate, resulting in a need to implement effective OHS policies and programs.

The field of occupational health and safety incorporates information and research from dozens of other fields including chemistry, physics, engineering, biology, medicine, physiotherapy, psychology, sociology, health care, and ergonomics. The general practitioner cannot be expected to be an expert in every field. This text is intended, therefore, to give the manager or human resource professional a basic understanding of the elements that combine to create an organizational health and safety program.

Health and safety information is generally presented in a nontechnical manner. Thus the text does not cover, for example, a highly technical topic such as constant air pump, but it does explain the requirement for calibration that is necessary for a legitimate air sampling study. There are specialists available who can be hired or contracted, as required, to perform many of the more complicated analyses that may have to be performed from time to time. This book is designed to help the practitioner identify the problem and, most important, understand and deal with the results of experts' studies.

The text begins with an overview of health and safety legislation (Chapter 2) and workers' compensation (Chapter 3). An understanding of the legally required duties and obligations of employers is essential to the implementation of an effective OHS program. Also of critical importance to the program is risk management, which involves hazard identification (Chapter 4), hazard control (Chapter5), accident investigation (Chapter 6), and emergency preparedness (Chapter 7). The implementation of programs to identify, evaluate, and control hazards is the most important step in the reduction of occupational injuries and illnesses.

The text next deals with chemical and biological agents (Chapter 8), physical agents (Chapter 9), the control of physical injuries through ergonomics (Chapter 10), occupational stress (Chapter 11), and sector-specific hazards (Chapter 12). The components of an effective OHS program are delineated in Chapter 13, while Chapter 14 draws upon social psychological principles in discussing strategies for reducing risk–taking behaviour among employees. The final chapter identifies emerging trends and issues in the field of occupational health and safety. Exercises and supporting references are provided at the end of each chapter.

Acknowledgments

I wish to acknowldege several individuals who helped to bring this book to fruition. Thanks to Mary Smith for writing Chapters 2 and 13, and most of Chapter 15; to Paul Nolis for contributing Chapter 3; and to Gerry Goldberg and Kim Ankers for providing Chapters 11 and 14 as well as the unique perspective on commitment found in Chapter 15. I also wish to thank George Pappas, director of education of the Industrial Accident Prevention Association of Ontario for preparing the Appendixes.

I am grateful to Renzo Dalla Via and Wayne Vollick for acting as sounding boards for some of the ideas and approaches used in this text and to my students at York University for "debugging" parts of the material. The manuscript of this work was reviewed at various stages of its development by a great number of my peers across Canada, and I wish to thank those who shared their insights and their constructive criticism. Among them are Renzo Dalla Via, Industrial Accident Prevention Association and Seneca College; Jerry Mendek, Confederation College; Carol Eamer, Southern Alberta Institute of Technology and Department of Labour, Occupational Health and Safety Services, Government of Alberta; Diane White, Seneca College; Lars Larsson, British Columbia Institute of Technology; George Pappas, Industrial Accident Prevention Association of Ontario; Jack O'Hara, Sir Sandford Fleming College; and Glen Towner, Centennial College. Finally, I wish to thank Monica Belcourt and Edward Ikeda, who are responsible for the HRM Series of which this book is a part.

James Montgomery
HUMBER COLLEGE, TORONTO
March 1996

Introduction

◆ ◆ ◆

INTRODUCTION

Occupational health and safety issues affect a wide range of players, from employees and their families, to all those who contribute to the insurance and compensation systems that are designed to assist and rehabilitate, to the workplace itself. Safety concerns are no longer limited to industrial-sector workers who face such hazards as mine explosions and transportation accidents. Employees in white-collar environments are increasingly anxious about repetitive-strain injuries and sick-building syndrome. The rising costs associated with work-related injuries and illnesses and, more importantly, the public's decreasing tolerance for work-related hazards, underlie the need to understand and implement effective occupational health and safety policies and programs.

Occupational health and safety (OHS) can be defined as the identification, evaluation, and control of hazards associated with the work environment. These hazards range from chemical, biological, and physical agents to psychosocial disorders such as stress. The goal of an organization's health and safety program is to reduce occupational injuries and illnesses. An *occupational injury* is any cut, fracture, sprain, or amputation resulting from a workplace accident. An *occupational illness* is any abnormal condition or disorder caused by exposure to environmental factors associated with employment.

◆ ◆ ◆

THE IMPORTANCE OF HEALTH AND SAFETY

Effective OHS programs have important and far-ranging benefits for both employers and employees. Employers and the general public should care about occupational health and safety for economic, legal, and moral reasons.

ECONOMIC CONSIDERATIONS

The example given in Box 1.1 shows some of the economic costs, both direct and indirect, that can result from a work-related injury.

BOX 1.1

A manufacturer of fibreglass cargo covers for campers and pickup trucks requires several skilled operators for the purpose of spraying a mixture of finely chopped fibreglass fibres and resins over the inside surface of the moulds. The sprayers are highly skilled workers. Their skill is the ability to spray a uniform layer of glass and resin approximately $\frac{3}{16}$ of an inch over the complete surface. Any thickness variations can add weight and cost to the product.

   While reaching to spray an inside edge, André twisted his ankle. He was deemed unable to work for six weeks. The Workers' Compensation Board covered his lost time and medical expenses. These costs were ultimately reimbursed by his company through an assessment. Since no trained worker was available to replace André, the company had to pay the two other operators overtime. The direct costs of André's injury were wages ($5000), overtime payments ($4000), and the Workers' Compensation Assessment. The indirect costs included André's personal suffering and potential loss of income from any long-term effects of the injury, as well as the stress imposed on the two operators by the extra workload.

The costs illustrated in this one example are repeated hourly across the country. In 1993, 423,000 workers were injured on the job. A work injury resulting in lost time happens every 15 seconds in Canada (Statistics Canada, 1994). The consequence is 15 million lost workdays (Milkovich et al., 1994), many times the amount lost to strikes and lockouts (Reasons, 1994). The cost is $4 billion a year in compensation payments alone, and $8–10 billion if indirect costs are included (Galt, 1991; Milkovich, 1994). The Economic Council of Canada estimates that indirect costs could range from two to ten times the direct costs.

Safety problems cost every man, woman, and child in Canada hundreds of dollars annually, based on the statistical direct and indirect costs of occupational injuries. But these figures represent costs associated with an injury once it has occurred. Other costs to the employer include work stoppages and strikes due to unsafe working conditions. In 1987, 1000 employees at McDonnell Douglas Canada refused to work after the Ontario Ministry of Labour cited the company for hundreds of infractions of the province's Occupational Health and Safety Act. Labour disputes involving such safety issues as pollutant levels, safety equipment, and first-aid facilities result in thousands of lost days of worker production. Incalculable costs include those associated with employees who quit or refuse to work in companies because of safety or health concerns.

Another indirect cost to companies is that of negative publicity when a death, accident, or serious health problem becomes public. The Occidental Chemical Company in California had a public-relations nightmare to cope with when the media learned that one of its chemicals caused sterility in the workers handling the compound. Managers who are committed to safety can turn adverse publicity into a marketing and recruitment advantage by advertising their concerns for employee safety.

Employers who are *not* concerned about the health and safety of their employees affect other employers and tax-paying citizens. Workers' compensation rates are determined by industry sector. A negligent employer forces the others in the sector to pay higher rates. These costs are significant. The 12 workers' compensation boards across Canada pay out $3 billion annually (Milkovich et al., 1994). The Alberta board estimates that a totally disabled young worker with children will receive $7 million in payments until age 72 (ibid). Unsafe working conditions cause insurance premiums to escalate and health expenditures to increase. For some employers, such as those in logging businesses, annual premiums are as much as $4000 per employee (ibid).

Industry estimates indicate that up to 90 percent of safety-related changes can result in positive paybacks (Kaminiskij, 1994). For example, the town of Markham, Ontario reported that its Workers' Compensation Board costs will be lowered by 15 percent when its New Experimental Experience Rating (NEER) program begins. Therefore, organizations have an economic interest in lowering the number of accidents and providing a safe working environment.

LEGAL CONSIDERATIONS

Every worker has the legal right to safe working conditions under occupational health and safety acts. The Ontario Occupational Health and Safety Act (section 25 (2) (h)) requires an employer "to take every precaution reasonable in the circumstances for the protection of a worker." The legal term for this requirement is *due diligence*.

From a legal perspective, due diligence is considered to be "such a measure of prudence, activity, or assiduity, as is properly to be expected from, and ordinarily exercised by, a reasonable and prudent person under the particular circumstances, not measured by any absolute standard, but depending on the relative facts of the special case" (Turner, 1995). In other words, due diligence is a standard of conduct measured by what could be expected of a reasonable person in the same circumstances. Due diligence does not require a business to prevent all unsafe conditions or acts, but it does require them to take precautions to prevent accidents that can reasonably be anticipated (Stammer, 1994).

Similarly, a worker is required to work in compliance with health and safety legislation. This legislation is discussed at length in Chapter 2.

MORAL CONSIDERATIONS

In 1993, 758 Canadian workers lost their lives in work-related illnesses and accidents, and another 423,000 reported disabling injuries (Statistics Canada, 1994). The actual figures could be even higher given the fact that most statistics of this nature are compiled by workers' compensation boards, and about one-quarter of the workforce is not covered by OHS legislation. A U.S. study suggested that the number of reported injuries may represent only one-tenth of actual injuries (Gordon et al., 1971).

Employers have a moral obligation to employees and their families to provide the safest working environment possible. Similarly, workers have a moral responsibility to learn about safety and health, to follow recommended workplace practices, and to be alert and responsible. A safe workplace will result in higher morale, lower turnover, and increased job satisfaction. Employees anxious about their own safety or traumatized by the death of a co-worker will not perform to the best of their abilities.

◆ ◆ ◆

HISTORY OF OCCUPATIONAL HEALTH AND SAFETY

Documented cases of work-related illnesses go back as far as ancient Egypt when stone masons and potters experienced respiratory problems. While the Egyptians did not understand the medical reasons for the physiological responses to the chemicals involved, they were able to describe silicosis and various types of pneumoconioses.

As societies became more technologically advanced, more cases of copper-induced dermatoses (skin diseases), vomiting, and hepatic (liver) degeneration began to occur. Labourers who worked with iron and the various alloying operations risked not only such symptoms as high fever, coughing, and headache, but also diseases like lung cancer (Janson, 1985).

Lewis Carroll identified the neurotoxic effects of mercury in tanning when he introduced the Mad Hatter to Alice in Wonderland. Some of the toxic effects of chronic exposure to mercury are loss of memory, tremors of the extremities, and manic-depressive psychosis (Key et al., 1977). The 19th-century architect A.W.N. Pugin, one of the designers of Britain's Houses of Parliament, died insane in his late 30s of systemic poisoning—the result of mercury compounds prescribed by his doctor.

The chimney sweeps of Victorian England and Europe were at risk of developing scrotal cancer as a result of their exposure to soot deposits. Miners were susceptible to such conditions as trench foot, silicosis, and coal workers' pneumoconiosis (lung lesions caused by coal-dust inhalation).

With the advent of the Industrial Revolution, machinists and others working in the new industries became exposed to oils used for lubrication during the cutting and removal of metal. These oils, in conjunction with poor personal hygiene practices, resulted in serious acne conditions and skin melanomas. When the spinning and weaving industries became mechanized, the resultant dusts from hemp and flax caused byssinosis (brown lung).

The English Factories Acts of 1833 were the first pieces of legislation to demonstrate concern for the health of the worker. Today, responsibility for occupational health and safety is divided among many players or stakeholders. Governments, employers and employees, organized labour, and the media all have important roles to play in ensuring safe work environments.

◆ ◆ ◆
THE STAKEHOLDERS

GOVERNMENTS

Government interest in the health and safety of workers was first demonstrated by the passing of the Chimney Sweepers Act of 1788 and subsequent English Factory Acts of 1833. In the United States, the first federal compensation act affecting certain civil employees was passed in 1908. The first state compensation laws were passed in 1919; by 1948, all the states were covered by compensation legislation. While compensation laws in the United States do not provide across-the-board coverage, they do allow the right to sue.

In Canada, Ontario was the first province to enact compensation legislation with the passage of the Workmen's Compensation Act in 1914. This legislation provided lost-time wages to almost every worker, thereby removing the right of workers to sue their employers. Following World War I, the federal and provincial governments began to enact legislation designed to protect the worker. The two main goals of this legislation have been (1) to ensure that the injured worker receives compensation, and that the employer accepts liability; and (2) to prevent accidents and illness through the establishment of safe work environments.

As a result of health and safety legislation, the number of workplace accidents has declined. Despite the addition of two million workers to the Canadian workforce between 1985 and 1993, the number of accidents dropped from 554,793 to 423,184 in the same period (Statistics Canada, 1994).

In addition to their legislative function, governments solicit or conduct research on health and safety issues and disseminate information. Ontario, Nova Scotia, and British Columbia are world leaders in the development of chemical exposure standards that are as low as reasonably attainable (ALARA) based on hard scientific evidence. The federal government created the Canadian Centre for Occupational Health and Safety (CCOHS) as a vital health and safety research and resource organization. CCOHS accesses a number of databases from around the world, in addition to creating and maintaining its own comprehensive database. The goal of this organization is to provide health and safety information to any worker who requests it.

One important contribution of CCOHS has been the creation of the CCINFO-DISC. This program's vast database contains information on chemicals, material safety data sheets (MSDS), toxicological effects of chemicals and biological agents, and health and safety legislation for all jurisdictions in Canada. CCOHS also produces a wide variety of safety Infograms and other publications.

EMPLOYERS

Although every player has a role in occupational health and safety, that of a company's management team is the most pivotal. Managers have the means and the authority to monitor the workplace and to ensure compliance with safe practices (Dunbar, 1975). Organizations have the resources to hire health and safety professionals.

The employer is responsible for preparing a written occupational health and safety policy and ensuring that it is prominently displayed in the workplace. Employers are also required to provide and maintain equipment, materials, and protective devices; to ensure that the manner in which the work is performed is safe, and that the environment is free from hazards and serious risks; to monitor their workplace and report minor, critical, disabling, and fatal injuries, as well as occupational illnesses and toxic substances (and to maintain the records of these occurrences for many years); to establish health and safety committees with strong employee representation; to alert employees to any known or perceived risks and hazards in the workplace; and to provide employees with health and safety training.

Managers themselves have to be trained in the recognition and control of unsafe work environments. They cannot monitor and control what they do not recognize as unsafe. Supervisors who participated in a study of 70 construction sites failed to recognize 44 percent of the workplace hazards, and felt that another 64 percent did not fall within their jurisdiction (Abeytunga and Hale, 1982). Further, these supervisors stated that 20 percent of the hazards were inevitable (ibid). Clearly, in order to fulfil their responsibilities, managers must receive health and safety training.

EMPLOYEES

Employees are required to perform their duties and tasks in a safe and responsible manner, and to wear protective equipment in compliance with company and legislative regulations. They are also required to report defective equipment and other workplace hazards to the safety professional, the joint health and safety committee, or the manager. Any employees who feel that a particular activity will endanger them or others have the right to refuse to carry out the activity.

ORGANIZED LABOUR

Voluntary and even legislated programs have not always treated as a priority the health and safety of workers. One role of organized labour is to bring to the attention of governments and employers emerging problems and issues in health and safety, and to pressure other stakeholders to take corrective action.

Unions also have a role to play in ensuring the proper management of safety at work. Organized labour and professional associations have used the collective bargaining process to incorporate safety and health provisions in many contracts. These labour contracts attempt to formalize voluntary measures and extend legislative programs. For example, some contracts state that a union representative must have a full-time safety function in all plants. Others bargain for more training on safety measures or more information on exposures to known toxic chemicals.

The United Auto Workers (UAW) in the United States have been prime movers in the area of health and safety. The union head office has a staff of very capable occupational hygienists, safety professionals, and occupational health physicians. In Canada, the Ontario Federation of Labour (OFL) develops policies and practices relating to health and safety. The Registered Nurses Association of Ontario (RNAO) and the Ontario Public Service Employees Union (OPSEU) regularly publish in their journals articles dealing with health and safety issues.

Organizational failure to adequately address health and safety issues can result in strikes and wildcat walkouts. Organized labour is expected to become increasingly strenuous in its enforcement of the right to refuse unsafe work (Reasons, 1984).

PARTNERSHIPS

The federal and most provincial governments require the establishment of joint health and safety committees (employer and worker representatives) in organizations with five or more employees. These committees respond to accidents; monitor the workplace; notify authorities about serious hazards, critical injuries, or death; hear complaints; and make recommendations.

MEDIA

The responsible reporting of occupational health and safety issues has resulted in many benefits. When the *London Illustrated News* blamed 19th-century mine owners for negligence in mine gas detection, proper safety lamps emerged some years later. In 1975, reports in the U.S. television media of sterility resulting from contact with 1,2-dibromo-3-chloropropane (DBCP) led to the withdrawal of this pesticide. In 1989, reports by Toronto-based media on the presence of asbestos in schools resulted in the establishment of a major program to remove or encapsulate the material.

◆ ◆ ◆
BARRIERS TO IMPLEMENTATION

While all stakeholders support the concept of safe working conditions, not everyone is committed to the implementation of OHS programs. Sexty (1979) discusses several reasons for stakeholders' lack of action in this area. Employers are more concerned with production quotas than safety records because the costs of production are more visible. Employers may "clean up" their locations just before an announced safety inspection, thus ensuring a pass on the safety inspection. Sometimes managers do not even recognize unsafe conditions or feel unable to do anything about those they do identify. Similarly, employers may be unaware of the methods and instruments by which rigorous monitoring of the workplace can be achieved.

Unions give higher priority to wages than safety. The general medical establishment is neither well versed nor well trained in OHS issues. In addition, the effects of some industrial diseases are not apparent for years, and are complicated by other factors such as the worker's lifestyle. Workers contribute to the problem by not following safety regulations; they may, for example, fail to wear safety glasses or other personal protective equipment. Worker health is affected as much by lack of exercise and smoking as by stress on the job.

One way to overcome these barriers to implementation is to form alliances among the stakeholders (Dennis, 1991). The three parties—employers, employees, and unions—have the same goal: the reduction of injuries and illnesses. It is a classic win–win situation in bargaining. The employer, by investing in health and safety programs, gains economically through the reduction in direct and indirect costs. The employer gains through an improved public image that may strengthen employee loyalty and increase marketing opportunities. Employees gain through reduced risk of work-related injuries and illnesses. Unions gain through their ability to successfully champion the health and safety interests of their clients.

One way to develop an effective OHS program is to employ health and safety professionals. Employing a health and safety professional can produce returns equal to factors of two or more times the salary paid. When the Oshawa Group employed safety professionals, its accident rate declined by 30 percent over a five-year period (Boyes, 1993). Managers who lack the technical expertise to investigate workplace hazards on their own must turn to health and safety professionals.

◆ ◆ ◆
HEALTH AND SAFETY PROFESSIONALS

Managers and human resource experts cannot be expected to develop, manage, and evaluate an OHS program, particularly when the issues cover the spectrum from chemical hazards to workplace violence. To assist managers in the operation of an OHS program, various types of safety and health experts may be hired or consulted.

SAFETY PROFESSIONAL

Safety is a multidisciplinary profession, combining engineering, psychology, preventative medicine, and industrial hygiene.

Safety professionals are trained to (1) identify and appraise workplace hazards, and evaluate the severity of the accident or loss; (2) develop and communicate hazard-control policies, methods, and programs; (3) devise motivational programs to integrate safety procedures into operations; and (4) measure and evaluate the effectiveness of these programs, and revise them as necessary. A *hazard* is any condition or action that could harm or injure people, property, or the environment (McLean, 1992).

To achieve certification, safety professionals must meet specified academic, experience, and examination requirements. The initials CRSP (Canadian Registered Safety Professional) are used to indicate certification. Many colleges, including Humber College in Toronto and BCIT in Vancouver, offer diplomas in Occupational Health and Safety.

OCCUPATIONAL HYGIENIST

Educated in a variety of fields (chemistry, engineering, physics, biology, and medicine), the occupational hygienist is trained to evaluate and control workplace hazards that may lead to sickness, impaired health, significant discomfort, and inefficiency (Berry, 1992). Specifically, the industrial hygienist is able to

> *a) recognize the environmental factors and to understand their effect on humans and their well-being; b) to evaluate, on the basis of experience and with the aid of quantitative measurement techniques, the magnitude of these stresses in terms of ability to impair human health and well-being; and c) to prescribe methods to eliminate, control or reduce such stresses when necessary to alleviate their effects (ibid., p. 572).*

The initials ROH (Registered Occupational Hygienist) or ROHT (Registered Occupational Hygiene Technologist) indicate certification, which requires post-secondary training and several years' experience. The use of the initials ROH requires a degree and ROHT a diploma. Ryerson Polytechnic University offers an undergraduate degree program in this specialty, as does Lambton College. Graduate programs can be found at McGill, the University of Toronto, and the University of British Columbia.

OCCUPATIONAL PHYSICIAN

Those who enter the field of occupational medicine must do postgraduate work in such subjects as industrial toxology, work physiology, industrial hygiene, respiratory diseases, and biostatistics. The occupational physician is concerned with the following:

> *a) appraisal, maintenance, restoration and improvement of the worker's health through application of the principles of preventative medicine, emergency medical care, rehabilitation and environmental medicine; b) promotion of a productive and fulfilling interaction of the worker and the job, via application of principles of human behaviour; c) active appreciation of the social, economic, and administrative needs and responsibilities of both the workers and work community; and d) a team approach to health and safety, involving cooperation*

with occupational or industrial hygienists, occupational health nurses, safety personnel, etc. (Zenz, 1992).

Within an organization, occupational physicians make decisions about medical equipment such as first-aid kits; put in place emergency-care services; undertake employee medical examinations; establish baseline records of physical condition, assess general health, and determine physical capacity to perform the functions; and provide health education and counselling to employees. Large companies such as General Motors and hospitals such as St. Michael's in Toronto employ occupational physicians.

OCCUPATIONAL HEALTH NURSE

The occupational health nurse is concerned with the prevention, recognition, and treatment of worker illness and injury (Cornyn, 1992). Applying nursing principles to employees, this individual develops and manages safety and health education programs that address such topics as nutrition and lifestyle changes. The occupational health nurse is typically engaged in primary and emergency care, assisting in medical examinations and rehabilitation efforts, maintaining medical records, promoting health education, and participating in health and safety committees.

SAFETY ENGINEER

The health and safety experts discussed above can be located through their associations, the Yellow Pages, or safety associations and provincial departments. A complete list of government departments, professional associations, and accreditation organizations is found in Appendixes 1 and 2. There are no legal requirements for the practice of occupational health and safety.

◆ ◆ ◆
SUMMARY

This chapter has established the importance of occupational health and safety. Discussion of the historical antecedents of the present health and safety movement was followed by a comparison of the concerns and roles of the various stakeholders. Barriers to the implementation of OHS programs were identified. Finally, the functions of various safety professionals were described.

EXERCISES

1. Who should speak for the health and safety of employees? Which of the stakeholders should play a more active role in lobbying for improvements to health and safety laws and programs? Discuss the roles of each of the stakeholders, and recommend ways in which they could be made more effective.

2. Are the media stakeholders? For one week, read the local newspapers and listen to the news. Make a note of the main topic of every article or item pertaining to occupational health and safety. What role are the media playing? What OHS issues are most likely to gain attention? Give reasons for your answers.

Questions

1. Why have people historically been more concerned with work-related injuries than work-related illnesses?

2. On what grounds beside humanitarian ones should workplace hazards be controlled?

3. Identify and discuss actions that have been taken in your workplace to improve the health and safety environment.

References

Abeytunga, P.K., and H.R. Hale. 1982 (July). "Supervisor's perception of Hazards on Construction Sites." Paper presented at the 20th Congress of the International Association of Applied Psychology, Edinburgh, U.K.

Berry, C.M. 1992. "The Industrial Hygienist." In P. Laing, ed., *Fundamentals of Industrial Hygiene*, 3rd ed. Washington, D.C.: National Safety Council, 571–84.

Boyes, S. 1993. "Doubles Strategy: When Human Resources and Occupational Health and Safety Work in Synchrony, Everybody Wins." *Human Resources Professional* 10, no. 7 (July/August): 17–19.

Cornyn, J. 1992. "The Occupational Health Nurse." In P. Laing, ed., *Fundamentals of Industrial Hygiene*, 3rd ed. Washington, D.C.: National Safety Council, 637–53.

Dennis, P. 1991. *Guide to Health and Safety Management*. Don Mills, Ont.: Southam Business Communications Inc.

Dunbar, R.L. 1975. "Manager's Influence on Subordinates' Thinking about Safety." *Academy of Management Journal* 18, no. 2, 364–70.

Galt, V. 1991 (March 14). "Workplace Accident Tab $4 Billion." *The Globe and Mail*.

Gordon, J.B., A. Akman and M.L. Brooks.1971. *Industrial Safety Statistics: A Re-Examination*. New York: Praeger.

Janson, H.W. 1985. *History of Art*, 2nd ed. Englewood Cliffs, N.J.: Prentice Hall.

Kaminiskij, A. 1994. *Safety Engineering Technology Study*. Humber College, Toronto.

Key, Marcus M. 1977. *Occupational Diseases: A Guide to Their Recognition*, rev. ed. Cincinnati, Ohio: U.S. Department of Health, Education, and Welfare, NIOSH.

McLean, W.T. 1992. "The Safety Professional." In P. Laing, ed., *Fundamentals of Industrial Hygiene*, 3rd ed. Washington, D.C.: National Safety Council, 585–606.

Milkovich, G.T., W.F. Glueck, R.T. Barth, and S.L. McShane. 1994. "Occupational Health and Safety." In H.C. Jain and P.C. Wright, eds., *Trends and Challenges in Human Resource Management*. Scarborough, Ont.: Nelson Canada.

Stammer, Brian J.1994. "Diligent Conduct." *Engineering Dimensions* (September/October).

Reasons, C.E. 1984. "Occupational Health: Material and Chemical Aspects." In K.M. Srinivas, ed., *Human Resource Management: Contemporary Perspectives in Canada.* Toronto: McGraw-Hill Ryerson.

Sexty, R. 1979. *Issues in Canadian Business.* Scarborough, Ont.: Prentice Hall.

Statistics Canada. 1994. *Work Injuries,1991–1993.* Ottawa: Ministry of Supply and Services.

Statistics Canada. 1991. *Accidents in Canada.* Cat. no. 11-612E, p. 65.

Turner, J. Ralph A. 1995. Correspondence from a partner with Field and Turner, Barristers and Solicitors, Toronto.

Zenz, C. 1992. "The Occupational Physician." In P. Laing, ed., *Fundamentals of Industrial Hygiene*, 3rd ed. Washington, D.C.: National Safety Council, 607–26.

2

Occupational Health and Safety Legislation Across Canada

INTRODUCTION

Knowledge of health and safety legislation is crucial. One company in Ontario was levied a fine of $500,000 due to a violation of the Occupational Health and Safety Act that resulted in the death of two employees (*Accident Prevention*, March/April). The human resource practitioner of the 1990s will discover a world of confusing and often conflicting legislation. The following sections will attempt to bring some clarity to the legislative jungle.

♦ ♦ ♦

LEGISLATIVE FRAMEWORK

An employer who operates a business in Canada is required to comply with hundreds of statutes and regulations. The human resource department is concerned with a small percentage of these laws. Laws that have consequences for employment may include employment standards, labour relations, pay equity, employment equity, workers' compensation, occupational health and safety, freedom of information, and, above all, human rights legislation. The effect of the Canadian Charter of Human Rights and Freedoms on all aspects of human resource management cannot be overstated. From the moment employees are hired to the moment they are retired or released, their rights must be assiduously protected by the employer.

However, the safety of an employee takes precedence over other individual rights. For example, the Supreme Court of Canada ruled that forcing an employee to wear a hard hat instead of a turban reflected a bona fide occupational safety requirement, not intentional discrimination on the part of the employer. Other court cases have supported the tenet that safety legislation overrides the individual rights of an employee.

---

*This chapter was written by Mary D. Smith, CRSP.

◆ ◆ ◆
STANDARDS AND CODES

Standards are design-related guides that assist engineers, building managers, and owners in the safe and efficient building and maintaining of structures. For example, Ontario's Building Code Act refers to the American Society of Heating and Refrigeration Engineers (ASHARE) for a design standard concerning ventilation in buildings. Occupational health and safety regulations frequently reference the Canadian Standards Association (CSA) standards for all manner of industrial, electrical, and construction applications. The CSA was chartered in 1919 and accredited by the National Standards Council of Canada and the National Standards System in 1973. CSA standards reflect a national consensus of producers and users, including manufacturers, consumers, retailers, unions, professional organizations, and government agencies. The U.S. counterpart of the CSA is the American National Standards Institute (ANSI). Canadian regulations frequently refer to ANSI when a Canadian standard does not exist. Of particular importance to the practitioner is the fact that, when a statute or regulation references a standard, it requires that the standard be met as minimum compliance in the eyes of the authorities that have jurisdiction. The standard thus has the power of the regulation under the statute.

Codes are often developed within regulations. For example, operating within Ontario's Power Corporation Act is the Ontario Hydro Safety Code; also, under various fire and building regulations there are fire and building codes. Codes carry the power of the law under the applicable Act.

Not all standards and codes refer to building and structural engineering. The practitioner should be aware that standards exist for such categories as office furniture (ergonomic designs), heat and cold stress, hospital and health-care equipment, recreational equipment, and personal protective devices.

◆ ◆ ◆
OCCUPATIONAL HEALTH AND SAFETY LAWS

The federal, provincial, and territorial governments are responsible for developing and enforcing occupational health and safety statutes and standards in workplaces across Canada. In the past, responsibility for health and safety was the sole responsibility of the separate provincial and federal jurisdictions. Responding to the pressures of labour organizations and multinational companies doing business in Canada, the ministers responsible for occupational safety have embarked on projects designed to harmonize health and safety legislation. One of the first pan-Canadian efforts was the Workplace Hazardous Materials Information System, which will be discussed later in this chapter.

◆ ◆ ◆
THE SCOPE OF OHS LEGISLATION

The scope of the OHS legislation differs from jurisdiction to jurisdiction (see Table 2.1 for a list of OHS Acts and enforcement agencies pertaining to each jurisdiction). The statutes and regulations that have been enacted to protect the rights of workers have also established duties that require compliance. The statutes provide the legal foundation, while the regulations enacted under the statute establish the framework within which the employer will conduct business in order to comply with the law.

Under common law, an employer is obliged to take reasonable precautions in ensuring the safety of an employee. This common-law duty is dormant in some jurisdictions because it has been superseded by other legislation relating to workers' compensation. The compensation legislation either bars or limits the employer's duty by proscribing civil actions between employees and their employers in exchange for awards or pensions that may be allowed following an occupational accident or illness. In most provinces and territories, occupational health and safety laws are separate from workers' compensation. One example of an exception occurs in British Columbia, where occupational health and safety programs can be instituted, amended, or removed by motion of the Workers' Compensation Board after a public hearing has been called following a 10-day notice and publication in the *Gazette*. No action by the legislature is required. The British Columbia regulations for industrial health and safety are among the most detailed in the country and include schedules of numerical requirements, diagrams, and tables. The legal force is different in British Columbia as well. First, the Workers' Compensation Board is responsible for enforcement. Second, the privative clause contained in Part I of the Workers' Compensation Act makes it impossible to appeal a WCB decision to any court.

TABLE 2.1 OCCUPATIONAL SAFETY IN CANADA

Jurisdictions	Legislation	Enforcement
Canada	Canada Labour Code, Regulations	Labour Canada
Alberta	Occupational Health and Safety Act	Department of Labour
British Columbia	Regulations under Workers' Compensation Act	Workers' Compensation Board
Manitoba	Workplace Safety and Health Act	Department of Environment & Workplace Health and Safety
New Brunswick	Occupational Health and Safety Act	Occupational Health and Safety Commission
Newfoundland	Occupational Health and Safety Act	Department of Labour
Nova Scotia	Occupational Health and Safety Act	Department of Labour
Ontario	Occupational Health and Safety Act	Ministry of Labour
Prince Edward Island	Occupational Health and Safety Act	Department of Fisheries and Labour
Quebec	Act respecting Occupational Health and Safety	Commission de la Santé et de la Sécurité du Travail
Saskatchewan	Occupational Health and Safety Act	Department of Labour
Northwest Territories	Safety Act	Commissioner of the N.W.T.
Yukon Territory	Occupational Health and Safety Act	Commissioner of the Yukon Territory, administered by the Workers' Compensation Board

Despite the existence of privative clauses in British Columbia and some other provinces, Canadian courts will still review provincial WCB decisions. However, the scope of the review is limited to the following issues:

(a) Did the tribunal have jurisdiction?

(b) Did the tribunal lose jurisdiction?

    (i)   by refusing to make a decision

    (ii) by making a decision based on the absence of evidence

    (iii) by failing to observe rules of natural justice.

(c) Did the tribunal commit a gross error or make a patently unreasonable decision?

All Canadian occupational health and safety legislation includes the following elements:

- An Act
- Powers of enforcement
- Rights of workers to refuse to do unsafe work
- Protection of workers from reprisals
- Duties and responsibilities assigned to employers and others

Other elements, which differ between jurisdictions, include mandatory establishment of joint labour/management health and safety committees, health and safety policies, accident-prevention programs, and advisory councils on occupational health and safety. Those responsible for the management of health and safety and workers' compensation should be familiar with the administrative structure as it relates to enforcement, education, and compensation in their particular jurisdiction. Multinational and transportation companies may fall under two or more jurisdictions, which increases the administrative complexities.

The general duty provision requiring employers to take every reasonable precaution to ensure employee safety is pan-Canadian. In the federal jurisdiction, the duty is sufficiently broad in scope that an employer could be held liable for having failed to ensure the health and safety of an employee even if there was an absence of a specific violation to a regulatory provision. The term "ensure" is applied across Canada and is accepted to mean the strongest responsibility possible short of a guarantee.

The application of the laws governing health and safety in Canada are well illustrated by the decision reached in a landmark case. Although the case did not deal directly with employment health or safety, the decision has been referred to by all courts at all levels dealing specifically with health and safety legislation. The case in question, *R. v. Sault Ste. Marie* (1978), dealt with a pollution charge under Ontario's Water Resources Act. As a result of this case, the Supreme Court of Canada ruled that there are three categories of offences:

1. *Criminal offence:* The accused must be shown by the prosecution to have had the intent to commit the offence.

2. *Absolute liability offence:* The prosecution merely has to prove that the accused committed the offence. The offences in this category are usually found in such statutes as the Highway Traffic Act.

3. *Strict liability offence:* The prosecution does not have to prove intent. The accused, who has the right to invoke a single defence of due diligence, believes that every reasonable precaution was taken to avoid the particular event.

Mr. Justice Dickson ruled that offences dealing with environmental pollution are public welfare offences and fit into the category of strict liability offence rather than absolute liability offence. The ruling allowed the accused a defence of due diligence.

The Supreme Court of Canada has ruled on appeals of two lower court decisions. *R. v. Ellis Don Ltd.* (1991) involved the death of a construction worker who fell down a shaft on a high-rise structure. The company was convicted on the basis that due diligence had not been demonstrated. The Ontario Court of Appeal quashed the conviction on the ground that the defence of due diligence was contrary to the Charter of Rights and Freedoms. The Crown appealed to the Supreme Court of Canada.

The Supreme Court of Canada subsequently released its decision on another case, *R. v. Wholesale Travel Group* (1991), which saw a conviction under the Competitions Act overturned. The decision clarified the Supreme Court's position on the legality of a due diligence defence. The court maintained that since the knowledge of what steps have been taken to comply with regulatory legislation is often solely in the hands of the accused, it is not unreasonable to require the accused to demonstrate precisely what has been done to prevent a contravention from taking place. The court noted that although the defence of due diligence was contrary to the Charter of Rights and Freedoms, the legal concepts that apply to criminal law should not apply to regulatory offences. In his ruling, Supreme Court Judge Cory stated:

> *Regulatory legislation is essential to the operation of our complex industrial society; it plays a legitimate and vital role in protecting those who are most vulnerable and least able to protect themselves. The extent and importance of that role has increased continuously since the onset of the Industrial Revolution. Before effective workplace legislation was enacted, labourers—including children—worked unconscionably long hours in dangerous and unhealthy surroundings that evoke visions of Dante's Inferno. It was regulatory legislation with its enforcement provisions which brought to an end the shameful situation that existed in mines, factories and workshops in the nineteenth century. The differential treatment of regulatory offences is justified by their common goal of protecting the vulnerable.*

The Ellis Don case was scheduled to be heard on March 31, 1992. Chief Justice Lamer requested that the lawyers for Ellis Don open with submissions on how the Ellis Don case differed from the Wholesale Travel case. The court heard the submissions and ruled that there were no compelling reasons to believe that a substantial difference existed. The Ontario Crown succeeded in its appeal without having to make an oral submission. The Supreme Court ruling that the defence of due diligence is constitutional will have a significant impact on the enforcement of health and safety legislation in jurisdictions across Canada. In Ontario, the emphasis is shifting from prosecutions to adjudication.

◆ ◆ ◆
DUTIES AND RESPONSIBILITIES OF THE MAJOR PLAYERS

The statutes in most provinces outline the duties and responsibilities of the major players in occupational health and safety. These include employers, contractors, supervisors, and workers.

Some provinces impose duties on joint health and safety committee or representatives, but the majority are silent on this subject. The human resource practitioner should be well versed in labour laws in order to make informed decisions with respect to the corporation's health and safety program. The OHS components attached to the various jurisdictions are listed in Table 2.2 .

TABLE 2.2 JURISDICTIONS AND OHS COMPONENTS					
Jurisdictions	Committees	Duties	Advisory Councils	Safety Policies	Accident Prevention Programs
Canada	✓	✓			
Alberta	Minister may order	✓ ✓	✓ to Minister, may hear appeals, other duties as assigned		
British Columbia	✓	✓			✓
Manitoba	✓	✓	✓		
New Brunswick	✓	✓			
Newfoundland	Minister may order	✓			
Nova Scotia	✓	✓		Director may order a code of practice	
Ontario	✓	✓		✓	✓
Quebec	Established by request of certified association, or Commission may order	✓	Sector-based advisory councils/ associations	Supply personal protective equipment free of charge	
Prince Edward Island	Minister may order	✓	✓		
Saskatchewan	✓	✓	✓		
Yukon	✓				
Northwest Territories	✓	✓			✓

Employers have a primary duty to provide a safe work environment. Other duties include providing supervision, education, training, and written instructions where applicable; assisting the joint health and safety committee/representative; and complying with statutes and regulations. In Ontario, the employer's responsibilities are extensive and include the following:

♦ Ensuring that equipment is properly maintained

♦ Appointing a competent supervisor

♦ Providing information (including confidential information) in a medical emergency

♦ Informing supervisors of possible hazards

♦ Posting the OHS Act in the workplace

♦ Preparing and maintaining a health and safety policy annually and reviewing it (see Box 2.1.)

BOX 2.1 DUPONT CANADA: SAFETY PHILOSOPHY

We are committed to excellence in safety and occupational health for all our people on and off the job. We are committed to the safe distribution and use of our products by our customers.

Safety management is an integral part of our business and is built on the belief that all injuries and occupational illnesses are preventable; that we are all responsible for our own safety and also that of our fellow employees; and that managers are responsible for the safety of those in their organizations.

Arthur R. Sawchuk
President
DuPont Canada Inc.

The Occupational Health and Safety Acts include "prescribed" duties that may come into effect by regulation at some time. The duties may include an employer's responsibility to establish occupational health services, or a description of the written procedures that may be required.

Constructors/primary contractors have responsibilities similar to those outlined for employers. In some jurisdictions, when a construction project is scheduled to commence, a constructor/primary contractor has a duty to notify the authority within a specified time. Some jurisdictions require a written Notice of Project to be filed outlining the approximate cost, scope, commencement date and duration of the project.

In Ontario, an owner is responsible for notification by way of tender when any designated substance is likely to be encountered during a construction project. Designated substances are those substances identified by regulation that when ingested, inhaled, or absorbed in the body can inflict either acute or chronic damage to a worker.

◆ ◆ ◆
DUTIES OF SUPERVISORS

The duties assigned to supervisors are similar across Canada. "Supervisor" is broadly interpreted to refer to a person (with or without a title) who has charge of a workplace and authority over a worker. Supervisors can be union members, association members covered under a collective agreement, plant managers, general managers, lead hands, forepersons, school principals, or self-employed individuals. The criteria used in Ontario to determine whether or not a person would be held to be a supervisor include authority to promote or recommend promotion, to discipline workers or to schedule or assign work.

A supervisor's duties include the following:

◆ Ensuring that workers comply with OHS Act and regulations

◆ Ensuring that workers use or wear safety equipment, devices, or clothing

◆ Advising workers of possible hazards

◆ Providing written instructions if applicable

◆ Taking every reasonable precaution to ensure the protection of workers.

Duties for workers are included in the majority of statutes. In some jurisdictions, the responsibilities are laid out by regulation. The inclusion of workers' responsibilities and duties is relatively new in health and safety legislation. Prior to the late 1970s, all responsibility for workplace health and safety rested with the employer.

A worker's duties include the following:

◆ Complying with the OHS Act and regulations

◆ Using safety equipment and clothes provided

◆ Reporting hazards, such as defective equipment, to the supervisor

◆ Reporting any contraventions of the Act or regulations

Workers are prohibited from making any safety device ineffective, using any hazardous equipment or machine, or engaging in rough or boisterous conduct.

◆ ◆ ◆

JOINT HEALTH AND SAFETY COMMITTEES

A recent addition to OHS legislation is the creation of joint health and safety committees in the workplace. These committees are required by law in nine jurisdictions; the minister responsible has the discretionary power to require the formation of committees in the remaining four jurisdictions.

The primary function of the joint health and safety committee is to provide a nonadversarial atmosphere where labour and management can work together to create a safer and healthier workplace. Joint committees are structured such that equal or better representation is required from workers who do not exercise managerial responsibilities. Ontario has embraced the joint health and safety committee concept wholeheartedly. The Occupational Health and Safety Act was amended in 1990 to create an agency, at arm's length from the Ministry of Labour, whose mandate included designing and administering a health and safety certification program for joint committee members. This agency will be absorbed into the workers' compensation Board in 1996 as a distinct branch responsible to the WCB Board of Directors.

Each workplace requiring a committee must certify at least one management member and one worker member of each workplace committee. Subjects taught during the training (which may run from one to three weeks) include law, general safety, hygiene, routes of entry (into the body), indoor air quality, chemical safety, certified workers' rights and duties, and joint committees. Certified members may be involved in inspections, work refusals, and bilateral work stoppage where there is an imminent hazard to a worker. They may also investigate critical accidents, attend at the beginning of hygiene testing, and respond to worker concerns.

A study conducted by Ontario's Workplace Health and Safety Agency suggests that joint health and safety committees may contribute to a reduction of injury rates (Worklife Report, 1994). Algoma and Stelco are among those companies that have experienced a decrease in lost-time injuries after implementing cooperative safety programs.

◆ ◆ ◆
WORK REFUSALS

The right to refuse unsafe work without fear of reprisals is now available to workers in every jurisdiction in Canada. Exceptions or limitations to the right to refuse unsafe work vary across the country. In essence, a worker does not have the right to refuse unsafe work if said work is a normal condition of employment or if the worker, by his or her refusal, places another life in jeopardy.

In Ontario, police, firefighters, teachers, and health-care workers are among those professionals who have been granted what is known as a limited right of refusal. For example, a firefighter has the right to refuse to use unsafe equipment during an exercise that is not an emergency. A teacher has the right to refuse to use equipment suspected to be defective until his or her concern has been investigated and resolved; however, a teacher does not have the right to refuse unsafe work if the lives of students are placed in jeopardy as a result.

The procedure for reporting a refusal to perform unsafe work is, for the most part, consistent across jurisdictions. Once the worker has apprised the supervisor of the suspected work hazard, an investigation is conducted by the supervisor and a worker representative (union, joint health and safety committee member, or co-worker).

The investigation results in either a return to work or a continued refusal. In the latter situation, a ministry inspector/officer conducts an investigation and then provides a written decision. In the meantime, a replacement worker may not be assigned the work that has been refused unless he or she has been informed about the circumstances surrounding the refusal; the refusing worker who continues to receive the regular remuneration for the job may be assigned alternate work.

In New Brunswick and Prince Edward Island, the supervisor and joint health and safety committee can make a judgment that the refusal is not based on reasonable grounds. The employee may then refer the matter to an occupational health and safety officer, who will make the final determination. As "reasonable grounds" is not defined, it appears to leave the door open for a subjective rather than an objective decision being reached.

◆ ◆ ◆
STOP WORK PROVISIONS (ONTARIO)

In 1990, an Act to Amend the Ontario Occupational Health and Safety Act was given royal assent. The amendments were far-reaching and promise profound changes in how employers will do business in Ontario. Among the most significant provisions were expanded powers for certified members of the joint health and safety committee.

The provisions for stopping work takes two forms, one bilateral and the other unilateral. A certified member of a joint health and safety committee may, in the course of an inspection or investigation, have reason to believe that a dangerous circumstance exists. The certified member will ask a supervisor (and possibly a second certified member of the joint health and safety committee) to investigate. Following the investigation and possible remedial actions taken by the supervisor, if the certified members, representing both management and labour, find that the dangerous circumstance still exists, they may direct the employer to stop work. The legislation defines "dangerous circumstance" as follows:

◆ a provision of the Act or the regulation is being contravened,

◆ the contravention presents a danger or a hazard to a worker, and

◆ the danger or hazard is such that any delay in controlling it may seriously endanger a worker.

The unilateral provision will apply in the case of an employer who has, in the opinion of a government-appointed adjudicator, taken insufficient steps to protect the employer's workers from serious risk to their health and safety. A second circumstance may allow the unilateral provision to apply. An employer may advise the joint health and safety committee in writing of a willingness to adopt the unilateral power of either of the certified members to stop work in dangerous circumstance.

◆ ◆ ◆
WORKPLACE HAZARDOUS MATERIALS INFORMATION SYSTEM

The origins of Workplace Hazardous Materials Information System (WHMIS) began in the United States in the early 1980s, in the form of the Hazard Communication Standard. The concept reflects the belief that citizens have the "right to know" about hazards that may be associated with certain chemicals used in the community and, by extension, the workplace.

WHMIS is the brainchild of industry, labour, and government representatives committed to developing regulations that would meet the "right to know" standard.

In Canada, all jurisdictions were involved in creating the first pan-Canadian health and safety legislation. The supplier legislation is administered by Consumer and Corporate Affairs Canada. The federal government created a Model OSH regulation that was used as a model by the provincial and territorial governments to ensure the desired consistency in regulations. The Hazardous Products Act defines a hazardous product and controls its use by requiring disclosure of the substance(s) and its concentration in a manufactured product. Other federal statutes and regulations governing controlled products include the Controlled Products Regulation, the Ingredient Disclosure List, and the Hazardous Materials Review Act and Regulation.

The federal legislation, which was limited in application to federally regulated workplaces, required the provinces and territories to create enabling legislation to empower the jurisdictions. The WHMIS legislation came into force across Canada between 1988 and 1990. The worker now has a "right to know" the potential hazards of the chemical being handled; handling, storage, and use instructions; and emergency measures for clean-up and disposal of a spill.

Pro Shield Corp. was fined for violating WHMIS legislation when it failed to inform an employee of the hazards of a product he was handling. The employee, who had been on the job for just three days, died from burns after the toluene in the product he was pouring exploded (*Accident Prevention*, September/October).

The WHMIS legislation is based on three elements:

1. Labels designed to alert the worker that the container contains a potentially hazardous product
2. Material safety data sheets outlining a product's potentially hazardous ingredient(s) and procedures for safe handling of the product
3. Employee training

In 1991, a WHMIS Enforcement Issues Subcommittee was formed for the purpose of ensuring that WHMIS is applied uniformly across the country. In addition, Consumer and Corporate Affairs Canada produces Policy

Issue Sheets and WHMIS information bulletins on a regular basis in an effort to keep employers and suppliers up to date on the legislation. For human resource practitioners responsible for health and safety, it is imperative that current information is made available to the corporation to ensure continued compliance.

There is a continuing need to harmonize the WHMIS legislation internationally. The federal government is engaged in ongoing consultations with the International Labour Organization (ILO) and exporting countries eager to do business in Canada. Although the United States, our major trading partner, does not have to comply with Canadian legislation, many multinational companies doing business in Canada are attempting to merge the U.S. Hazard Communication Standard into the WHMIS format.

SUPPLIER AND EMPLOYER RESPONSIBILITIES

A supplier is defined in the Hazardous Products Act as a person who imports or sells or distributes a controlled product. It is the responsibility of the supplier to determine whether a material that is manufactured or imported is a controlled product. In order to do this, the supplier is guided by a list of chemicals that appears under the Controlled Products Regulation. The supplier then determines the maximum quantity of any controlled chemical that is present in the mixture that is supplied for sale or use. The supplier must then prepare and apply labels conforming with the regulation, and prepare and supply safety information in a material safety data sheet as prescribed under the Controlled Products Regulation.

The employer is defined under the Act as anyone who employs workers to use, handle, store, and dispose of controlled products that contain potentially hazardous substances. It is the responsibility of an employer to provide information to an employee by way of workplace labels and material safety data sheets. As far as is reasonably practicable, the employer is responsible for ensuring that the program for worker instruction results in the employee being able to apply the information as needed to protect his or her health and safety.

LABELS

The need to label is the most widely understood element of the WHMIS program. Following are some important definitions:

◆ Controlled product (Hazardous Products Act, ss.2 and 12) means any product, material, or substance included in any of the classes listed in the HPA Schedule III unless it is exempted under s.12 of the HPA.

◆ Container (Hazardous Products Act, s.11(1)) includes a bag, barrel, bottle, box, can, cylinder, drum or similar package, or receptacle, but does not include a storage tank.

◆ Manufacturer includes a person(s) who manufactures, processes, packages, imports, distributes, or sells controlled products.

There are two types of WHMIS labels: supplier labels and workplace labels. The supplier label, the more comprehensive of the two labels, must be attached to the container by some means when it is delivered to the workplace. The supplier label must contain the following seven items of information (in both French and English):

1. Product identifier (Controlled Product Regulation, s.2(1)) including the brand name or code number. Information may include the chemical name, generic name, or trade name.

2. Supplier identifier (Controlled Product Regulation, s.2(1)) is the name of the manufacturer or supplier as defined.

3. A statement that the material safety data sheet is to be referred to for more information.

4. Hazard symbol(s) (Controlled Product Regulation, s.11) that must correspond to the class and division that allocates the product as a controlled substance.

5. Risk phrases (Controlled Product Regulation, s.2(1)) that must correspond to the class and division to which the product is allocated.

6. Precautionary measures to be followed when handling or using the controlled product.

7. First-aid measures to be taken in the event of an exposure to a controlled product.

The requirement for workplace labels takes effect when, upon receipt of the container, the employer at the workplace takes the product out of its original container to use or distribute. Workplace labels would also be required for storage tanks or large in-house containers. The workplace label must contain: a product identifier, safe-handling instructions, availability of a material safety data sheet. See Box 2.2 for an example of a workplace label.

MATERIAL SAFETY DATA SHEETS

The objective of safety data information is to identify potentially harmful ingredients in products the worker may be handling, to present some factual information about the ingredient's form, and to provide guidance in the use and disposal of the product.

The material safety data sheet (MSDS) must contain information as set out by the Hazardous Products Act, s.11(1) and the Controlled Products Regulation, ss.12 and 13. The information must be comprehensive, up to date (revisions are required every three years), and made available in the two official languages. The following nine categories are a minimum standard:

1. Product information including the name, address, phone number, of the supplier/manufacturer and the product identifier and use.

2. A hazardous ingredients list including all controlled substances in the product and their concentrations. The list generally includes the Chemical Abstract number (when available); the allowable concentration limits, known as Threshold Limit Values (TLV), set by the American Council of Government Industrial Hygienists (ACGIH), and the lethal-dose range tested for a specific animal population.

3. Physical data including information on appearance, odour, density, boiling point, corrosiveness, etc.

4. Fire and explosion information including data on flammability of the hazardous ingredients.

5. Reactivity information outlining the conditions under which the material may react with other chemicals or materials. The section will also identify the hazardous products produced by decomposition in a fire situation.

6. Toxicological data including all available information on the possible health effects due to chronic or acute exposure.

7. Preventative measures to be used while dealing with the product, including information on personal protective equipment, ventilation requirements, storage, handling, and waste disposal.

8. First-aid measures providing specific recommendations for treatment for exposure to the material.

BOX 2.2 WHMIS Class Symbols and Subclass Designations

The symbol represents ...

Class A —
Compressed Gas

Class D, Division 2 —
Poisonous and
infectional material:
other toxic effects

Class B —
Combustible and
flammable material

Class D, Division 3 —
Poisonous and
infectional material:
biohazardous
infectious material

Class C —
Oxidizing material

Class E —
Corrosive material

Class D, Division 1 —
Poisonous and
infectious material:
Immediate and
serious toxic effects

Class F —
Dangerously
reactive material

9. Preparation information including the name of the person(s) who pre-pared the MSDS, a phone number for contact, and the date of the issue of the MSDS.

The manufacturer or supplier must develop or cause to be developed an MSDS for each product supplied for use in the workplace. The MSDS must be transmitted to the purchaser on or before the date of sale or delivery of the product. The information on the MSDS must be current at the time of sale or delivery, and the MSDS must be dated no more than three years prior to the date of sale or delivery. See Box 2.3 for an example of an MSDS.

The requirement for supplying MSDS is twofold. Suppliers are regu-lated by the federal legislation under the Controlled Products Act while employers are regulated under provincial or territorial regulations. Should an employer also be a manufacturer or produce research products not intended for sale, the responsibility for creating an MSDS becomes the employer's leg-islated responsibility.

TRAINING

Education in WHMIS is commonly defined as the process of acquiring knowledge through systematic instruction. By contrast, training is defined as bringing a person to a desired state or standard of efficiency by instruction and practice. One area that often escapes the scrutiny of the inspector/offi-cer's application of a performance-based regulation is the application of the education received. A worker may know to check for labels, know where to find the MSDS, and know the employer's procedures for handling a spill; however, the same worker may not know how to read the MSDS or under-stand it in sufficient depth to apply it in the workplace. Training and educa-tion should include a practical process to ensure that the worker understands how to apply the knowledge acquired.

After completing a training program, the worker should understand the purpose and origin of WHMIS and be able to:

◆ Identify WHMIS hazard symbols

◆ Read WHMIS supplier and workplace labels

◆ Read and apply the information on an MSDS

The WHMIS program must be reviewed annually or as changes occur in products or processes in the workplace.

BOX 2.3 MATERIAL SAFETY DATA SHEET

Form #CH3   **MATERIAL SAFETY DATA SHEET**   name of product:

SECTION I – HAZARDOUS INGREDIENTS

Chemical Identity	Concentration	CAS Number	PIN Number	LD_{50} Species and Route	LC_{50} Species and Route

SECTION II – PREPARATION INFORMATION

Prepared by (Group, Department, Etc.)	Phone Number	Date of Preparation

SECTION III – PRODUCT INFORMATION

Product Identifier

Manufacturer's Name		Supplier's Name	
Street Address		Street Address	
City	Province	City	Province
Postal Code	Emergency Tel. No.	Postal Code	Emergency Tel. No.

Product Use

SECTION IV – PHYSICAL DATA

Physical State	Odour and Appearance		Odour Threshold
Specific Gravity (water = 1)	Co-efficient of Water/Oil Distribution		Vapour Pressure
Boiling Point (°C)	Freezing Point (°C)	pH	Vapour Density (Air = 1)
Evaporation Rate (BuAc = 1)	Percent Volatile (by volume)		

BOX 2.3 (continued)

Form #CH3 **MATERIAL SAFETY DATA SHEET** name of product:

SECTION V- FIRE OR EXPLOSION HAZARD

Conditions of Flammability

Means of Extinction

Explosion Data
Sensitivity to Mechanical Impact   Sensitivity to Static Discharge

Flashpoint (°C) and Method	Upper Flammable Limit %	Lower Flammable Limit %
Autoignition Temperature (°C)	Hazardous Combustion Products	

SECTION VI- REACTIVITY DATA

Stability

Incompatible Materials

Conditions of Reactivity

Hazardous Decomposition Products

SECTION VII- TOXICOLOGICAL PROPERTIES

Route of Entry
☐ Skin Contact   ☐ Skin Absorption   ☐ Eye Contact   ☐ Inhalation   ☐ Ingestion

Effects of Acute Exposure to Product

Effects of Chronic Exposure to Product

Exposure Limits	Irritancy of Product	Synergistic Products
Evidence of Carcinogenicity, Reproductive Toxicity, Teratogenicity or Mutagenicity?		Sensitization to Product

BOX 2.3 (continued)

Form #CH3 **MATERIAL SAFETY DATA SHEET**   name of product:

SECTION VIII- PREVENTIVE MEASURES

Personal Protective Equipment

Gloves (specify)	Respiratory (specify)

Eye (specify)	Footwear (specify)

Other Equipment (specify)

Engineering Controls (e.g. ventilation, enclosed process, specify)

Leak and Spill Procedure

Waste Disposal

Handling Procedures and Equipment

Storage Requirements

Special Shipping Information

SECTION IX- FIRST AID MEASURES

Inhalation

Ingestion

Eye Contact

Skin Contact

Additional Information	Sources Used

♦ ♦ ♦
ENVIRONMENTAL LEGISLATION

Environmental and occupational health and safety legislation are solidly entwined. In recognition of this fact, many companies and institutions have Environmental Health and Safety departments. The health and safety professional will be conscious of the overlap in environmental and OHS statutes and regulations. Chemicals that can cause damage to a worker may also cause damage to the ecosystem if released into the environment. Federal and provincial/territorial statutes relating to some aspect of environmental or health and safety management are listed in Tables 2.3 and 2.4 respectively.

Regulatory legislation having to do with environmental assessment, public health, waste disposal, buried fuel tanks, and storage/use of pesticides impacts on both the environment and the occupational health and safety of employees and the public. As the following scenario indicates, the practitioner is required to understand environmental and OHS jurisdictions and the potential for overlap:

> *If a release of a potentially hazardous substance occurs within a building (other than residential) it falls under the jurisdiction of the authority enforcing the health and safety*

TABLE 2.3 FEDERAL STATUTES
Canadian Environmental Protection Act, R.S.C. 1985
Hazardous Products Act, R.S.C. 1985
Canadian Charter of Rights and Freedoms, Part I of the Constitution Act 1982
Pest Control Products Act, R.S.C. 1985
Radiation Protection Act, R.S.C. 1985
Radiation Emitting Devices Act, R.S.C. 1985
Transportation of Dangerous Goods Act, 1992, S.C. as amended
Canada Labour Code, Part IV

TABLE 2.4 PROVINCIAL AND TERRITORIAL STATUTES

Province	Transportation	Environment	Other
Alberta	Transportation of Dangerous Goods Act, S.A. 1982	Environmental Protection and Enhancement Act, S.A. 1992	
British Columbia	Transportation of Dangerous Goods Act, S.B.C., 1985	Waste Management Act, S.B.C. 1982/Amended 1990, 1992	
Manitoba	Dangerous Goods Handling and Transportation Act, R.S.M. 1987	Environment Act, S.M. 1987–88 Waste Reduction and Prevention Act, S.M. 1989–90	
New Brunswick	Transportation of Dangerous Goods Act, S.N.B. 1988		
Newfoundland	Dangerous Goods Transportation Act, R.S.N. 1990	Department of Environment and Lands Act, R.S.N. 1990/ Waste Material Disposal Act, R.S.N. 1990/Water Protection Act, R.S.N. 1990	
Northwest Territories	Transportation of Dangerous Goods Act, 1990, S.N.W.T.		
Nova Scotia	Dangerous Goods Transportation Act, R.S.N.S. 1989	Environment Act (draft)/ Litter Abatement Act, S.N.S. 1989	
Ontario	Dangerous Goods Transportation Act, R.S.O. 1990	Environmental Protection Act, R.S.O. 1990 as amended/ Environmental Bill of Rights, 1993, S.O. 1993/Ontario Water Resources Act, R.S.O. 1990/Waste Management Act, R.S.O. 1992/Environmental Assessment Act	Gasoline Handling Act, S.O. 1990/ Health Protection and Promotion Act, R.S.O. 1990/ Municipal Act, R.S.O. 1990/ Pesticides Act, R.S.O. 1990/Public Health Act, R.S.O. 1980/Energy Act, R.S.O. 1990
Prince Edward Island	Dangerous Goods Transportation Act, R.S.P.E.I. 1988	Environmental Protection Act, R.S.P.E.I. 1988	
Quebec		Environmental Quality Act, R.S.Q. 1990	
Saskatchewan	Dangerous Goods Transportation Act, S.S. 1984–85–86	Litter Control Act, R.S.S. 1978	
Yukon Territory	Dangerous Goods Transportation Act, R.S.Y.T. 1986	Environment Act, S.Y. 1991	

legislation. If the release is outside the building, or if the potentially hazardous substance is released into the sewer, storm system, water or air, it falls under the jurisdiction of the authority enforcing the environmental legislation. Any single occurrence might involve both authorities.

The parallels between environmental and OHS legislation have extended to the courts. In *R. v. Bata Industries Ltd., Bata, Marchant and Weston*, Bata Industries Ltd. and three of its directors were charged with allowing a large chemical waste storage site containing many deteriorating and leaking containers to discharge known toxic industrial chemicals to the ground environment. The defendants used the defence of due diligence, arguing that the legislation was vague and imprecise and contrary to the Canadian Charter of Rights and Freedoms. The company was convicted, as were two of the directors (the third director was acquitted). The court found that the two defendants had not exercised due diligence. The court stated that, while it did not expect Boards of Directors to make all environmental decisions, these decisions were too important to be delegated to subordinates.

◆ ◆ ◆

TRANSPORTATION OF DANGEROUS GOODS

The regulation of environmental hazards, occupational health and safety, and transportation of dangerous goods is not the exclusive domain of either the federal or provincial governments. Therefore, the practitioner should be familiar with the statutes relevant to his or her particular jurisdiction. In essence, the environmental and transportation legislation seeks to supply the framework within which society can protect itself from the risk that attends the transportation of inherently dangerous materials.

The federal legislation governing the transportation of dangerous goods applies to all persons who handle, offer for transport, transport, or import any dangerous goods. The provincial legislation does not always go this far, making it sometimes impossible to determine whether federal or provincial statutes apply. Notwithstanding some provincial limitations, dangerous goods legislation applies to carriers, shippers, and transportation intermediaries such as freight forwarders and customs brokers. Various regulations exist with respect to identification and placarding, quantities, training and certification of workers. The regulatory wording complements the WHMIS requirements and the OHS responsibility of employers and supervisors to educate and train workers.

In *R. v. Midland Transport Ltd.* (1991), the New Brunswick Provincial Court made the following observation about the legislation:

> *The Transportation of Dangerous Goods Act and the Regulations thereunder fall in the category of legislation which creates public welfare offences. Recognizing the potential dangers, it establishes safety guidelines for the handling of hazardous materials to ensure the protection of the public and the environment.*

◆ ◆ ◆
CORPORATE LIABILITY

Whereas in the past, directors and officers of incorporated entities were responsible solely to the corporation and shareholders, their zone of accountability now extends to the public at large. Environmental and occupational health and safety statutes have been amended to include broad responsibilities for directors and officers. Liabilities directors and officers now face include the following:

◆ Fines or imprisonment for corporate pollution, causing or permitting the discharge of liquid industrial waste into the ground.

◆ Clean-up costs associated with a property the corporation owns, controls, or occupies.

◆ Fines for failing to comply with regulatory legislation. In Alberta, a worker was killed when a piece of equipment collapsed onto a machine he was operating. Suncor was fined $150,000 for failing to ensure that machinery was used and maintained according to the manufacturer's specifications [COSHN, 1995].

Canadian jurisprudence has followed the lead of the United States in extending legal responsibility to the boardroom. The directing minds of a company are no longer permitted to hide behind the laws of incorporation.

SUMMARY

The complexities associated with OHS legislation in Canada continue to grow. This chapter has outlined the scope of this legislation and the changing climate surrounding it. The human resource practitioner must constantly monitor labour legislation pertaining to health and safety in the workplace. The federal and provincial governments have made significant headway toward harmonization of some regulations, but consistent OHS and environmental laws across Canada are still a long way off.

EXERCISE

1. An auto-parts manufacturer employs 500 workers in his factory. The plant operates on three shifts and its various lines include large punch presses, conveyors, paint-spray booths, and overhead cranes. A worker has been killed following an accident on the overhead crane line. The worker was guiding the load hoisted by the crane when the load slipped, causing a failure of the supporting cables. The worker was killed when the falling load struck him.

   Create a hypothetical case that would provide the employer with a strong due diligence defence.

Questions

1. What is the difference between the responsibilities assigned to companies under occupational health and safety and those assigned under environmental legislation?
2. What three components make up WHMIS compliance?
3. A defence of "due diligence" has been ruled to be constitutional when applied to regulatory statutes. In your own words, describe why this decision is important with respect to health, safety, and environmental contraventions.

References

"Reduced Fine for Company Disappointing." *Accident Prevention* (September/October1995): 6.

"Top Fine for Company after Workers Die." *Accident Prevention* (March/April 1995): 6.

"The Effectiveness of Joint Health and Safety Committees." *Worklife Report* 9, no. 3 (1994): 12–13.

WHMIS Regulations Consulted

Model OSH Regulations

Alberta Chemical Hazards Regulation

British Columbia, Workplace Hazardous Materials Info System Regulation

Manitoba, Workplace Hazardous Materials Info System Regulation

New Brunswick, Workplace Hazardous Materials Info System Regulation

Newfoundland, Workplace Hazardous Materials Info System Regulations (WHMIS)

Northwest Territories, Work Site Hazardous Materials Information System Regulations

Nova Scotia, Workplace Hazardous Materials Information System (WHMIS) Regulations

Ontario, Workplace Hazardous Materials Information System (WHMIS)

Prince Edward Island, Workplace Hazardous Materials Information System Regulations

Quebec, An Act to Amend the Act respecting Occupational Health and Safety

Saskatchewan, The Occupational Health and Safety Act 1993, Part IV, Workplace Hazardous Materials Information System

Yukon, Workplace Hazardous Materials Information System Regulations

3

Workers' Compensation

♦ ♦ ♦

INTRODUCTION

Workers' compensation is a form of insurance that is governed by an Act of Parliament for the purpose of helping workers who are injured on the job return to work. Consider the example of a construction labourer who has sustained an injury on the job and is now unable to work due to his disability. Workers' compensation will ensure that the injured worker receives (1) first-aid treatment either on the job or at the nearest local treatment facility; (2) benefits while he is at home recuperating from his injuries; and (3) proper treatment for his injuries. If necessary, rehabilitation will be provided to help the worker return to his former job or some modified version thereof if circumstances dictate.

♦ ♦ ♦

HISTORICAL ROOTS

Workers' compensation, which had its origin in Germany in 1884, was not established in Canada until 1915, when the Ontario Workers' Compensation Act was passed by Parliament. This time lag was something of an advantage because it allowed for consideration of the American and European experience. In 1900, an inquiry was made by the Ontario government into the German system. This was followed in 1912–1914 by an intensive and prolonged study of the existing laws in Europe and the United States, under the guidance of Sir William Ralph Meredith, Chief Justice of Ontario. On the basis of his findings, the first Act in Canada was passed.

Acts were subsequently passed in all of the provinces, and although they have been amended many times (largely for the purpose of increasing coverage and benefits), they have retained many of the principles set forth in the Ontario Act of 1914, namely:

---

*This chapter was written by Paul Nolis.

1. Collective liability for employers, with some recognition of risk in the amount of contribution paid by individual employers

2. Workers compensated regardless of the financial condition of the employer

3. Compensation based on loss of earnings

4. No-fault system

5. Nonadversarial process (no recourse to the courts)

◆ ◆ ◆
ADMINISTRATION AND RESPONSIBILITIES

The provincial Acts throughout Canada are administered by Workers' Compensation Boards (WCBs) that are appointed by the Lieutenant-Governor in council within each province, and that hold office during pleasure. The various boards are empowered to fix and collect assessment, determine the right to compensation, and pay the amount due to the injured worker. In all these matters, the workers' compensation system has exclusive and final jurisdiction. The Ontario Workers' Compensation Act is representative of the type of legislation that exists in all jurisdictions in terms of its authority and power.

With respect to injured workers, the boards' responsibilities are as follows:

(a) the injured worker is entitled to be paid while he or she is off work and is entitled to have all of the medical bills paid, if the injury happened while at work and because of work;

(b) the injured worker will receive a pension if the disability proves to be permanent;

(c) the injured worker will receive benefits if it is shown that as a result of the accident, he or she cannot earn the same amount of money earned prior to the accident;

(d) the injured worker's immediate family and dependents will be entitled to benefits if the worker was killed as a result of an injury on the job;

(e) the workers' compensation boards will decide which employers will fall in which classification, to ensure that there is consistency;

(f) the workers' compensation system will decide whether an individual is a worker, a subcontractor or employer, because it does make a difference as to the type of responsibility that this class has to the board, and how much money they pay to the board;

(g) the workers' compensation system will pay benefits if a worker is affected by an industrial disease, that resulted from his occupation.

In relation to most of the industries within the scope of the provincial Acts, the system of compensation is one of compulsory and collective liability. Under collective liability, the various industries are classified according to their end product, and each employer therein is assessed at a rate of percentage of its payroll, which is determined by the accident cost of its classification. From the accident fund thus collected payments are made for compensation, medical aid, rehabilitation, accident prevention, and administrative expenses. Each employer is liable for assessment irrespective of the cost of accidents sustained by its workers. As a result, each is relieved of individual liability. In most provinces, liability is further distributed by a disaster reserve fund.

Public authorities and certain large corporations such as railways and shipping/telegraph companies are excluded from the collective liabilities' scheme and are individually liable for compensation; however, all disputes are determined by the WCB. Such corporations contribute their portion of the cost of administering the various Acts.

Most WCBs at one time had responsibilities for the accident-prevention or OHS aspects of workers' compensation. In the 1970s and 1980s, the combined role was seen as a conflict of interest by some governments, and these WCB functions were placed under a department of government in most provinces. Although the OHS function is separate in most jurisdictions, all WCBs cooperate with the responsible government department by sharing and making information available. A number of WCBs have input into the experience rating or merit/demerit program and work with government in developing programs designed to reduce workplace injuries.

Employers or injured workers who disagree with a WCB decision can turn to various appeal bodies and mechanisms. In Prince Edward Island, Saskatchewan, and Yukon, the WCB is the final level of appeal.

Most WCBs within Canada do enter into agreements among themselves to avoid duplicate assessments and to assist the worker in claiming and receiving compensation when two or more jurisdictions are involved. These agreements are intended to ensure that the worker receives the best possible benefits, and that coverage is extended in a province often at the request of the injured worker.

The provincial Acts generally cover all employment in industries such as lumbering, mining, fishing, manufacturing, construction, engineering, and transportation. Covered occupations include operation of electrical power lines, employment in water works and other public utilities, navigation, operation of boats and ships, operation of elevators and warehousing, street cleaning, painting, decorating, renovating, and cleaning. Those types of employment that are exempted from this list may be admitted at their own request.

Personal injuries resulting from accidents arising out of and in the course of employment are compensated except in cases where the accident is attributed to the worker's serious and willful misconduct and does not result in serious disablement. Certain specified occupational diseases also give the various workers' compensation systems the right to compensate.

◆ ◆ ◆
COMPENSATION RATES AND METHODS

There are two standards in place for determining the rate for payment of compensation. Eight jurisdictions base the payment on a percentage (generally 90 percent) of net earnings; the other four base payments on 75 percent of average earnings. Jurisdictions like Nova Scotia have used both methods depending on the date of the accident. A worker's average earnings are generally calculated on the basis of his or her earnings during the last 12 months. Since a large number of workers have not worked for the same employer for 12 months, other ways of establishing earnings are sanctioned.

Each Act also stipulates a maximum amount of earnings that can be used to determine the amount of compensation. This figure ranges from above $50,000 in Ontario to below $30,000 in Prince Edward Island. The minimum weekly amount that can be paid for total disability ranges from around $60 in Prince Edward Island to around $320 in Saskatchewan.

The method used to determine the average wages of a worker is the one that gives the best representation of the worker's weekly earnings and seems fair and reasonable. Work is made available and the worker still suffers an earnings loss, the payment for the continuing disability may be adjusted, whether or not the worker accepts the work. A payment for noneconomic loss (functional impairment) is also made in several jurisdictions. This figure is based on such factors as the worker's age, degree of impairment, and number of dependents. For example, a 40-year-old worker with three children would receive a larger payment than a 60-year-old worker with no children.

Compensation may take two forms: cash benefits or wage or earnings loss. Cash allowance is based on the degree of severity of the disability. Payments continue as long as a permanent disability lasts in accordance with the entitlement established by the province. In cases of permanent partial disabilities, the worker receives a life pension based upon rating scales established by the provincial boards. There are allowances for economic losses and noneconomic losses. An injured worker could receive noneconomic loss if he was unable to perform some of the things that he was able to do before his accident. In the case of a worker unable to golf as a result of the accident, a benefit would be paid for that noneconomic loss.

Wage or earnings loss refers to situations where the worker can no longer earn the same amount of money that he was earning prior to the accident as a result of his disability. For a worker who was earning $20 per hour before his accident and now, as a result of his accident, is capable of earning only $10 per hour, the potential compensation is $10 per hour. The earnings loss is calculated and paid as long as the worker is unable to return to work or carry on employment; is considered totally disabled; and is undertaking treatment and following medical advice. When a partial recovery has taken place, a reduction of payment may occur. When a permanent recovery has occurred, compensation will cease if the recovery is total and will be fixed if the recovery is partial.

In the event of the death of a worker, the spouse receives a pension in accordance with the schedules established by the various jurisdictions, and allowances are given to children. In addition, most provincial boards allow an immediate lump-sum payment and variable expenses.

❖ ❖ ❖
MEDICAL AID AND ACCIDENT PREVENTION

Accompanying compensation in all cases is the provision of medical aid. This aid includes medical and surgical care, hospitalization, nursing care, drugs and supplies, physiotherapy and occupational therapy, and the provision and maintenance of prostheses. An employee who sustains a work-related injury is compensated for not only loss of earnings but also loss of *functional capacity*. Workers who, as a result of their accident, are no longer able to perform some of their duties on the job such as lifting, twisting, or bending are considered to have suffered loss of functional capacity for which benefits are payable.

Employers within a particular industry may form safety associations and make rules for accident prevention that, upon approval of the WCB and lieutenant-governor in council in the provincial jurisdiction, are binding upon all employers in that industry. WCBs pay the expenses of these associations out of the accident fund, and have the authority to investigate the premises of employers to ensure compliance with safeguards required by law. The goal of safety associations is to provide training in the area of accident prevention and health and safety.

◆ ◆ ◆
SOCIAL GOALS OF WORKERS' COMPENSATION

Workers' compensation is driven by two main social goals: (1) to provide services intended to prevent injuries or reduce the psychological impacts of injuries that have occurred; and (2) to provide the training and development necessary to prepare an injured worker to return to work. The various WCBs have come to look upon compensation as a means for society to share with the worker the consequences of industrial accidents, and to ensure the restoration of the worker to active participation in the life of the community. The focus is more on restoring earning power than paying for its loss. In no sense is compensation considered a reward for being injured.

This social conception of compensation is grounded in the following standard provisions contained in the various Acts:

1. Unlimited medical aid

2. Artificial appliances

3. A fund to encourage re-employment (known as Second Injury and Enhancement Fund (SIEF) in some provinces)

4. Liberal compensation

5. Rehabilitation maintenance income

Not only does the compensation system in Canada provide greater benefits than most insurers, but it also ensures that benefits are not prejudiced by earnings after rehabilitation. In contrast many compensation laws in the United States hinder rehabilitation either by cutting off compensation for permanent injury as soon as workers begin to earn as much money as they did before the injury, or by paying compensation for only a limited period, leaving workers stranded before they can be retrained. In Canadian jurisdictions, permanently injured workers draw compensation for life and are able to keep their pensions, even if the sum of their pensions and supplement to earnings amount to more than their wages before they were hurt.

◆ ◆ ◆
PROVISION FOR SECOND INJURIES

The Canadian workers' compensation system provides for a "second injury fund" whose purpose is to facilitate the re-employment of disabled workers. Without this provision for multiple injuries, employers within Canada are liable to discriminate against workers with disabilities because an additional injury to such persons might cause disability out of proportion to the last injury considered by itself. Thus, a worker who has lost one arm will be given a total disability rating if he or she loses the second arm. By charging the excess liability resulting from the cumulative effect of a prior disability, and the subsequent injury to a disaster reserve fund, the various Acts distribute the burden throughout industry as a whole rather than letting it rest on one particular class. In this way, employers are relieved of the extra risks associated with the employment of workers with disabilities.

◆ ◆ ◆
REHABILITATION

In earlier times, persons with disabilities were left to fend for themselves. Some were placed in poorhouses while others survived through begging. Gradually, society began to realize that the best way to deal with these individuals would be to help them become productive. But accomplishing this proved to be a difficult and frustrating experience. Persons with disabilities found that although they were allowed an opportunity to earn a living, they could do so only by accepting menial jobs that no one else wanted. It took World War I, and the return of thousands upon thousands of injured soldiers, to elevate the social status of persons with disabilities and provide the impetus for rehabilitation programs.

Rehabilitation is a financial necessity as well as a moral and social obligation. Only with the assistance of effective rehabilitation can the future cost of the workers' compensation system be maintained at a reasonable level. There are three types of rehabilitation. *Vocational rehabilitation* refers to the steps undertaken by WCBs to help injured workers return to their place of employment or find similar or suitable work elsewhere. Placement services, vocational testing, and retraining or training may all be part of this process. *Physical rehabilitation* refers to the steps taken to restore, whether fully or partially, the worker's physical function. *Social rehabilitation* refers to the psychological and practical services that help workers with severe disabilities cope with daily life (e.g., assistance with cooking, bathing, household chores).

A scenario in which the full range of compensation benefits was provided to an injured worker is outlined in Box 3.1.

◆ ◆ ◆
INDUSTRIAL DISEASES AND WORKPLACE STRESSORS

A significant issue facing workers' compensation today concerns industrial diseases and the degree to which they are work-related. Examples of industrial diseases would include various cancers, skin diseases, and allergic reactions to materials and components within the workplace.

Industrial disease has been part of workers' compensation ever since six specific diseases were cited in Ontario's Act of 1914. The last 30 years have seen a broadening of the definition of "accident" and "injury," which has allowed for greater consideration of industrial disease claims. Today, many industrial disease claims can be considered in the same way as any other claim. The need to isolate the point at which the disease was contracted has given way to a recognition that the disease could be the result of exposure or injury over time.

Because some diseases may stem from nonindustrial sources, the schedules of each jurisdiction may contain specific requirements that must be met before the presumption of work-relatedness will be evoked by the WCB. A disease like lung cancer may be attributable to either industrial or nonindus-

BOX 3.1

In 1987, Mr. X lost his left hand in an industrial accident. Over a period of 10 years, he had risen from the position of delivery truck driver to plant manager at a small aluminum fabricator in northwest Toronto.

Mr. X recalled the accident. "We were having problems with the alignment. The mechanic was on lunch and repairs had to be made. I had done the same thing a thousand times before. It was a stupid accident. There was a piece of paper on the floor and I instinctively kicked it out of the way. Unfortunately, I didn't know that the foot pedal was beneath the paper. The press came down in the blink of an eye and my hand was left attached to my wrist by a single tendon."

Mr. X had been thinking about a career change before the accident. In addition to his duties as plant manager, he had begun to do some selling and marketing and found it was something he enjoyed. After the accident, Mr. X knew that he would not be able to work in the plant again so he began to consider retraining.

After his surgery, Mr. X spent four weeks in hospital recovering. A WCB representative came to see him two days after the accident and initiated his claim so that he could continue to pay his bills. Before Mr. X could be fitted with a prosthesis, his physical wounds had to heal. He spent the next couple of months getting better and receiving treatment.

Around this time Mr. X decided to pursue a marketing career. Thanks to the sponsorship of the WCB, he enrolled in Seneca College's marketing program. Upon graduation, Mr. X received further assistance from a WCB placement adviser. Within months, a job was located. After completing a training program with his new employer, Mr. X began work as a full-time marketing representative.

In this scenario, the full range of compensation benefits was provided, including benefits, medical aid, prosthetic devices, vocational rehabilitation, placement services, and counselling in social services.

trial causes. As we know, lung cancer may be caused by smoking or other environmental factors; however, it can also be caused by particles (such as asbestos) inhaled on the job. It is the responsibility of WCBs to determine cause-and-effect relationships. There are those who argue that the industrial disease schedules should be eliminated from the Acts either because they are not current or because they are being used to restrict rather than expand coverage.

Industrial disease claims, unless very straightforward, are often adjudicated by a special claim unit and may require additional expert medical opinion as well as exposure and employment histories. Some WCBs use separate claim forms for specific industrial diseases. The latency period is quite often a major factor in determining the acceptability of the claim.

Stress-related disabilities can be divided in three groups: (1) physical injury or industrial disease leading to a mental disability; (2) mental stress resulting in a physical disability, traumatic occurrence, or series of occurrences; (3) mental stress resulting in a mental condition.

Generally speaking, stress claims in the first group have been dealt with in the same way as any other claims. Those in the second group have been subject to some selection. If the disability (say, a cardiac attack) is acute, it will be considered for compensation. If the disability (say, an ulcer) is a result of accumulated stress, it will likely not be considered for compensation. With respect to the third group, an unusual incident that provokes the mental reaction and results in a disability will probably be considered for compensation; chronic stress resulting in a mental disability is seldom compensated. The adjudication of stress claims is currently receiving a great deal of attention from all insurance parties.

◆ ◆ ◆

HOW ORGANIZATIONS CAN MANAGE DISABILITY

Every company, including small businesses, should create and implement strategies to manage disability and reduce the period of compensation claims. Seven strategies for managing disability are outlined below.

1. *Create and run an effective corporate culture that values employees and establishes them as an integral part of the workforce.* An effective disability management program cannot conflict with the organizational culture. Specifically, it is the culture that makes it easier to create a disability management program. The corporate culture best able to enhance a disability management program is one that includes the following:

   (a) Regular collaborative communication between supervisors and employees

(b) Helpful cooperative relationships among co-workers

(c) Training for new managers on how to handle personnel issues effectively, including evaluating employee performance

(d) Favourable work conditions

(e) Opportunities for career growth

(f) Clearly defined and flexible work roles

(g) A willingness on the part of senior management to invest money up front in order to save money in the near and distant future

(h) Giving local managers incentives to make disability management part of their decision-making process

2. *Ensure senior management support.* To be successful, a disability management program requires support and cooperation from staff at all levels of the company. At times, the most effective way to obtain this cooperation is to enlist senior management support for a strong effective disability management program.

3. *Intervene early and regularly.* All corporations should have a policy of contacting employees early and regularly throughout the disability absence. Contacting employees sooner rather than later produces three distinct benefits:

(a) Employees tend to come back to work more quickly.

(b) Employees who return to work tend to stay at work.

(c) Employees generally return to earn a higher wage.

The early-return and regular-contact strategy must be supplemented with an effective return-to-work policy that must be in place before an employee becomes disabled.

4. *Develop case management capacities.* Case management refers to the coordination of health and social services so that injuries or disabilities receive care that is appropriate, timely, and efficient. The goals of case management are to enhance the injured worker's quality of life and, if possible, reduce the costs associated with care. Case management should therefore begin early in the process to ensure that injured workers are receiving the most effective and most cost-efficient services available.

5. *Create modified and light duty jobs to allow an early return to work.* The most cost-saving strategy is to bring employees back to work when they can perform at least part of their tasks. This concept can speed up recovery by giving an employee practical goals to achieve during the rehabilitation process. It can serve a work-hardening function by gradually strengthening the employee's ability, thereby reducing the risk of injury on the first day back at work.

6. *Train supervisors to encourage and facilitate early return to work.* This is perhaps the most difficult step in any disability management program. The company can begin by expanding the role of the supervisors to include assistance for employees with disabilities.

7. *Create data systems.* An effective disability management system can greatly minimize costs by identifying problem areas, by creating a baseline for measuring improvement, and by increasing the efficiency with which workers' compensation absences are tracked. Companies can obtain a system tailored to individual needs and budget. Up-to-date data allow a company to track trends and identify problem areas within the corporation.

◆ ◆ ◆
ASSESSMENTS

Employers are grouped together according to the type of operation or industry in which they are engaged and assessed on the base. The groups are referred to as industries, classes, subclasses, or classifications. In some jurisdictions, the terms "unit" and "sector" are used; employers are not grouped by occupation, although occupation may help determine a subdivision of an industry or class.

Separate accounts are generally used when an employer is involved in more than one industry or when an industry or employer's operation includes several departments. Assessments are determined by the WCB at least once a year when the board sets a percentage or rate to be applied to the payroll of the employer. Payrolls are estimated and then the employer is required to submit a certified payroll statement.

The workers' compensation system in Canada is based on the concept of dividing employers into three broad categories: (1) those who contribute to the accident fund and benefit from its collective liability; (2) those who are individually liable for their own employees' accidents; and (3) those in certain low-risk industries who are excluded under the various Acts across the country. Employers who pay directly for the accidents of their employees are generally public enterprises such as provincial and municipal governments and certain transportation and communication companies within Crown corporations.

All employers within a particular industry are assessed at the same rate based on the accident experience of the industry as a whole. In most jurisdictions, within the general accident fund, provision is made for a rate stabilization and disaster reserve fund. One group by itself cannot sustain the heavy costs associated with a major disaster that might occur in any one year or with a sharp decline in assessable payroll due to massive layoffs in the industry. Continued financing can be provided by the rate stabilization and disaster funds, which are maintained by the various WCBs.

◆ ◆ ◆
EXPERIENCE RATING

Experience rating in workers' compensation refers to an accident insurance premium-pricing scheme that takes into account the clear cost experience of the individual employer. Under experience rating, the assessment for each firm may be higher or lower than the basic rate for the relative industry group. Firms with lower-than-average accident costs per worker pay lower premiums than firms with above-average accident costs. In essence, experience rating reduces or eliminates the cross-subsidization of relatively unsafe firms by relatively safe firms. Given two otherwise similar firms, a safer employer will face lower workers' compensation costs and hence lower production costs. Thus, the primary effect of the experience rating is to create a financial incentive for relatively unsafe firms to begin caring for their workforce.

Experience rating is intended to offer an incentive to employers to reduce accidents and to return workers to their jobs as early as possible. In this way, employers benefit because the amount of dollars that are spent on compensation is reduced, and workers benefit because they are returned to their job quickly. Experience rating is thus a process of rewarding good performers and penalizing those organizations that are not making efforts to reduce accidents and return workers back to work as quickly as possible.

Experience rating, for WCBs assessment rate setting, generally shifts a greater degree of the responsibility for workers' compensation costs, from the industry of a group as a whole, to the particular employers actually incurring the injury cost. When experience rating is used, the rate of assessment payable by an employer may vary above or below the standard rate applicable to the rate group or subclass. Most experience rating programs modify an individual employer's assessment by comparing the firm's claims cost of average experience for the industry or class in which the employer falls. Some modify reassessments by comparing the firm's claim costs experience with the firm's assessments.

Experience rating is intended to serve as an incentive for employers to reduce both the number of workers injured and the length of lost time by encouraging employers to establish and maintain safety and prevention programs, and to assist the worker to return to work as soon as possible. Employers can accomplish these goals by preventing accidents and injuries in the workplace, effectively tracking the progress of claims, and rehabilitating and rehiring injured workers.

Generally speaking, if an employer on experience rating has a three-year average accident cost lower than that of the entire industry within the group, that employer will receive a rebate on his annual assessment. On the other hand, employers who have an average accident cost higher than the industry will receive demerit charges on top of their regular assessments.

One of the most important reasons for mandatory experience rating is the reduction of industrial accidents and their costs. Professor Paul Weiler, in his report to the government on the study of the Workers' Compensation Act, states: "It is the employer who is in control of the workplace. Senior management must be influenced to pursue industrial safety. Business reacts to economic incentives." Consequently, Professor Weiler recommends that individual experience rating be made the rule, rather than the exception. This concept has been accepted.

The profit-maximizing, cost-minimizing firm will respond to incentive by investing in activities that reduce its workers' compensation claim costs to the point where the expected marginal benefits (i.e., incremental reduction in the expected cost of accidents) equal the marginal cost. Given the existence of workplace risk, and assuming full information about such risk, the firm may allocate resources to safety practices or pay the costs associated with work injury. Profit-maximizing firms operating in competitive markets will strive to minimize some of the costs associated with the work-place accident—e.g., workers' compensation premium payments (including experience rating service charges/refunds as well as material costs), fixed employment costs, lost production time, and damage to equipment) by pre-venting accidents (i.e., reducing the probability of a hazardous state) as well as by engaging in activities that minimize costs once accidents do occur. Post-accident employer actions that can result in claim cost reduction include implementing early-return-to-work programs and appealing WCB decisions on workers' benefits.

The Workers' Compensation Board in Ontario operates three experi-ence rating plans. The Voluntary Experience Rating plan was established in 1953, while the New Employer Experience Rating (NEER) plan and the council amended draft #7 (CAD-7) plan were both initiated in 1984. All of these plans require participation by the entire rate group. Individual employ-ers within the industry group may not opt out of an experience rating plan.

The NEER plan provides for a refund or surcharge based upon the dif-ference between the firm's actual and expected claims costs, adjusted by a rating factor that varies by the size of the firm. A very small firm would receive or pay 10 percent of the difference, graduating up to 80 percent for larger firms. Thus, the smaller the firm, the more NEER resembles a tradi-tional collective-liability insurance scheme.

The CAD-7 plan applies exclusively to 11 construction industry groups. Employers receive assessment refunds and surcharges based on a formula that takes into account both injury frequency and claim cost. The magnitude of the refund or surcharge varies directly with the size of the firm.

◆ ◆ ◆
WORKWELL PROGRAM

The Workwell program is designed to promote health and safety in Ontario workplaces by levying additional assessment on employers that do not main-tain safe and healthy work environments.

The Workwell program has two major components. The first compo-nent is intended to assist those employers who have demonstrated good occupational health and safety programs and who have exemplary accident costs and frequency histories. These employers may receive lump sum pay-ments for their good work.

The second aspect of the Workwell program is targeted at employers who have demonstrated poor accident costs and frequency experiences, and thus penalties may be levied to these employers if they do not amend the programs or implement new programs to promote health and safety.

1. Accident Costs

The history of a firm's cost experience is reviewed in relation to the assessment monies that the firm has paid to the board. The objective of this comparison is to identify firms whose performance has been consistently excellent. The standards for defining excellence is dependent upon the accident cost per assessment ratio and the size of the firm. Development ratios are set out below:

FIRM SIZE ACCIDENT COST WCB ASSESSMENT X 100

5-20 employees   an accident cost to assessment ration of 0% in each of the past five years

21-35 employees   an accident cost to assessment ration of 0% in each of the past three years

35 + employees   an accident cost to assessment ration of 5% or less in each of the past three years

2. Experience Rating

The employer must not be issued a surcharge under an experience rating plan or under section 103/8 of the Workers' Compensation Act at any time in the past three to five years. The specific time period under review, which is dependent upon firm size, is for a firm with (a) more than 35 employees (3 years); (b) 21 to 35 employees (3 years); or (c) 5 to 20 employees (5 years).

3. Orders Under Occupational Safety and Healthy Acts

During the past three years, the employer must have received no orders representing violation of the Occupational Health and Safety Act or regulations made thereunder. Examples would include lock-out procedures or confined space requirement and ventilation. In addition, the employer must not have experienced any critical injuries as defined by regulations 714/82 under the

Ontario Health and Safety Act or any refusals to work that resulted in a potentially dangerous decision.

NOTIFICATION OF STATUS

If the criteria are met, the firm will be contacted in writing and informed of their status. These exemplary firms will be invited to apply for an award under section 103/6 of the Act.

EMPLOYERS' ADMISSION OF HEALTH AND SAFETY PROGRAMS EXAMPLES

When a firm applies for the section 103/6 award they will submit examples of their firm's occupational health and safety program. Examples would include some of the following:

- a copy of the firm's health and safety manual;
- the firm's health and safety goals for the year;
- job descriptions for workers and supervisors;
- a procedure for a particular risk orientation and operation;
- copies of the first page of the health and safety committee minutes for the last three meetings; or
- copies of the first page of the last three worksite evaluations.

EVALUATION PROCESS

The board staff will review the occupational health and safety material submissions prior to visiting the firm to perform an on-site Workwell health and safety program evaluation.

AWARDS

In section 103/6, awards of the Workwell evaluation are in recognition for consistent exemplary accident and illness performance and for the health and safety program in place at the worksite location. Those firms that meet the threshold criteria and that achieve the highest scores on the Workwell evaluation will receive section 103/6 awards.

WORKWELL PROGRAM EVALUATION METHOD

The Workwell evaluation form, covering the basic elements of any generic occupational health and safety program, is part of this document. Each question specifies what the evaluator will be reviewing during the audit process.

The number of workers at the firm is one of the factors used to determine employer size, and the evaluator will also consider the complexity and diversity of the operation. A small employer may have one distinct level of management, a medium employer may have two distinct levels of management, and the large employer may have three or more distinct levels of management.

VERIFICATION

Evaluators will verify the existence, consistent application, implementation, and enforcement of the firm's occupational health and safety programs. The verification process requirements are listed on the evaluation and include the following:

"D" DOCUMENTATION

The evaluator shall review and, where necessary, attach copies of the firm's health and safety program documentation. The documentation may include written policies, rules, procedures, work procedures, job descriptions, inspection reports, and minutes of health and safety committee meetings.

"I" INTERVIEW - MANAGEMENT - WORKERS

The evaluator will discuss the entire evaluation process with representatives of both management and labour. In addition, the evaluator will perform a worksite tour. The purpose of the worksite tour is to conduct random informal contact with the firm's workers. During the tour, the evaluator will be asking employees questions about different aspects of the firm's health and safety program, in order to verify the level of program implementation and the employees knowledge and understanding. The evaluator will record, wherever possible, the names and titles of the employees questioned during the tour.

"O" OBSERVATIONS - MANAGEMENT - WORKERS

While at the worksite, the evaluator will observe the process and procedures related to health and safety. Examples of observations include: notice boards, housekeeping, production processes, job performance, machine equipment function, use of personal protective equipment or clothing.

◆ ◆ ◆
SUMMARY

Workers' compensation was established in Canada in 1915 with the passage of Ontario's Workers' Compensation Act. Since then, coverage and benefits have increased, as have the associated costs. The thrust of the workers' compensation system today is to create more safety-conscious work environments and to work actively to reduce the number of work-related accidents, disabilities, and diseases. Primary responsibility rests with the employer to ensure that the compensation system is administered efficiently and funded equitably through assessments on employers. The underlying philosophy of workers' compensation is that employers are as much accountable to their employees as they are for the bottom line.

EXERCISES

1. Outline the responsibilities of WCBs today. Describe how these responsibilities have changed over the years since the inception of workers' compensation in 1915.

2. Imagine that you are a truck driver. An accident on the road has left you with two broken legs and a head concussion. What types of assistance might you expect from workers' compensation? What could your manager do to expedite your return to work?

3. If you are employed, talk with the health and safety manager in your organization. (If you are a student, ask to speak to the safety officer at your school.) Obtain information about the organization's sector, assessment, and record of experience ratings.

4

Hazard Identification and Evaluation

◆ ◆ ◆
INTRODUCTION

Virtually every workplace has recognizable hazards to which people are exposed. A hazard is any existing or potential condition in the workplace that, by itself or interacting with other factors, can result in deaths, injuries, property damage, or other losses (Firenze, 1978). Hazard identification and evaluation refers to the process of determining those factors likely to cause incidents and accidents. Hazard control is the subject of Chapter 5. This chapter will focus on the first steps in the hazard-control process: identification of the sources of workplace hazards, methods to systematically examine these hazards, and ways to assess the probability, severity, and consequences of the hazards. Following is a list of pertinent terms and their definitions.

1. **Hazard.** A *hazard* is any condition or changing set of circumstances that has the potential to cause an injury. A hazardous condition would include a damaged ladder, an icy porch and steps, or a frayed electrical wire. A changing set of circumstances would include the substitution of a nontoxic solvent by a toxic solvent.

2. **Event.** An *event* is any activity that may occur on a day-to-day basis as a direct or indirect result of some human or human-related undertaking. Operating a forklift or word processor are events.

3. **Incident.** An *incident* is any observable human activity that is sufficiently complete as to allow predictions about the consequences of the performance of the act (Laing, 1992). Examples of incidents include failing to wear protective goggles when operating machines, wearing loose clothing around equipment, handling hot objects with unprotected hands, and cleaning a machine that is in motion.

4. **Accident.** An *accident* is any unwanted event that causes harm to people or property. Accidents usually result from direct contact with some form of energy that is greater than the strength of the body or structure to

resist. These energies may be electrical, mechanical, thermal, radiative, gravity, kinetic, or chemical in nature. When a worker falls off a ladder and breaks an arm, the energies involved are gravity (the fast trip to the ground), mechanical (not enough grip between the worker's feet and the ladder rung), and kinetic (the sudden stop).

5. **Injury.** An *injury* is any trauma, whether physical or mental, direct or indirect, acute or chronic, experienced by a human being. *Physical injury* includes any damage to tissue (resulting from cutting, abrasion, burn, etc.), and can include the inhalation of a toxic substance. A physical injury is very easy to identify. *Mental injury*, which includes such conditions as anxiety or depression, is more difficult to identify and prove.

A *direct injury* is the immediate or primary result of an action, such as leaning against a hot stove and getting burnt. An *indirect injury* would include a serious complication, like infection, resulting from the same stove burn. *Acute* trauma is an injury that occurs quickly (e.g., a burn from a welder). The term *chronic* is used to describe a condition that takes many years to develop and manifest itself; the development of a malignant tumour 25 years after exposure to a toxic material is considered a chronic injury.

◆ ◆ ◆
SOURCES OF HAZARDS

The identification of hazards examines three areas of analysis: human factors, situational factors, and environmental factors.

HUMAN FACTORS

Incidents involving humans fall into two main categories, *predictable* and *random*. An incident that is a result of a predictable action is something that the perpetrator did knowingly. For example, a worker who locks out a machine before making some adjustments is performing a voluntary action. In some cases, potential sources of accidents are predictable (e.g., a worker knows that it is possible for a ladder rung to break). A random event, in contrast, is by its very nature difficult to predict. For example, the worker climbing the ladder could have fallen because another worker walked into the ladder. No one could have predicted this event. If the worker had placed the ladder in a crowded corridor, however, the event could be considered predictable. A change in conditions can thus transform a random event into a predictable one.

When a worker or another person causes an accident by commission (some action) or omission (failing to do something), the cause is labelled the human factor. However, analysts distinguish between fact finding and fault finding. A human action may have been directly or indirectly involved in the event, but "human error" or blame will neither be used nor implied. In a similar vein, no one will willingly or intentionally injure himself or herself. No matter how many backup systems are in place, some shortcut or personal foible can cause the system to fail. The intent of hazard identification is not to scapegoat, but to correct procedures and behaviours so that the likelihood of the accident occurring is reduced.

An *unsafe act* generally refers to a deviation from standard job procedures or practices that increases a worker's exposure to a hazard. Unsafe acts may be direct and indirect. A human action that may cause an immediate event of any type, and over which the person has control, is considered a direct, unsafe act (sometimes referred to as a *substandard practice*). An indirect, unsafe act is one in which the human action is only indirectly involved. Consider the example of a designer of a machine who makes a decision that results in a defect that occasionally causes a breakdown of the operation or function. If this defect was the cause of an accident or injury, it would be considered an indirect act. There could be overlap between an indirect unsafe act and an unsafe condition. The machine defect started as an indirect unsafe act, which resulted in an unsafe condition.

Some safety professionals differentiate between the terms "unsafe act" and "substandard practice" by suggesting that the latter implies a much broader application. In this text, the term unsafe act will be used to indicate acts or practices that are unsafe or potentially unsafe. Following are some examples of unsafe acts:

◆ Unauthorized operation of equipment

◆ Improper use of equipment

◆ Use of defective equipment

◆ Failure to lock out power when servicing equipment

◆ Removal or disabling of safety devices

◆ Failure to warn or secure

◆ Improper lifting, loading, or positioning

◆ Failure to use personal protective equipment

◆ Improper use of personal protective equipment

◆ Alcohol or drug abuse

◆ Horseplay

SITUATIONAL FACTORS

Situational factors, also known as *unsafe conditions*, exist when a company does not provide proper equipment, tools, or facilities, or when its operations are unsafe. Following are examples of unsafe conditions:

◆ Defective equipment and materials

◆ Airborne toxic chemical agents

◆ Physical agents

◆ Fire and explosion conditions

◆ Poor housekeeping

◆ Adverse temperature conditions

◆ Improper illumination

◆ Poor exhaust or ventilation systems

◆ Poor indoor air quality

◆ Ineffective personal protective equipment

◆ Continuance of improper procedures or practices

The above situational factors can be grouped into four categories (Laing, 1992): (1) defects in design; (2) substandard construction; (3) improper storage of hazardous materials; and (4) inadequate planning, layout, and design.

ENVIRONMENTAL FACTORS

Environmental factors, including physical factors, chemical factors, biological factors, and ergonomic factors, can play either a direct or indirect role in accidents. For example, physical factors such as noise, vibration, illumination, and temperature extremes have an obvious relation to safety. A noisy work environment may prevent a worker from hearing approaching vehicles or may damage hearing over time. Similarly, under the chemical category, toxic gases may not only cause illness but may impair a worker's reaction, judgment, or concentration. Contact with biological agents such as viruses or parasites may cause illness.

◆ ◆ ◆
CHOOSING A HAZARD IDENTIFICATION PROGRAM

Safety professionals have several choices to make when determining the type of hazard identification program they will undertake. The factors influencing this decision include the source of the request for information, the nature of the hazards to be identified, and the costs associated with the program.

SOURCE OF REQUEST The identification of workplace hazards may be prompted by a request from the Ministry of Labour (resulting from the presence of specific substances in the workplace) or from the joint health and safety committee (resulting from a complaint or inspection). Alternatively, the program may be initiated as part of an organization's safety program. The safety expert may decide to survey one procedure, one area, or the entire plant, depending on the request.

NATURE OF HAZARDS Some tests can be performed on a single employee, while others require samples from many workers. Similarly, some hazards (such as a broken tool) can be identified within minutes; other hazards, such as chemical agents, may require months of testing.

COST Cost will also determine the extent of the program. For example, to obtain an air sample for benzene contamination, sampling may have to be done in several locations over an eight-hour shift. Several air samples, including blanks, may have to be taken at each location. (A blank is an unopened sample device, such as a charcoal tube, which is used as a baseline or zero point for comparison.) The cost of obtaining three samples, plus a blank, in five locations (including the eight hours of the safety professional's time) would be over $2000. Unless it is a legal assessment or a due diligence requirement, then a cost/benefit analysis would have to be done.

◆ ◆ ◆
COMPONENTS OF THE HAZARD
IDENTIFICATION PROGRAM
USE OF SAFETY EXPERTS

Most organizations have a network of associations with people who have a great deal of knowledge about safety in the workplace. These experts include occupational health and safety inspectors, the suppliers who manufacture the tools and equipment used at the worksite, insurance company loss control specialists, safety personnel in the same industrial sector, labour representatives specializing in safety issues, and agencies such as the Industrial Accident Prevention Association.

A safety professional can enter a worksite and, by walking through, be able to note hazards. The utility of a walk-through survey is increased by arranging to have the supervisor or a member of the health and safety committee accompany the safety expert. *Safety sampling*, often referred to as *behaviour* or *activity sampling*, is a systematic survey procedure undertaken by safety personnel who tour the plant or operations. These experts record their observations of unsafe practices on a safety sampling sheet. They might observe, for example, workers without hard hats.

Actual and observable exposures to hazards are the focus of the survey. Examples of exposure include chemical substances such as solvents or physical agents such as noise. Safety personnel might observe escaping smoke, or open containers, or the type of personal protective equipment worn by employees. However, potential and inferred exposures would not be ignored. The former includes any substance for which an intended control procedure is being considered. The latter includes any observable accumulation of material such as dust, which might be an airborne hazard.

Following the walk-through survey, the safety personnel code and count their observations. A report is then submitted to management to provide an objective evaluation of the type and number of unsafe conditions.

Management can ask workers who represent a variety of tasks and jobs to identify hazards and unsafe conditions. Employees might report that they are required to adapt tools (thus rendering them potentially hazardous) in order to meet production quotas, or that a machine is dripping oil, rendering a corridor slippery and treacherous.

These discussions with both the experts and the employees should be supplemented by an analysis of the job site and the work performed.

ANALYSIS OF THE PLANT, TASKS, AND JOBS

GEOGRAPHICAL INFORMATION The company should have a detailed layout of the plant, showing processes, machinery, materials storage, shipping, and so forth. A drawing showing the location of any toxic materials must be available under WHMIS requirements.

TASK AND JOB INVENTORY A description of the job and its associated tasks should be obtained by department, operation, or product. The human resources department can assist by providing job descriptions and job specifications. Flow process charts that incorporate standard industrial engineering symbols can clarify the relationships between tasks, jobs, and procedures (see Figure 4.1).

TASK ANALYSIS *Task analysis* refers to the systematic examination of a job's many components. It consists of a list of tasks and the job of which they are a part; the number of workers who perform the same or similar tasks; the time spent on each task; the importance of the task to the job; the complexity and criticality of the job; the learning curve and effort. The analysis identifies the various demands on the worker, tasks that are susceptible to worker error and stress; and potentially hazardous conditions. Industrial engineering methods are best for performing this kind of analysis.

REPORTS AND AUDITS

A review of the reports filed after an accident or as part of a safety inspection will provide valuable information on hazards. Occupational health and safety departments can also provide written information about the type of accidents in similar industries. Accident rates published by governments are another source of information. Audit information, which is obtained by reviewing records of all injuries, accidents, incidents, workplace design changes, and environmental sampling, is an extremely useful source for cataloguing hazards.

Most large organizations are using computers to store, analyze, and report on hazards and incidents, thus facilitating the identification of hazards by type or department (Rampton et al., 1996).

MONITORING INSTRUMENTS

Monitoring refers to the collection of data that are used to detect and measure any deviations from standards. In monitoring air quality, Gastec, MSA,

FIGURE 4.1   Flow Chart for Ping-Pong Paddle Assembly

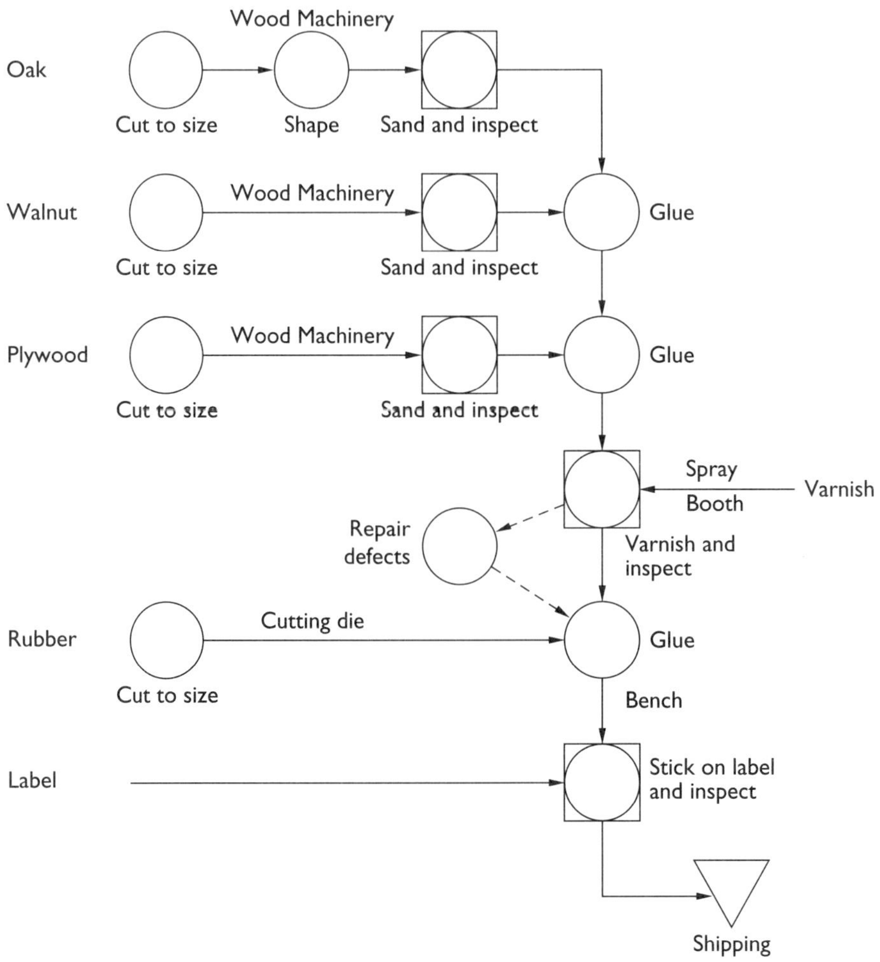

or Draeger pumps with the appropriate colourimetric glass tubes may be used to get an instant reading of the amount of airborne impurities for one chemical at a time. Alternatively, constant air-flow pumps with the proper cassette, impinger, or charcoal tube may be used to provide an accurate analysis of samples of dirty or contaminated air. The former method is relatively inexpensive and not very accurate; the latter is very accurate, but costly. Both methods provide results after the air has become contaminated, and require a knowledge of the specific materials being tested.

Safety professionals should ensure that the instruments are calibrated for air-flow rate by using a primary flow calibrator. The calibration for air flow must show three consecutive readings within +/- 5%. Should the company need to mount a compliance defence based on test surveys, the test evidence will be suspect if the calibration is not done and recorded. Recording information must include time, date, weather conditions, name of the operator, and so forth. This check must also be conducted during and after the survey to ensure that no changes have occurred.

Recording the results is a critical step in establishing the validity of the testing. Some of the necessary information to be recorded includes the type of instrumentation with model and serial numbers; calibration method and results; battery test; leak test; location of the measurements that are taken; check of calibration, battery condition, and leak immediately after the test. The sample is then analyzed in the laboratory, supplemented by a written report. At this point, the safety professional determines if the results are within acceptable levels. A detailed report including complete conclusions and recommendations is prepared. In the follow-up, retesting may be required. Quick corrective action, if necessary, will not only be proof of due diligence on the part of the company, but will also demonstrates concern for safety.

◆ ◆ ◆
HAZARD ANALYSIS

Hazard analysis is used to acquire specific hazard and failure information about a given system (Firenze, 1978). Hazard analysis is an orderly, analytical technique that examines a system for the most probable hazards, with the severest consequences, for the purpose of establishing corrective or control mechanisms. The most common form of hazard analysis is the analytical tree of which there are two types. The *positive tree* shows, graphically, how a job should be done. The more frequently used tree is the *fault tree*, which provides an illustration of things that can go wrong.

FAULT TREE ANALYSIS

Fault tree analysis is a useful technique for evaluating hazards and risk (Fabrycky and Mize, 1976). The process, developed from decision tree theory (Raiffa, 1968), is unique in that it reasons backward from a series of conditions to some predetermined, undesired result called a *top event*. The key to its success is the determination of the origin of the top event (undesired result).

Following are some examples of top events:

1. *Injury to a person.* A worker is injured while performing a task.
2. *Equipment activated.* Some piece of machinery that was shut down is turned on while work is being done.
3. *Equipment failure.* A piece of equipment fails to start or else operates improperly.
4. *Worker exposure.* Airborne toxic chemicals or harmful physical agents may contaminate the worker.
5. *Explosion or sudden release of energy.* High concentrations of solvents or dust may explode, or a source of high pressure may be released into the atmosphere.

Fault tree analysis uses a series of symbols (see Figure 4.2) to illustrate the various conditions, situations, or event sequences that could result in the undesired or top event. The events or conditions that lead into the top event filter through a gate (see Figure 4.3) that specifies the sequences for the lower conditions and their effect on the top event.

To set up the initial fault tree:

1. Identify the top desired top event (e.g., "foreign particle in eye").
2. Identify the possible causes or conditions that could result in the chosen top event, and list them horizontally.
3. Determine whether the gate should be "and" or "or." This will depend on whether the noted conditions will act independently ("or") or in concert ("and").
4. Determine whether the conditions or events in item 2 require further investigation or consideration. A rectangle indicates further information is required.
5. For each rectangle, repeat steps 2 through 4.
6. Once the tree has been constructed (see Figure 4.4 for an example), estimate and note at each event or condition the probabilities of occurrence for each element.

There are two methods of dealing with these probabilities of occurrence. The first (shown in Figure 4.5) considers each row leading into a gate

FIGURE 4.2 **Fault Tree Analysis Symbols**

A condition or event requiring further development or examination (e.g., an injury).

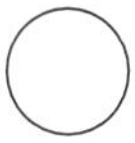

A basic event not needing further analysis – failure data assigned (e.g., a bulb burns out).

"AND" gate: All inputs must act together in order for the event to occur.

"OR" gate: Any of the inputs individually will cause event failure.

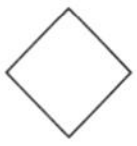

A secondary event with assumed risk, with insufficient data to develop (e.g., a break in a telephone connection).

A human factor. A special secondary event situation (e.g., power not locked out).

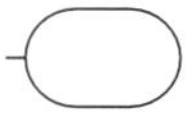

A constraint that further explains or qualifies an event at the gate.

An event normally expected to occur (e.g., fire creates heat).

as a separate set of conditions. The probability of occurrence is estimated for each element in the row. The sum of the probabilities must equal 1.00. The critical path can now be highlighted by starting at the lowest element with the highest probability and tracing the path back to the top event. Thus, in this example, the condition at H—the person entering the area for a reason—will be the probable initiating source for the top event.

In the second method (shown in Figure 4.6), a probability is assigned to each element randomly. Using the relationships noted, the probability at each rectangle can then be calculated.

The advantage of the second method is its flexibility without bias. Once an estimation and identification of the hazard and the associated risk has been made, prevention strategies can be developed.

Obviously, a technical expert is needed to do a fault tree analysis. When should management use such expertise? Any job, operation, or task that has

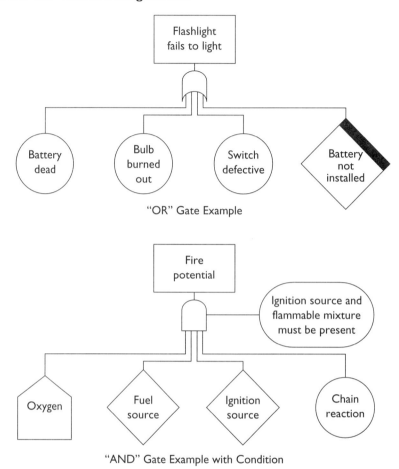

FIGURE 4.3 Gate Arrangements

a history of accidents should receive top priority. Fault tree analysis might also be used in situations where the severity of the accident is great or where there is a high potential for accidents. When new equipment or operations are introduced, fault tree analysis can be used as a preventative tool.

DOMINO THEORY

Every event—accident or disaster—is composed of a series of happenings that results in some negative condition. The domino theory, developed by H.W. Heinrich (1959), is based on a set of five dominos labelled as follows:

FIGURE 4.4 Example of a Fault Tree

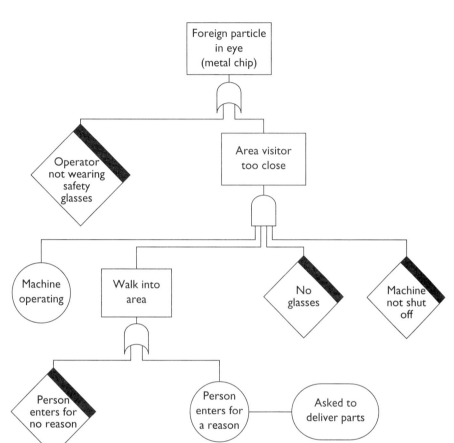

1. *Background*: a lack of control over the management function (planning, organizing, leading, and controlling).

2. *Personal defects*: personal factors such as physical or mental problems, and job factors such as normal wear and tear.

3. *Unsafe acts and conditions*: (described earlier).

4. *Accident:* a series of undesired events with releases of energies that can cause harm.

5. *Injury:* the most undesired result (e.g., trauma or property damage).

FIGURE 4.5 **Fault Tree with Probabilities Added**

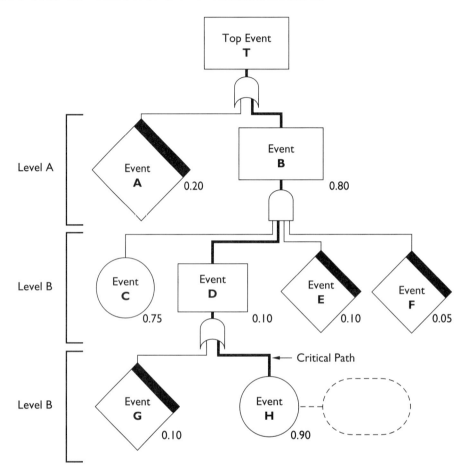

While there are other models, such as those dealing with the release of energy (Haddon, 1970) and with the theory of multiple factors (Gross, 1972), the domino model is the easiest to illustrate or demonstrate. The domino theory asserts that if any one of the domino classes does not happen, then the injury will not occur. (see Figure 4.7). For example, if a worker was trying to make a production quota (background), was wearing loose clothing (personal defects or unsafe conditions), and operated a machine at unsafe speeds (unsafe act), then an accident or injury would be more likely to occur.

FIGURE 4.6 Fault Tree Example with Simplified Probabilities Added

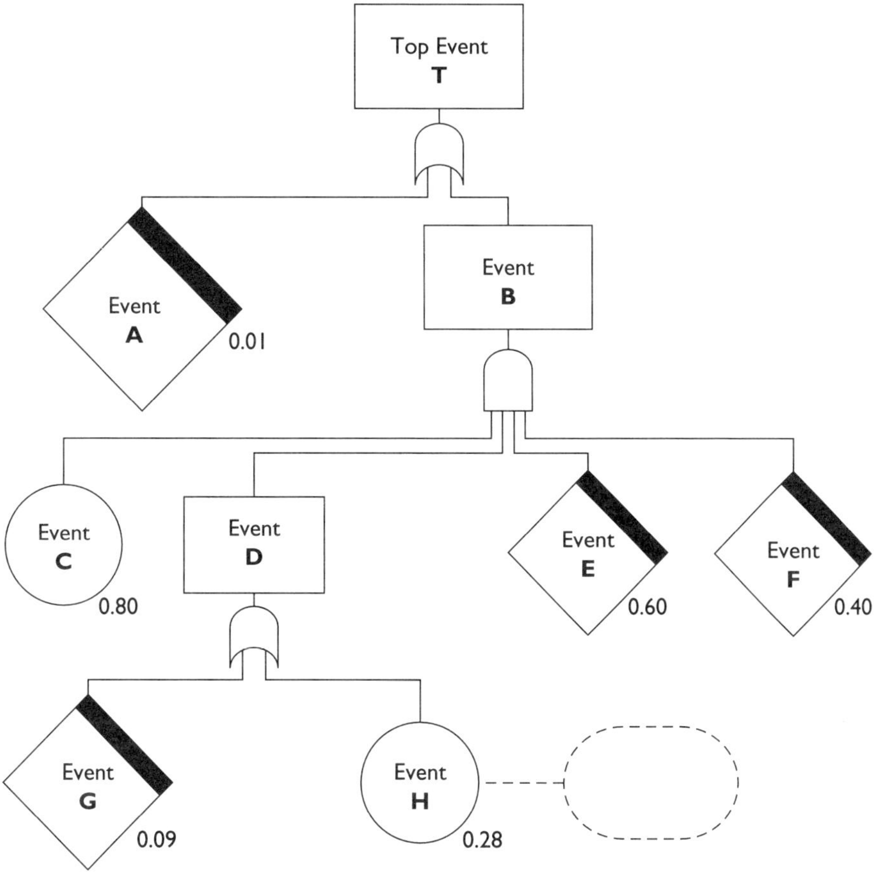

"AND" Gate Probability: $P_B = P_C \times P_D \times P_E \times P_F$
"OR" Gate Probability: $P_D = 1 - (1 - P_G \times P_H)$

◆ ◆ ◆
RISK ASSESSMENT

Once hazards have been identified, the risk of an incident or accident must be determined. Insurance companies have long used risk evaluation to determine the susceptibility of humans to have accidents and even to die. The rates that subscribers pay are predicated on this type of evaluation. For example, younger drivers pay higher insurance rates because they are involved in a disproportionate number of accidents. Insurers similarly

BOX 4.1   Fault Tree Analysis at a Missile Centre

In 1988, a consulting firm performed, at the request of the military, a fault tree analysis on the American Intercontinental Ballistic Missile (ICBM) program. The military itself had estimated that the probability of a deliberate, unauthorized launch was about 1,000,000 to 1.

The consulting firm was asked to evaluate the possibility of an accidental launch based on the human factor. Its final analysis indicated a 1500 to 1 probability of an accidental firing based on workers performing unsafe acts while working on the equipment.

At that time, accidental firings and explosions had been documented at some ICBM silo sites. One of these accidents was attributed to an electrician who had held a missile program access door open with a piece of wood, which then slipped into the exposed launch circuitry. The missile firing sequence was initiated near the end of the actual sequence. The missile engine ignited, but the security clamps did not release; the result was a devastating explosion.

measure the relative risk of such events as theft, fire or flood damage, and vandalism. The same concept can be applied to health and safety.

Risk is the probability of an injury expressed as a percentage. The assessment of risk is calculated by determining probability, consequences, and exposure expressed as:

$$Risk = Probability \times Consequences \times Exposure$$

Probability refers to the chance or likelihood that an event will happen. The range of probabilities for risk run from about .001 percent to about 99.9 percent. For management purposes, probability can also be measured in the following terms (Laing, 1992):

(a) Likely to occur immediately or shortly after exposure to the hazard

(b) Probably will occur in time

(c) Possibly will occur in time

(d) Unlikely to occur

Any measurement of the risk of an accident occurring will have to take into account the degree of *worker exposure* to the hazard. This estimate includes not only the number of people who are regularly exposed, but the frequency of the exposure. The more contact one has with a known hazard, the greater the risk. A worker who operates a lathe continuously throughout an eight-hour shift has more exposure than the worker who uses the lathe

FIGURE 4.7 **Heinrich's Domino Model**

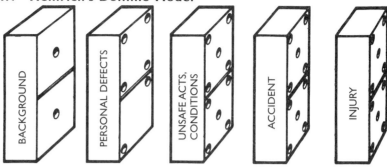

(a) Five factors in accident sequence

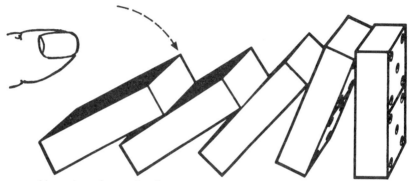

(b) Injury caused by action of preceding factors

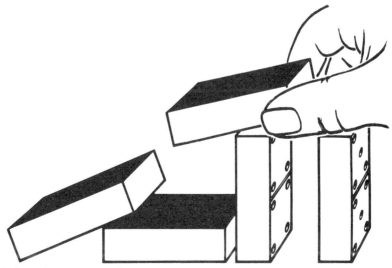

(c) Removal of one factor prevents final injury

only once or twice. However, consideration must also be given to the worker's level of experience. Generally, the more experience a worker has in dealing with a potentially dangerous work situation, the lower the possibility of injury. A professional race-car driver should be at a lower risk of injury when driving on a busy highway than a regular commuter. Even a driven who has done skid-school training should be at a lower risk on the same roadway. The number of workers exposed to a hazard could be used in a ranking or weighting system as part of the risk formula.

Factors such as noise and light can increase the probability of an accident. The machine-generated noises in an assembly plant may mask the sound of an approaching vehicle. Dimly lit workstations and pathways may increase the risks associated with potential hazards such as sharp tools and steps. The loud talk of a co-worker may distract a worker who is engaged in a potentially hazardous task.

Consequences have to do with the severity of the injury, and can range from dust in the eye to amputation of a finger to death. Below is a subjective ranking system that can be used to classify the degree of hazard consequence (Laing, 1992):

1. *Catastrophic:* may cause death or loss of a facility.

2. *Critical:* may cause severe injury, occupational illness or major property damage.

3. *Marginal:* may cause minor injury or minor occupational illness resulting in lost workday(s) or minor property damage.

4. *Negligible:* probably would not affect personnel safety or health, but still in violation of specific criteria.

By estimating the probability, the consequences, and the exposure, safety personnel can determine the relative amount of risk. Table 4.1 shows a sample layout that can be used for hazard inventory and risk evaluation. The first column will include a brief description of the job or task being inventoried (weld assembly in our example). The second column will show the hazard or hazards associated with the task (flash burns, skin burns, toxic fumes, lifting sprains, etc.). The third column will show an estimate of the percent probability for each hazard, while the fourth column will list the corresponding consequences of each hazard (e.g., "vision loss" for flash burns).

TABLE 4.1 SAMPLE LAYOUT FOR HAZARD INVENTORY AND RISK EVALUATION					
Job/Task	Hazard(s)	Risk			
		Probability	Consequence	Exposure	

Once the table is completed, the hazards can be rated using a scale of 1 to 10 for each of the three risk columns (probability, consequence, and exposure), as shown in Table 4.2. The final formatted table is exemplified by Table 4.3.

The factors in Table 4.2 correspond to the numbers shown in Table 4.3. Thus if the worker's risk of coming in contact with toxic fumes as a result of welding is calculated from the values assigned, out of a maximum of 1000, as a percent then

$$Risk = 6 \times 4 \times 8 = 192 \ / \ 1000 \ or \ 19.2\%$$

In this example, the worker would have a 19.2 percent risk of contact with toxic fumes while welding. To determine whether or not this value is too high, the chemical content and toxicity of the fumes would have to be known. This information appears on the labels of hazardous products.

TABLE 4.2 SAMPLE HAZARD INVENTORY AND RISK EVALUATION					
Job/Task	Hazard(s)	Risk			
		Probability	Consequence	Exposure	
Weld assembly	Flash burns	6	Temporary or partial blindness, lost time	4	Daily while welding	8
	Skin burns	2	Discomfort	3	Rarely	3
	Lifting strains	5	Back injury if heavy material lifted, lost time.	4	Occasionally	6
	Toxic fumes	6	Respiratory difficulty without personal protective equipment	4	Daily while welding	8

TABLE 4.3 FACTORS FOR EVALUATING RISK

Probability		Consequence		Exposure	
10	Predicted or expected	10	Catastrophic	10	Continuous daily
9		9		9	
8	Almost certain	8	Fatality	8	Frequently daily
7		7		7	
6	Possible	6	Serious injury	6	Occasional (1/wk.–1/mo.)
5	50/50 chance	5		5	
4	Coincidence	4	Disabling injury	4	Usual (1/mo.–1/yr.)
3	Never occurred before	3	Minor	3	Rare
2	Almost impossible	2	Nerves ("close call")	2	Remotely possible

◆ ◆ ◆
FOLLOW-UP

The information obtained through hazard identification and evaluation should be communicated to the plant manager, the immediate supervisor, and the health and safety committee. Some reports may be forwarded to the Ministry of Labour (if the substance is under assessment) or the Ministry of Environment, or even to the corporation's lawyers. Safety professionals and supervisors who do not pass information about unsafe conditions to a responsible manager could be charged under the Occupational Health and Safety Act.

When presented with information about hazards, management may decide (1) to take no action, (2) to take corrective action, or (3) to consider a cost-benefit analysis to determine if the anticipated losses are worth the cost of correcting the problem.

◆ ◆ ◆
SUMMARY

The primary goal of hazard identification is to reduce injuries, accidents, and property-damage numbers. A variety of methods are used to identify hazards: safety experts; analysis of the plant, task, and jobs; reports and audits;

and monitoring instruments. Hazard analysis is then used to acquire specific information about the hazards in a given system. The hazards are then rated according to their degree of risk, calculated by a formula that takes into consideration probabilities, consequences, and exposures.

EXERCISES

1. Outline all the methods that a manager of a small plant could use to identify hazards. What could a safety professional add to this manager's hazard-identification program?
2. Choose any operation in your workplace or at school and identify the hazards associated with it. Perform a risk analysis to determine whether these hazards are dangerous or not. Outline the changes that could be made to reduce the level of risk associated with the hazards.

References

Fabrycky, W.J., and J.H. Mize, eds. 1976. *System Analysis and Design for Safety*. Englewood Cliffs, N.J.: Prentice Hall.

Firenze, R.J. 1978. *The Process of Hazard Control*. Dubuque, Iowa: Kendall/Hunt Publishing.

Gross, V.L. 1972. "System Safety in Rapid Rail Transit." *ASSE Journal* (August).

Haddon, William, Jr. 1970. "On the Escape of Tigers: An Ecological Note." *Technology Review* (May).

Heinrich, H.W. 1959. *Industrial Accident Prevention*, 4th ed. New York: McGraw-Hill Book Company.

Laing, P.M., ed. 1992. *Accident Prevention Manual for Business and Industry: Administration and Programs*, 10th ed. Washington, D.C.: National Safety Council.

Raiffa, H. 1968. *Decision Analysis*. Reading, Mass.: Addison-Wesley.

Rampton, G., I. Turnbull, and G. Doran. 1976. *Human Resources Management Systems*, Nelson Canada Series in HRM. Scarborough, Ont.: Nelson Canada.

5

Hazard
Control

♦ ♦ ♦
INTRODUCTION

Hazard control refers to the program or process used to establish preventative and corrective measures. The goal is to eliminate, reduce, or control hazards so as to minimize injuries and losses. The first step in hazard control is hazard identification, the subject of the previous chapter. This chapter will examine the next three steps in the hazard-control process: (1) *pre-contact control* (addressing issues before an incident or accident occurs); (2) *contact control* (identifying ways in which a hazardous situation can be prevented from harming workers); and (3) *post-contact control* (putting in place cleanup operations and ensuring that the event cannot be repeated).

♦ ♦ ♦
PRE-CONTACT CONTROL

The best time to deal with an accident is before it occurs. Ways of determining the likelihood that an accident will occur were discussed in Chapter 4. Ways of actively preventing accidents from occurring would include purchasing quality materials and equipment and providing effective supervision. Training, safety awareness, engineering controls, purchasing, housekeeping, preventative maintenance, and machine guarding are some of the other means by which hazards can be controlled or eliminated.

TRAINING

Safety training should be an integral part of any new employee's orientation program. Ongoing training and upgrading is a most important part of an employee's development. In fact, under provincial OHS legislation training is mandatory (training requirements are spelled out in WHMIS legislation). Teaching employees about physical and chemical hazards is a good investment of time and effort, because employees educated about hazards are not only alert to them but able to take corrective action. Senior-level managers should also receive training in health and safety. Increasingly, managers are being held responsible for health and safety. How can they effectively discharge this function without some basic knowledge?

Health and safety training is based on technical information, and must be adapted to suit the worker. The ability to absorb and retain safety information will depend to a great extent on worker motivation. This motivation can be increased by establishing, in the employee's mind, the need for such information and the effect it can have on daily work. General information about industry-wide accidents should be supplemented with information directly relevant to the worker's own experience. Thus, a trainer might discuss with the employee the suitability of his or her personal protective equipment.

The learning environment can be made more stimulating through the use of audio, video, and class discussions. At the end of the training period, the worker should be given a wallet card or certificate to indicate completion of training. This will signal to the worker that the company is serious about the training. Moreover, the company will have a record of the worker's training. The employee's training record can impact the company in legal action as was demonstrated in a recent case.

A large Toronto company trained its assembly-line workers to properly apply a joint sealer, which required a respirator and gloves for additional protection. One of the employees instituted a work refusal that eventually involved the Ministry of Labour (MOL) because the worker claimed he had not been properly trained in the application of this sealant. Company training records, which the worker and trainer signed, showed that the worker had been instructed and was qualified to do the task. However, no mention of any health and safety (toxicological) precautions were in the documentation, and the worker won the work refusal and retraining, because the company had taken that part of the task for granted. Had this case gone to court as the result of a serious injury and Ministry of Labour (MOL) charges, the company probably could not have proven due diligence and could be found culpable.

An effective job training program should convey the following information:

- Company safety rules and practices
- Duties of the employer, supervisor, and the worker as specified in OHS legislation
- Importance of strict compliance with warning and emergency signs and signals
- Types and use of emergency equipment (e.g., extinguishers, and/or spill retainers)
- Use, care, and acquisition of personal protective equipment
- Company benefits
- Known hazards and safeguards against them
- Importance of reporting other hazards (e.g., defective equipment) and mechanism for doing so
- Emergency procedures (fire, spills, toxic exposure, etc.)
- Need for good housekeeping
- Where applicable, generic courses in first aid, CPR, and defensive driving

An effective way to disseminate information on an ongoing basis is to hold the occasional short safety meeting during working hours. Attendees should share common interests. Thus, welders and spray painters should not be together unless the material is relevant to both groups. Workers should be encouraged to participate in these meetings by, for example, giving presentations or demonstrating new procedures or equipment.

SAFETY AWARENESS

Promoting and maintaining awareness about health and safety matters is a critical component in a hazard-control program. Following are some approaches to hazard control.

VISIBLE REMINDERS Posters and signs at worker entrances and other points of entry are one way to promote safety awareness. A company-designed booklet dealing with safety issues can be issued to employees. Safety message inserts can be added to paycheques. Place mats and napkins in the dining area can be imprinted with safety messages. Decals (self-adhesive labels) can be applied to specific objects as a safety reminder.

In addition, safety displays can be set up at entrances as well as in cafeterias. These displays can feature photographs of the Safe Employee of the Month or brief statements by workers who were saved from injury by, for example, correct use of personal protective equipment. Newsletter, bulletin boards, and billboards are other vehicles for promoting safety awareness. Finally, safety campaigns can be used to target a specific hazard or unsafe practice.

AWARDS AND INCENTIVES The Industrial Accident Prevention Association (IAPA) in Ontario is among the many safety associations that give awards to organizations and individuals who have made a significant contribution to accident and injury prevention. These awards come with a certificate, an on-site presentation, and coverage in the organization's newsletter. The staffs of departments that have a good safety and noninjury record can be recognized (not rewarded) with ballpoint pens, coffee and snacks, or lapel buttons.

Employees can be given incentives to maintain good safety performance. These incentives can range from individual payoffs to team rewards. DuPont Canada employees were given special scratch-and-win lottery tickets (Schuler and Dolan, 1994). Other organizations recognized good safety performance through such incentives as private parking spaces or dinners. In addition, supervisors may receive a reward based on the number of employees who attend safety talks or on the number of safety deficiencies that are corrected in an expeditious fashion. Contests may be held in which employees compete to produce the best safety slogan. Finally, safety records can be used as one factor in the evaluation of supervisory and managerial performance. Care must be taken with this approach, since some supervisors may be tempted to "hide" problems and serious hazards.

ENGINEERING CONTROLS

Hazard control should be built into the design of the work itself. *Engineering control* refers to the modification of work processes and materials in order to reduce exposure to hazards (Pilger, 1994).

Before equipment and materials are purchased, specifications for efficient and safe operations should be determined. For example, noise-emission limits for noisy equipment can be specified before the equipment is purchased, thus reducing worker exposure at the source of the hazard. Engineering control also refers to the installation of auxiliary equipment, such as physical barriers and ventilation systems, in order to reduce hazards. Various methods of controlling hazards through engineering are discussed below.

SUBSTITUTION Safety professionals can sometimes replace hazardous equipment or materials with those that are less hazardous. For example, replacing a light, fluffy powder with the same material in granular form will result in a reduction of airborne dust levels. Lead paints can be replaced with less toxic compounds of iron or zinc. Similarly, electric trucks can be substituted for gasoline-powered ones with a resultant decrease in exposure to carbon monoxide. The substitute should, of course, be checked for different types of hazards.

PROCESS MODIFICATION Sometimes changing the manner in which the work is done can increase safety. Moving from a manual operation to an automated one, or from batch processes to continuous processes, may result in fewer hazards.

Effective job design is key to worker safety and efficiency. Frederick Taylor (1856–1915), the founder of industrial engineering, tried to increase both by breaking a job into its basic components and then assigning to each task specific times and methods (motions). Taylor's ideas were applied to the shovelling of coal at the Bethlehem Steel Company in what was to become a classic motion study. This application demonstrated that a stoker could shovel more coal into the blast furnace by using a larger shovel and engaging in fewer work cycles. Decreasing the repetition of the task served to reduce fatigue and back strains.

Subsequent efficiency experts addressed the tedium associated with simple task repetition. Inspired by the Hawthorne studies of the 1920s, the sociotechnological approach to work design was concerned with enhancing worker involvement and satisfaction. What has this to do with health and safety? The more interested and motivated the worker, the lower the probability of an serious accident or injury.

ISOLATION OR SEGREGATION In this approach, the hazardous job or task is isolated from the employees in order to reduce their exposure. Isolation strategies may be as simple as a physical barrier around a chemical or noise source, removal of a hazardous operation to a separate facility. Robots can handle tasks that are too dangerous for humans.

Segregating the hazardous operation in time as well as space is also advisable. Cleanups, maintenance, and particularly hazardous tasks such as spray painting can be done on weekends or nights, when fewer workers are present.

PURCHASING

Purchasing agents have an important role to play in the control of hazards. In addition to price, quality, and efficiency, the purchasing agent must consider safety. At a minimum, the equipment must meet the regulatory requirements of the Canadian Standards Association.

Purchasing machinery without proper or minimal safety specifications or compatibility can result in equipment failure or injury. Workers can have their toes crushed by safety shoes with inadequate metal caps, or they can suffer from headaches because their safety goggles have imperfections in the lenses. The best time to eliminate hazards is at the design stage.

Once specifications have been met, the safety features of competing brands can be compared. The purchasing agent should consult the safety records for accidents and incidents that resulted from defects in equipment, machinery, or materials. He or she can use the information contained in these records to defend certain purchasing decisions on a cost-benefit basis.

HOUSEKEEPING

Ensuring that the worksite is clean and that workers have access to cleaning facilities will contribute to the control of hazards. A clean, orderly workplace can reduce hazards and at the same time increase efficiency. Every worksite contains potentially hazardous tools and equipment. For example, a plant site may have containers of chemicals such as solvents, tools such as drills, and processes that generate dust or scrap material. Maintaining a clean and orderly job site reduces the risk of injury due to falls, fires, and so forth. Furthermore, it is easier to locate first-aid equipment or exits in an environment where all tools and equipment are in their assigned places.

The cleaning process itself should be evaluated. Besides the obvious hazards posed by solvents used for cleaning, other hazards may be involved in operations such as dust removal. Workers using compressed air may be tempted to blow dust off work surfaces and even clothing; however, compressed air can be forced through the skin, enter the bloodstream, and cause death.

Organizations that employ workers who handle toxic materials should ensure that washing facilities are located close to the work area. Workers should wash before drinking or eating to prevent the ingestion of toxic materials. No food or drinks should be permitted at the worksite. Workers exposed to chemicals should have showers and change clothes before leaving the worksite.

PREVENTATIVE MAINTENANCE

Preventative maintenance refers to the orderly, continuous, and scheduled protection and repair of equipment and buildings. The primary goals of preventative maintenance are the determination of potential problems and the implementation of corrective action. The primary benefits of this process are uninterrupted production and the reduction of potential hazards caused by equipment failure.

Generally speaking, equipment failures do not happen without warning. We are all familiar with the atypical noises our cars or air conditioners produce as a signal that something needs to be fixed. However, maintenance should enter the picture before the emergence of warning signs. It is more cost-effective to perform maintenance routines while the equipment or machines are still operating than it is after they have failed, necessitating shutdown of the entire operation. Checking the level of oil in your car at every second fuel stop is preventative maintenance. To let the oil level drop and the engine seize is expensive and unnecessary.

Recordkeeping is an essential part of any preventative maintenance program. Maintenance information should be recorded at the time the maintenance work is being done. Pertinent data would include part replacement and frequency, lubrication, bearings and drive repairs, electrical failures, and cleanliness. Once the historical information is available, failure trends—commonly referred to as failure mode analysis or maintenance hazard analysis—can be anticipated and addressed.

WORK PERMITS Before any high-risk work is undertaken, a series of work permits must be in place, one for each type of activity. These permits are, in effect, in-house licences to perform dangerous work. Permits are required for confined space entry, cold work (the machinery is shut down and isolated), hot work (the machinery is active and in operation), electrical work, excavation work, safety-valve work, scaffolding work, radiation work, and equipment disconnecting work (lockout procedures). A sample work permit for scaffolding is shown in Figure 5.1.

FIGURE 5.1 Example of Scaffold Use Permit

CHECKLIST FOR THE AUTHORIZED CRAFTSMAN

PREPARATIONS
- SPECIFICATIONS/DRAWING PROVIDED?
- FOUNDATIONS/FOOTING PREPARED?
- LIFTING DEVICES NEEDED?
- ERECTION PERSONNEL EXPERIENCED?
- SUPERVISION APPOINTED? COMPETENT?
- AREA HAZARDS/SAF. RULES KNOWN?
- ADDITIONAL JOB DEMONSTRATION NEEDED?
- STRUCTURE INSPECTION/APPROVAL BY A COMPETENT PERSON NEEDED?

STABILITY & CONSTRUCTION
- ANCHORING POINTS SELECTED? APPROVED? SUFFICIENT?
- SCAFF. MATERIAL INSPECTED? SELECTED? IN GOOD CONDITION?
- FOOTING FIRM?
- STANDARDS SPACING ADEQUATE?
- BRACING USED? SUFFICIENT?
- PLATFORMS FULL? TRIPPING? OPENINGS?
- GUARDRAILS? TOE BOARDS?
- ACCESS ADEQUATE? LADDERS FIXED?

IN USE
- STRUCTURE INSPECTED DAILY?
- TRAFFIC HAZARDS?
- OVERLOADING?
- USE OF PERSONAL PROTECTION?
- RESPONSE TO EMERGENCY KNOWN?

DISMANTLING
- METHOD AGREED TO?
- HAZARD CREATED TO SURROUNDING?
- FINAL SITE CLEARING ENSURED?

SPECIAL INSTRUCTIONS

Side 2

BIRTE OIL COMPANY

SCAFFOLDING PERMIT

DATE	TIME	
FROM:		TO:

PLANT:

EQUIPMENT & LOCATION:

DESCRIPTION OF WORK TO BE DONE: ☐ ERECTION ☐ REMOVAL

SCAFFOLD DUTY: ☐ LIGHT ☐ GENERAL ☐ HEAVY ☐ CONSULT CIVIL ENG. GROUP
HEIGHT = ___ M WIDTH = ___ M

ANSWER WITH (X) WHERE APPLICABLE: YES
1. FAMILIAR WITH AREA HAZARDS/SAF. RULES?
2. SCAFFOLD TYPE/MATERIAL AGREED TO?
3. SCAFFOLD ANCHORING POINTS APPROVED?
4. FOUNDATION/FOOTING PREPARED?
5. HAZARD CREATED TO/FROM TRAFFIC?
6. AREA FREE OF COMB./TOXIC GAS?
7. ACCEPTANCE APPROVAL NEEDED?

SPECIAL PROTECTION REQUIRED
- MONITOR FOR:
- LIFTING DEVICE APPROVAL
- BARRIERS/ROPING OFF
- SAFETY BELTS/LINE
- STANDBYS
- (SPECIFY)

THE EQUIPMENT AND / OR LOCATION WHERE THE WORK IS TO BE DONE HAS BEEN INSPECTED & POINTS 1-7 ABOVE HAVE BEEN INVESTIGATED TO MY SATISFACTION.

_____
SIGNATURE OF PERSON AUTHORIZING THIS PERMIT

I UNDERSTAND THE HAZARDS INVOLVED IN THE ABOVE PERMITTED WORK AND THE LIMITATIONS REQUIRED HAVE BEEN EXPLAINED TO ME.

7-3 SHIFT	9-11 SHIFT	11-7 SHIFT

SIGNATURE OF AUTHORIZED CRAFTSMAN

PERMIT CLOSED OUT		WORK COMPLETED	
DATE	TIME	YES ☐	NO ☐
AUTHORIZED CRAFTSMAN		OPERATING SUPERVISOR	

APPROVAL FOR USE OF COMPLETED SCAFFOLD	NAME	SIGNATURE	DATE

Side 1

◆

LOCKOUT PROCEDURES When maintenance or adjustment is performed on any machine, the machine must be shut off and locked out. For example, to replace the signal light on a stove, one must access the interior of the appliance. Shutting off the stove would entail turning off the switches; locking it out would entail turning off the power in the basement and removing the appropriate fuses in either the power panel or the stove. As a result of these precautions, no one can turn the stove on and cause an electrical shock or burn injury. A more complicated appliance like a furnace would necessitate not only the removal of fuses but also the shutting off of fuel lines and disassembly of a flange joint.

Following are some of the precautions that must be taken during the lockout process:

1. Only one person should be in charge of the lockout procedure.

2. The worker must ensure that the machine is shut off completely; that all internal pressure sources (hydraulic, air, and steam) are bled off to atmospheric level and the valves are locked open; and that any movable parts, such as flywheels or rams, are immobilized.

3. After the machine has been shut down, all of the disconnect points, such as the electrical panel, must be left open.

4. Before work begins, complete testing must be undertaken to ensure that all energy sources are inoperative.

5. The worker must use an approved lockout tag and padlock to secure equipment.

6. Only the worker who installed the lock is permitted to remove it.

7. Each worker must sign off the work permit as the lock is removed.

When the project is finished, the equipment will be activated in the reverse sequence to the shutdown. Checks must be made to ensure that guards are in place, isolation devices have been removed, all tools are accounted for, energy controls have been closed and put back into operating condition, and tags and locks have been removed.

CONFINED SPACE ENTRY Confined space refers to a space that is potentially deficient in oxygen. Sewers, tanks, and boilers are all examples of confined spaces. Examples also include any long, small tunnel, a shower stall, and some specialty rooms such as computer equipment rooms that are completely independent from any adjacent spaces.

At home, cleaning the shower stall in the bathroom using a tile cleaner, with the door closed, will trap the vapours from the cleanser. These vapours may accumulate near the floor where the work is being done, displace oxygen, and cause drowsiness or fainting.

Two cleaners were killed in 1988 when the cleaning solutions they were using combined to create chlorine gas. The work area was a self-contained computer mainframe room that was being refurbished for use as office space.

Entry into industrial confined spaces is addressed in various OHS regulations. One of the first things to determine is whether the space to be entered is, in fact, a confined space. The flow diagram shown in Figure 5.2 can be used to determine if confined-space procedures are necessary. The diagram shown in Figure 5.3 can be used to determine the extent of the testing that will be required before actual entry.

Once it has been established that a confined space exists, the following steps should be taken:

FIGURE 5.2 Hazard Rating of Confined Space Prior to Entry

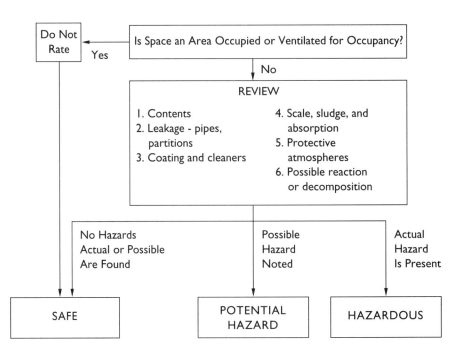

FIGURE 5.3 **Review of Confined Space Prior to Entry**

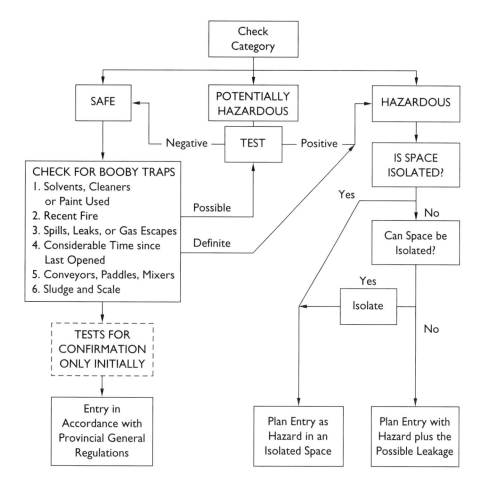

1. Issue a proper work permit and follow all of the lockout procedures.

2. Determine the ease of access to and from the space and develop appropriate contingency plans.

3. Make sure that all of the proper tools and equipment are on hand to do the job.

4. Communicate to workers that no smoking or open flames are to be permitted at or near the worksite.

5. Purge the space of all contaminants and test the air quality several times to ensure that all impurities have been removed.

6. Ensure that constant forced air flow into the space is provided.

7. Clean the interior of the space to ensure that no hazardous scale or deposits are present.

8. Post a trained safety lookout outside the space. (The inside workers should be kept in full view at all times.)

9. Attach a lifeline to each worker in the space. (The free end should be controlled by the safety lookout.)

Upon completion of the confined-space work, equipment start-up can be undertaken in the reverse order to the shutdown. The permit and lockout systems should be followed without deviation.

MACHINE GUARDING

Machine guarding is necessary to protect a worker from the hazards and energies created by moving machinery. According to Ontario's Ministry of Labour, more orders are written for nonexistent or improper guarding than for any other regulation (Somasunder, 1993). The problem is serious enough to have prompted the Canadian Standards Association to issue standard Z432-94, *Safeguarding of Machinery* (C5A, 1994), which covers the topic of machine guarding thoroughly.

The following basic guidelines for machine guarding apply, regardless of the type or operation of the equipment:

1. The guard must be sturdy enough to resist external source damage that will interfere with the operation of the machine.

2. The guard must permit required maintenance tasks without excessive dismantling or reassembly labour.

3. The guard must be properly and securely mounted to prevent rattles or part interference.

4. There should be no parts that, if removed, will compromise the protection provided by the guard.

5. Construction should be relatively simple so that problems can be immediately identified and corrected during an inspection.

Thoroughness in guard design is essential. An incomplete guard may be as much of a hazard as no guard at all. The guard must not create a false sense of security that may cause accidents and possible injuries. When the guard is in operation, all parts of the body must be excluded, and no access is permitted. The barrier or guard will prevent a worker from being caught in, on, or between moving equipment (kinetic energy), or from being struck by flying, sliding, or falling objects (gravity energy).

Floor barriers installed around pumps and other hazardous equipment must be strong enough to resist damage by, for example, fork truck impact (mechanical energy), and high enough so that a worker will not trip or fall over them. Expanded metal should fill the open spaces to prevent parts from rolling into the hazard area.

A number of devices of can be used to control point-of-operation hazards.

Barrier or *enclosure guards* prevent workers from entering a hazardous area. The barrier may be mechanical (a cage that covers the work action) or electrical (a photocell that will not permit the machine to cycle while the beam is broken). The emergency stop button is another form of guard; in order for it to be effective, the machine must be equipped with a braking system that will stop the machine in mid-cycle.

Guarding by distance involves keeping workers physically removed from the machine hazard. One of the most common methods is the two-handed trip guard or control, which is located near but not in the midst of the hazard site. Both hands are required to press each button simultaneously for the machine to cycle.

Hand-removal devices are designed to physically remove the worker's hands and arms from the activated machine. The "hand pull-out" is a harness-like system fastened to the worker's wrists at one end and to the machine at the other end. When the machine (say a punch press) is activated, the harness mechanism physically pulls the worker's hands out of the way. Short of removing the harness, the worker cannot win the ensuing tug of war.

The "sweep away" is a device with one or two arms (single sweep or double sweep) that, when activated by the machine cycle, will swing across in front of the worker, forcibly removing his or her hands from the danger area. A small panel attached to each arm screens the swept area to keep the worker's hands from re-entering the danger zone after the sweep arm passes. This is not a recommended type.

The *photoelectric eye* is a light beam that, when broken, will not allow the machine to cycle. This type of device has the advantage of not adding to the machine obstructions that can make maintenance difficult. It is generally expensive to install and maintain, but very effective.

Feeding tools include hand-held tongs, push sticks, or clamps that allow the operator access to the machine while keeping his or her hands out of the way. Metal tools are usually made of aluminum or magnesium, which will crush easily if caught in the machine, thereby saving the die sets and not allowing the type of kickback that could direct the worker's hands into the machine. A press forge operator will use a set of special tongs to hold a red-hot piece of metal in place in the dies while the machine forms the part. In a similar manner, a set of handles secured to sheet glass or metal by vacuum will permit a worker to handle the material without being cut by sharp edges.

◆ ◆ ◆
CONTACT CONTROL

If the machine or equipment or the plant cannot be modified to control the hazard, then the worker has to be protected. *Personal protective equipment* (PPE) such as hard hats, safety glasses, earplugs, and safety footwear shield the worker from hazards. While engineering controls are the preferred hazard-control option, PPE may be a legitimate alternative during emergencies or temporary breakdowns (Pilger, 1994). However, PPE does nothing to eliminate the hazard and should therefore not be relied upon.

Following are some steps that should be taken in the contact phase of an accident or incident:

1. **Suppression.** Reduce air contaminants by adopting procedures that control at the source. For example, dust in mining operations can be controlled by spraying water at the rock surface; floors that need to be swept can be dampened to control dust.

2. **Barriers.** Put in place barriers between workers and sources of energy as discussed earlier in the chapter.

3. **Modifications.** Identify and modify contact surfaces such as low ceilings in stairwells (to prevent head injuries) or projecting ends on guard rails (to prevent abdominal injuries).

4. **Substitution.** Eliminate potentially harmful energies through substitution or replacement. If possible, use a natural solvent instead of a petrochemical-based one.

5. **Reduction.** Reduce the amount of energy utilized. Lower the thermostat on hot-water sources (thermal energy); lower the speed of plant vehicles (kinetic energy). Both actions will reduce costs as well as potential injuries.

6. **Isolation.** Isolate energy sources from the workers. Install high-potential electrical equipment outside the building (electrical energy). Mount expensive, sensitive equipment at ceiling height to prevent contact damage (mechanical energy).

7. **Enhancing strength.** Encourage physical fitness among workers. Being fit will increase their ability to absorb higher levels of energy contact.

◆ ◆ ◆
POST-CONTACT CONTROL

Following are some steps that should be taken in the aftermath of an event:

1. Ensure that the injured worker receives immediate and thorough emergency care. The injury could be physical (a blow on the head) or from an exposure to hazardous chemical. Provisions for first aid and emergency care should be made during the pre-contact control process. The extent of these provisions will depend on the number of workers in an organization and the types of hazards they face.

2. Lock out the machinery involved until the accident investigation is complete and the damage repaired.

3. Keep unauthorized people out of the area.

4. Determine what can be salvaged and what waste must be disposed. Environmental regulations may prohibit the easy removal of certain hazardous waste (e.g., PCB-contaminated oils from a damaged power transformer).

5. Apprise the joint health and safety committee, affected managers, and government agencies of the event.

6. Complete all accident reports to determine what happened. Use report recommendations to ensure the accident will not be repeated.

7. Review all company procedures and revise where appropriate.

8. Communicate with workers about the event. If necessary, implement safety retraining.

Another way to think of controlling hazards is isolate the three areas in which hazardous conditions can either be eliminated or controlled: the source, the path, the human. This next section examines this perspective.

◆ ◆ ◆
SOURCE-PATH-HUMAN

Hazards can be controlled or eliminated by identifying and attacking the source of the hazard, the path it travels, and the employee or recipient of the hazard. The strategies discussed in this chapter can be regrouped along these lines as shown in Figure 5.4.

This schematic provides a useful summary of the information on hazard control. Placing control strategies in categories is less important than having a thorough understanding that hazard control is necessary and possible.

◆ ◆ ◆
MONITORING/AUDITING

Monitoring is an important part of the hazard-control process. Audits are done to ensure that hazard controls are functioning effectively, as well as to identify new hazards. Monitoring can be done daily by supervisors and maintenance personnel, weekly by department heads, monthly by health and safety committees, and as needed by compliance officers (Laing, 1992). The auditing process itself impacts safety. A 50 percent decrease in accidents in one organization over a two-year period was attributed to the fact that managers began to audit (Taylor, 1991).

An audit program can be used to evaluate health and safety performance in the workplace. There are a number of audit methods available. One very effective technique, which involves the application of total quality control methodologies and trend analysis, relates the number of incidents to some predetermined goal. If it seems from the number of events in a particular time frame that a safety goal failure is imminent, then steps can be taken to prevent the occurrence.

The audit program should do the following:

FIGURE 5.4 Source-Path-Human Controls

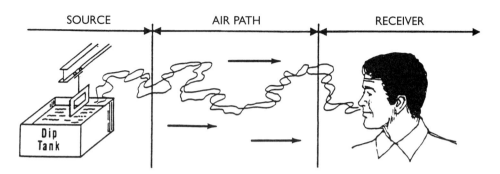

Source Controls	Path Controls	Human Controls
Substitution	Barricades	PPE
Modification	Process modification	Training
Housekeeping	Isolation	Safety awareness
Purchasing	Reduction	Personal hygiene
Preventative maintenance		Strength enhancement
Guarding		

1. Ensure that safety programs are being carried out without restrictions.

2. Ensure that safety programs are up to date and that deficiencies are documented.

3. Be carried out by people with some understanding of both the audit methods and the material being examined. (The various members of the joint health and safety committee should be able to carry out this inspection.)

4. Stimulate discussion among all managers and workers, and ultimately produce conclusions and recommendations.

5. Be conducted at least annually by companies with high-risk hazards.

6. Include all documentation (WCB statements, Ministry of Labour citations, air sampling results, first-aid and incident reports, hazard analyses, discipline records, cost-benefit studies, etc.).

◆ ◆ ◆
RECORDKEEPING

Information obtained at all stages of the hazard-control process should be stored in a database. These records are used to identify frequency of events as well as trends in hazards. They are also a source of information on worker training and equipment maintenance. The provision of monthly updates to managers will assist them in their efforts at ongoing hazard control.

◆ ◆ ◆
SUMMARY

The control of hazards has multiple payoffs for organizations. Eliminating or controlling hazards can be done at the pre-contact stage through training, safety awareness, engineering controls, purchasing, housekeeping, preventative maintenance, and machine guarding. Strategies at the contact stage include the use of personal protective equipment and barriers. Post-contact control is intended to minimize the damaging effects of hazards.

EXERCISES

1. Explain why hazard control at the pre-contact stage is better than hazard control at other stages.
2. Identify a hazard at your workplace. List all the approaches you could undertake to control or minimize the hazard.
3. You have been asked to conduct a training session in health and safety. Outline how you would conduct and coordinate a three-day session.
4. A maintenance crew has been hired to enter an underground sewer line to do some minor repair work. They call and ask you for advice about necessary equipment and procedures. Briefly outline your response.

References

Canadian Standards Association. 1994. *Safeguarding of Machinery.* Standard Z432-94.

Dessler, G. 1994. *Human Resource Management*, 6th ed. Englewood Cliffs, N.J.: Prentice-Hall.

Laing, P., ed. 1992. *Accident Prevention Manual for Business and Industry: Administration and Programs*, 10th ed. Washington, D.C.: National Safety Council.

Pilger, C.W. 1994. "Hazard Control Procedures." Presentation at the 23rd Intensive Workshop in Industrial Hygiene, September 27.

Schuler, R., and S. Dolan. 1994. *Human Resources Management: A Canadian Perspective.* Scarborough, Ont.: Nelson Canada. Greene,

Somasunder, Sam. 1993. "Machine Safeguarding." *OH&S Canada* 9, no. 5 (September/October): 30–31.

Taylor, J. 1991. "Guide to Health and Safety Management: 20 Proven Programs." *Safety Auditing.* Don Mills, Ont.: Southam Business Communications Inc.

6

Accident Investigation

INTRODUCTION

The investigation of incidents and accidents is a critical component of an organization's health and safety program. This chapter describes the rationale for accident investigations, the critical factors in the investigative process, the types of information to be collected, and the investigative methods and tools used to conduct an investigation. The importance of reporting and keeping records is also discussed.

◆ ◆ ◆

RATIONALE FOR ACCIDENT INVESTIGATION

The investigation of accidents is an important component in a hazard identification and control program, which in turn is an integral part of a health and safety program. Laing (1992) identifies the benefits of accident investigation as follows:

1. *Determines direct causes.* An investigation will uncover the direct causes of an accident, thereby allowing for the subsequent exploration of corrective measures.

2. *Identifies contributing causes.* Some accidents may be the result of many factors. For example, although the direct cause of an accident may be the loose clothing worn by an employee, contributing factors may include inadequate safeguards on the equipment, and a lack of instruction in the proper procedures for equipment use.

3. *Prevents similar accidents.* Once the direct and contributing causes are identified, corrective measures such as training programs or equipment design improvements can be implemented to prevent similar accidents.

4. *Creates a permanent record.* The reports generated by an investigation can be used by safety specialists to identify trends (i.e., sites of frequent accidents), inefficient layouts and designs, and substandard operating

procedures. Reports can also be valuable in the case of litigation or compensation claims. Actions taken to improve safety records can be cost efficient, in the sense that money and time will be allocated to sites or equipment where the most frequent or most severe accidents occur.

5. *Determines cost.* The delineation of the exact situation may help the organization determine the actual costs accruing from an accident.

6. *Promotes safety awareness among employees.* If a thorough investigation is conducted, employees will realize that management is serious about safety and interested in their well-being. This should motivate employees to show a greater concern for safe practices.

◆ ◆ ◆
CRITICAL FACTORS IN THE INVESTIGATIVE PROCESS

Accident investigations are strongly influenced by the factors of timing, severity, and legal requirements.

TIMING Timing is a critical factor in the investigation of accidents. Time impacts several types of information. Delays in investigation may lead to witness memory loss, changes at the accident site, and removal of important evidence. Furthermore, those directly involved in the accident, whether witnesses or late arrivals, tend to discuss the accident, and details may be distorted in the retelling.

Of course, the investigation should start only after the injured person receives medical attention and the accident site has been secured to prevent further injuries and attempts by helpful observers to "fix" the hazard.

SERIOUSNESS Given the time-consuming nature of investigation, companies tend to examine only those accidents that have the most serious consequences. However, accidents that result in minor injuries are often signals of a hazard that may one day have more serious consequences.

One corporate director of health and safety recommends that the following types of accidents be investigated: those resulting in lost-time injuries beyond the day of the accident; accidents in which the injury was minor but the employee was treated by a doctor, and there was potential for a serious injury; near misses; accidents without injuries but property damage in excess of $1000; and lost-time accidents resulting from aggravation of a previous injury (Ryan, 1991). Regardless of the system used to judge seriousness, organizations have a legal obligation to report certain types of accidents.

LEGAL REQUIREMENTS Depending on the seriousness of the accident, and the jurisdiction in which the accident happened, employers have to fulfil reporting requirements. Certain types of accidents, such as those requiring medical aid or resulting in lost time, must be reported to the Workers' Compensation Board, normally within three days. Forms are supplied by the WCB.

◆ ◆ ◆
TYPES OF INFORMATION COLLECTED

Most incidents and accidents are the result of many direct and contributing factors. The Three Mile Island disaster was preceded by multiple contributing factors ranging from inadequate emergency training to equipment shutdown to fail-safe systems that failed to take into consideration the human equation. Although no lives were lost in the incident, public trust in the nuclear-power industry plummeted.

When investigating an accident, the safety specialist should concentrate on gathering information relating to human, situational, and environmental factors.

HUMAN FACTORS

Studying the worker as a source of accidents does not mean that the investigator is looking for a scapegoat. As underlined throughout this text, the intent is fact finding, not fault finding. Following are some questions that could be asked when investigating human factors:

◆ What was the worker doing at the time of the accident? Was he or she performing a regular task, doing maintenance work, or helping a co-worker?

◆ Was the work being performed according to procedures? Were the tasks or procedures new?

◆ Was the worker trained to do the task? Was hazard recognition part of this training?

◆ Was a supervisor present?

◆ What was the employment status of the worker—seasonal, part-time, or full-time?

◆ How much experience did the employee have with respect to this particular operation?

◆ What were the sequence of acts leading to the accident/incident?

◆ What was the posture and location of the employee?

SITUATIONAL FACTORS

An analysis of the unsafe conditions that led to the accident is a critical step in an accident investigation. The equipment and tools must be examined. Was the machine operating in a satisfactory manner? Were all of the control and display positions ergonomically sound? Were the safety measures satisfactory and functioning? The analysis of failed materials or equipment can indicate how the accident happened. If a shaft broke, causing a machine part to fly off, an engineer can examine the break and determine the mode of failure. Failure of metal through shear or bending modes will leave definite patterns in the failed ends. Once the mode is known, the cause is usually easily determined.

The following questions could also be asked:

◆ What was the site/location of the accident?

◆ What tools and equipment or objects were involved in the accident?

◆ Was the correct equipment available and being used to do the job?

◆ What personal protective equipment (gloves, goggles, etc.) was being worn?

◆ Were guards in place?

◆ What time of day did the accident occur?

◆ What shift was being worked?

ENVIRONMENTAL FACTORS

Sometimes environmental factors such as light and noise may increase the likelihood that an accident will occur. The setting sun may blind the driver of a delivery truck; the noise of a machine may mask the approach of a vehicle; the vibrations of a certain piece of equipment may dislodge another tool.

Box 6.1 describes an accident in which all three factors—noise, light, and vibration—play a role.

BOX 6.1 ANALYSIS OF AN ACCIDENT

A carpenter is making some tool holders for the company where he is employed. He finds that he needs to trim about ¼ of an inch off the length of a piece of 4 × 4 wood. The 4 × 4 is 48 inches long. The carpenter spends 15 minutes adjusting the table saw to remove the correct thickness of material. He also removes the legally required saw guard because it tends to interfere with cutting. The supervisor had been after the company to purchase a new and proper guard for the saw. The usual answer was: "Why buy a new guard when one came with the machine?"

The carpenter decides not to replace the guard for this cut because the last time he did the same operation, the wood snagged on the guard support and allowed the blade to burn the cut surface. This necessitated extra sanding to remove the stain. This time, even though the carpenter uses the proper hand pusher and guides, the saw hits a knot and the work piece jumps up from the spinning blade. The cut is just starting when the worker removes his hand. He has received only minor lacerations.

The *unsafe acts* in this accident would include: (1) the carpenter removing of the guard and leaving it off during the operation; (2) the supervisor allowing the saw to be used with the poor guard and not insisting on replacing the defective guard; (3) the carpenter continuing to use a piece of unsafe equipment; and (4) the company purchasing the saw without specifying the correct type of guard.

The *unsafe conditions* would include: (1) having the improper guard on the machine; (2) providing a machine without a proper guard; and perhaps (3) the supervisor being unaware of the use of the improper guard.

In most provinces, a company official such as the plant manager could be found liable if an identified unsafe act or condition is ignored. The carpenter displayed voluntary risk in that he used the saw even though he knew it had a defective guard.

Can you identify the human, situational, and environmental factors that contributed to this accident?

◆ ◆ ◆

INVESTIGATIVE METHODS

OBSERVATIONS OR WALK-THROUGHS

At the beginning of the investigation, an overall picture of the total environment is achieved by means of a walk-through. Observation of causal factors, physical conditions, and work habits will help the specialist to identify potential causes of the accident. Because the manager may not be totally familiar with the details of the operation, the specialist may turn to the supervisor for any necessary information.

INTERVIEWS

Following are some basic rules for conducting an interview:

1. Interview witnesses on the spot and as soon as possible after the event while their memories are still fresh. Inform each witness of the purpose of the interview and what you hope to accomplish.

2. Interview witnesses separately and in a neutral location such as the cafeteria. Do not use your office, since there could be an authority stigma associated with it. The witness should be permitted to have a worker representative present, if he or she desires. Make sure that this individual listens and says little or nothing.

3. Put the witness at ease. If the person witnessed a serious injury, he or she may well be shaken up. If the person witnessed a death, counselling may well be necessary before any discussion can take place. Reassure the witness that you are trying not to lay blame, but simply to gather information.

4. Let the individual recall the event in his or her own way. Do not try to bias the account with questions that are pointed or directed. "Will you please tell me in your own words what you saw or heard?" is much better than, "Can you think what prompted John to do what he did?"

5. Ask any necessary questions at some appropriate time without interrupting the speaker's train of thought. The questions serve to clarify a point or fill in any gaps, not to support your own forming conclusions. "Can you explain again how you knew that the machine was turned off?" is preferable to, "You commented that the table saw was not running—did you see the worker turn it off?"

6. Give the witness feedback. "Based on what you said, my understanding of what you saw is ... If there is something I missed or confused, please add or clarify it." When you are finished, both you and the witness should be able to agree that the statement is a factual representation of what was said.

7. Make sure that critical information—either from the witnesses or your own observations—is recorded in a timely fashion. The longer the delay,

the more bias will affect the results. Supplement your written record with visuals (e.g., sketches, photographs, video).

8. End the interview on a positive note by thanking the witness for his or her valuable time and assistance. Encourage the witness to come to you with any further information that may emerge.

RE-ENACTMENTS

Re-enactment is a powerful method of incident recall that requires very careful handling and planning. The most obvious problem is the danger that simulating an actual injury will produce another one.

Circumstances will often dictate whether a re-enactment is essential to the building of a thorough investigation. In one documented case, the safety professional was on site when a worker was impaled between the couplers of two box cars in the rail yard of the company. The safety specialist filmed the car separation and the removal of the body. Then, while all of the witnesses were present and all of the details were fresh—horribly so—in their minds, he had each witness walk through what he or she saw. The local coroner complimented the safety officer on the thoroughness of the evidence.

Following are some guideline for conducting a re-enactment:

1. A qualified observer is necessary. If none is available, then the house specialist will have to do the job. If it appears that evidence is being gathered for an inquest or court hearing, then every possible explanation, even suicide, must be considered.

2. Do not show—tell. Have all of the witnesses relate in their own words what they observed. You as the analyst have to know precisely what took place during the event in question. Their stories will provide that information. You cannot afford any surprises that might lead to additional injury.

3. Shut every energy source down and lock them out. Follow the lockout procedures discussed in Chapter 5. Have the professional who is conducting the re-enactment control the major key for the lockout.

4. Carefully act out the events. The witness will describe what happened at each step (just as he or she did when verbally describing the events), and then, with the control person's approval, will act out that step. For obvious reasons, the re-enactment will stop prior to the point of accident.

BOX 6.2 INVESTIGATIVE TOOLS

The walk-through, the interview, and the re-enactment can be supplemented by the following:

Photographs

Accident photography is helpful and even necessary for efficient accident investigation. When pictures are being taken, make sure that they show the whole area as well as every angle and every "nook and cranny." Colour is best, although black and white is also useful. One advantage of black-and-white photographs is that they can be scanned and included in the accident report. Investigators with limited photographic experience will find a Polaroid camera relatively easy to use. Photographs taken with this camera can be examined on the spot for focus and framing problems. Point and shoot cameras also require minimal operator skill. Video cameras are effective.

Drawings

After the interview, prepare a series of sketches or drawings of the accident scene. These can be complemented by Polaroid or video photography. A good CAD program such as Cadkey or Cadkey Lite will facilitate the drawing process. If you do not have access to CAD software, then a scale pencil sketch is fine. Make sure all parts of the drawing are well labelled.

Computers

Incident recall involves the gathering and recording of large amounts of information and recording it. A computer with a user-friendly database is a necessity. Portable laptops can be taken directly to the scene of an accident. Any computer will facilitate the structured entry of data and facts into the safety files.

Other Tools

Depending upon the circumstances of the event, other tools such as tape measures, clipboards, water-resistant pens and flashlights may be of assistance to the investigator.

RECORD CHECK

Training records and maintenance/production schedules can offer the investigator some valuable insights. A careful review of training records can provide the answers to a number of questions. Was the worker properly instructed in the accepted and safe methods of doing the job or task? Was he or she aware of the rules of operation and were they followed? Has the worker signed a training attendance or test form? Maintenance logs and records should provide information about potential hazards within the company and what, if anything, was done about them. Preventative maintenance data are particularly important, since they can be used to predict possible future failures in equipment.

◆ ◆ ◆
ACCIDENT/INCIDENT REPORTS

Once all of the information from the investigation has been gathered, the accident/incident reports must be completed. These reports should provide some explanation of causal factors. While the principal causes remain unsafe acts (e.g., not using a personal protective device) or unsafe conditions (e.g., a broken guard), other explanatory conditions may exist. The factor most closely associated with the cause of an accident is referred to as the *agency*. Following are some examples of agents:

◆ Animals (insects, dogs, etc.)

◆ Pressure vessels (boilers, piping)

◆ Chemicals (solvents, explosives)

◆ Materials handling systems (conveyers, fork trucks)

◆ Dust, fumes, smoke, mists (silica, wood)

◆ Electrical equipment (motors, fuses, wiring)

◆ Elevating devices (elevators, vertical stop belts)

◆ Tools (hammers, wrenches)

◆ Flammable materials (solvents, gasoline)

◆ Lifting devices (hoists, cranes)

◆ Machine tools (lathe, drill press)

◆ Motive power sources (engines, vehicles)

◆ Radiation (X-ray, ultraviolet)

The agency part refers to the subgroup of the factors listed above. For example, a dog bite would be the agency part of the animal group.

Another consideration in reports is the *accident type*, which attempts to categorize the nature of the accident. Some examples:

◆ Caught in or between (e.g., crushed between two moving machines)

◆ Struck by (impact or blow to the body by an object)

◆ Struck against (walking into a door)

◆ Fall to the same level (tripping on a level walkway)

◆ Fall to a lower level (falling off a ladder)

- Fall to a higher level (tripping while walking up the steps)
- Abraded, scratched, or punctured (an injury such as hitting the face when falling)
- Overexertion (sprains, strains, etc., caused by a greater-than-average effort)
- Contact with an energy (mechanical, kinetic, electrical, chemical, thermal, gravity or radiation)

Personal factors (e.g., lack of knowledge, fatigue, restricted vision) should also be included in the accident investigation form to assist in entry, recordkeeping, and analysis.

The actual report format will vary by company. (Samples of short and long reports are provided in Figures 6.1 and 6.2 respectively.) Organization and layout should be straightforward. Accuracy and thoroughness are also important. Where information is unknown or is not applicable, the respondent should indicate "information unknown" or "not applicable" as the case may be. Abbreviations such as n/a for "not applicable" should not be used (it can mean "not available" as well).

Reports that must be submitted to outside parties such as OHS agencies or WCBs should include basic information about the company (type of industry, number of employees, etc.).

A description of any injury that was sustained should be included. A separate physician's report (see Figure 6.3) should also be provided, along with a witness report (see Figure 6.4).

Completed reports are submitted to the senior managers, the joint health and safety committee, others directly involved, and possibly the Ministry of Labour if the accident involved serious injuries. It is then up to the senior manager directly responsible for the operation in question to implement the recommendations contained in the report.

CALCULATING ACCIDENT FREQUENCY AND SEVERITY RATES

Copies of the reports of accidents involving injuries should accompany the firm's WCB claim forms. WCB requires injury not accident frequency and severity rates in order to determine the assessment for the organization.

Frequency is determined by dividing the number of medical aid injuries by the number of hours worked expressed as a ratio of 200,000 (or 1,000,000). (In some firms and jurisdictions, the factor may be 1,000,000 person hours worked rather than 200,000.)

Take, as an example, a company that employs 300 people who work 8-hour shifts for 250 days in one year. The total number of hours worked is

$$250 \times 300 \times 8 = 600,000$$

This company has a record of 6 medical-aid injuries with no lost time; 15 minor injuries with 5 days lost; 3 major injuries with 55 days lost; and 6 property-damage accidents with no lost time. The total number of injuries thus is

$$(6 + 15 + 3) = 24$$

The frequency is calculated as

$$\frac{\text{Total injuries} = (6 + 15 + 3) = 24}{\text{Total hours worked} = (250 \times 300 \times 8) = 600,000} = \frac{8}{200,000}$$

Therefore, this organization has an accident frequency ratio of 8 per 100 persons (2000 hours/year $\times$ 100).

Property-damage accidents are not considered since there is no associated injury. However, some organizations calculate their own accident frequency values by dividing the number of property-damage accidents by the total number of hours worked. In the above case, this value would be 6/600,000 or 2 per 200,000 hours.

Severity of work-related injuries is the ratio of the number of days lost per 200,000 hours worked. Severity is calculated by applying the above formula to the number of days lost to injuries, instead of lost time injuries. The severity, or total number of days lost, in the above case would be calculated as

$$\frac{\text{Total lost days} = (5 + 55) = 60}{\text{Total hours worked} = 250 \times 300 \times 8 = 600,000} = \frac{20}{200,000}$$

The severity is thus 20 per 200,000 hours, or 100 person years.

These ratios facilitate comparison between years and companies and help identify trends. Records of accidents can also be used as a basis for risk and fault tree analyses.

FIGURE 6.1 Short Report

PE+E Supervisor's Accident/Incident Report

A. General Information

last name: first name: gender: [ ] male [ ] female

department: job title:

type: [ ] full time   [ ] part time   [ ] casual

date of injury: time of injury: [ ]am [ ] pm

date reported: time reported: [ ]am [ ] pm

incident category: [ ]illness   [ ]injury   [ ] first aid   [ ] medical aid

B. Accident Investigation

Nature and extent of injury: [ ] left   [ ] right

What job was the employee performing:

Was this part of regular duties: [ ] yes   [ ] no

Length of time employee performing this type of work:

Exact location of accident:

Describe sequence of events leading to accident. Name tools, machines, materials used. Provide sketch on reverse if necessary.

Describe any unsafe mechanical or physical condition involved in accident:

Describe any unsafe act involved in accident:

Name and address of hospital or clinic: [ ] company doctor:

Doctor's name: Doctor's estimate of lost time:

Measures taken to prevent similar accidents:

FIGURE 6.1 (continued)

C. Diagrams

Diagrams or photographs may be placed here:

Witness name: _____   Witness name: _____

Address: _____   Address: _____

Phone: Res: _____   Phone: Res: _____

       Bus: _____   Bus: _____

Supervisor's signature: _____   Date: _____

Employee's signature: _____   Date: _____

Please have this document processed and forwarded to: Original to: Manager, Safety and Environment

                        Copies to: Vice President, Manufacturing,

                                    Manager, Human Resources

                                    Department

The information you provide on this document will enable PE+E to effectively manage claims. Thank you for taking as much time as possible.

FIGURE 6.2 Long Report

Supervisor's Accident / Incident Report

To be completed by the Supervisor with the Employee immediately after an accident / incident
Please Print

last name   first name   gender

street   apt   city   prov

postal code   telephone   date of birth   marital status

date of employment   department   job title

[ ] full time   [ ] part time   [ ] casual   hrs/week

years experience   social insurance number

accident/incident occurred: yyyy mm dd (   )   hhmm (   ) am/pm

reported to employer: yyyy mm dd (   )   hhmm (   )am/pm

who was accident reported to:

location of accident (dept, machine, location of machine)

supervisor's name

witness name(s)

Has this employee ever had a similar work-related injury or non-work-related injury? [ ] yes   [ ] no

If yes, explain:

List the employee's job description / task analysis at the time of the injury

(Include job title, duties, weights, sizes of equipment, tools, etc.)

What physical effort was involved? (List job function plus weights and sizes of materials used.)

FIGURE 6.2 (continued)

investigation of accident / incident (*who, what, why, where, how*)

Who was involved?

Where did the accident / incident occur?

What happened to cause the accident / incident? (explain—facts only)

Why did the accident / incident occur? (be objective, do not lay blame)

How did the accident / incident occur? (based on facts only)

injury

[ ] lost time   [ ] medical aid   [ ] first aid   [ ] information only or [ ] hazardous condition, no injury

treatment memorandum sent   [ ] yes [ ] no   modified work form sent   [ ] yes   [ ] no

causes

[ ] unsafe act   [ ] unsafe condition   [ ] information only or [ ] poor/damaged equipment

[ ] no / poor training   [ ] no/poor procedures   [ ] other

explain

FIGURE 6.2 (continued)

accident type

[ ] overexertion / strain   [ ] caught in / between   [ ] slip / fall   [ ] struck by / against   [ ] exposed to

[ ] motor vehicle   [ ] contact with/by   [ ] other

explain:

_____

_____

_____

injury type

[ ] bruise   [ ] burn (heat)   [ ] burn (chemical)   [ ] cut   [ ] crush   [ ] strain

[ ] twist   [ ] lift   [ ] electric shock   [ ] inhalation   [ ] occupational illness

[ ] rash   [ ] other

explain:

_____

_____

_____

part of body injured   *[ ] left   [ ] right*

[ ] head	[ ] face	[ ] eye	[ ] ear	[ ] neck	[ ] chest
[ ] lungs	[ ] abdomen	[ ] groin	[ ] back-upper	[ ] back-middle	[ ] back-lower
[ ] buttock	[ ] shoulder	[ ] arm	[ ] wrist	[ ] hand	[ ] finger th 2 3 4 5
[ ] leg	[ ] knee	[ ] ankle	[ ] foot	[ ] toe big 2 3 4 5	[ ] other

explain:

_____

_____

_____

suggested corrective action

[ ] review procedures   [ ] protective equipment   [ ] repair equipment   [ ] develop procedure

[ ] re-instruction of staff

explain:

_____

_____

_____

_____

_____

_____

FIGURE 6.2 (continued)

name & address of hospital or clinic
_____

_____

_____

name of attending doctor _____ estimated time off work _____

name of family physician _____

address _____

date & hour last worked _____ Work hours: from _____ to _____

shift information: _____ [ ] Day [ ] Afternoon [ ] Midnight

hours worked: from: _____ to: _____ days/week: _____

provide average gross earnings _____ [ ] hourly [ ] daily

additional information

_____

_____

_____

_____

_____

diagram of accident

employee's signature _____ date _____

supervisor's signature _____ date _____

MAKE COPIES AND SEND TO:

[ ] Manager, Loss Control (*original*)   [ ] *Human Resources*   [ ] *Department*

FIGURE 6.3 Physician's Report

INJURY/ILLNESS ASSESMENT FORM
to accompany employee to physician

For use in on-duty instances of sickness or injury to determine the rehabilitation duties to which an employee can return to in the workplace as presented in Bill 162 of the Worker's Compensation Act

To be completed by an Employee's Supervisor (please print)

A. Personal Data   Date:_____

Employee's Name: _____   Signature: _____

Job Title: _____   SIN No.: _____

Date of illness or injury on duty: _____   Date of birth: _____

Date absence commenced: _____   Health No.: _____

Nature of injury: _____

Supervisor's Name: _____   Department: _____   Telephone: _____

To be completed by Physician (please print)

B. Assessment of fitness to work

1. [ ] Employee is fit to return to regular work.

2. [ ] Employee is fit to return to modified work - with restrictions as indicated in C & D (reverse).

    Indicate number of hours to be worked and on what basis?

    [_____] hours   [ ] daily   [ ] weekly

    Estimate date of return to modified work:_____

3. [ ] Not fit for work at this time.

    Employee to return for medical reassessment on: (yyyy mm dd) _____

See reverse side for Physical Evaluation to be completed by the Physician

Please return this completed form to the Manager, Loss Control via the Employee

FIGURE 6.3 (continued)

To be completed by the treating Physician

C. Physical Evaluation

Step 1 *Location of problem*

a) head include vision, hearing, speech
b) neck
c) upper back, chest or upper abdomen
d) lower back, lower abdomen or genetalia
e) shoulder or upper arm
f) elbow or lower arm
g) wrist or hand
h) hip or upper leg
i) knee or lower leg
j) ankle or foot
k) systemic or internal organ

Right   Left

Step 2 *Please indicate restrictions for modified work*

1. Walking: [ ] only short distances   [ ] other
2. Standing, not more than: [ ] 15 minutes [ ] 30 minutes [ ] other
3. Sitting, no more than: [ ] 30 minutes [ ] 60 minutes [ ] 2 hours [ ] other
4. Bending and twisting, explain:
5. Lifting, floor to waist, not more than: [ ] 7 kg   [ ] 14 kg   [ ] 25 kg   [ ] other
6. Lifting, waist to head, not more than: [ ] 7 kg   [ ] 14 kg   [ ] 25 kg   [ ] other
7. Carrying, not more than: [ ] 7 kg   [ ] 14 kg   [ ] 25 kg   [ ] other
8. Climbing stairs: [ ] no stair climbing   [ ] 2 or 3 steps only   [ ] only short flight
9. Climbing ladder: [ ] no climbing   [ ] 2 or 3 steps only   [ ] 4 to 6 steps only
10. Manual dexterity, not able to: [ ] type   [ ] sort   [ ] other
11. Pushing and pulling trolley, not more than: [ ] 16 kg   [ ] 25 kg   [ ] other
12. Can operate motorized equipment: [ ] any vehicle [ ] forklifts [ ] not recommended
13. Vision, potential safety hazard   [ ] yes   [ ] no   [ ] other
14. Other comments (explain)

D. Treatment

1. Is the employee's prescribed treatment likely to impair performance or safety?   [ ] yes   [ ] no

2. Is the employee referred to: [ ] physiotherapy   Date commenced:_____

                          [ ] occupational therapy   Duration:_____

Physician's Name: _____   Telephone: _____

Address: _____

Date: _____   Signature: _____

FIGURE 6.4 Witness Report

Accident/Incident Witness Statement

Injured employee: _____ date of injury: _____

Witness Name: _____

Does the witness have knowledge of the accident or injury?   [ ] yes   [ ] no

Did the witness see the injury happen?   [ ] yes   [ ] no

If yes to either of the above, please explain below:

Knowledge of Injury: Explain what you know about the injury/accident. e.g.: what type of work was being done at the time of the injury / accident, what happened to cause the injury / accident, how seriously was the injured employee hurt, etc. _____

_____

_____

_____

_____

What witness actually saw: Please identify what you saw before the injury/accident, during the injury/accident and immediately after the injury/accident. _____

_____

_____

_____

_____

Give your **opinion** as to how this injury/accident could have been prevented. _____

_____

_____

_____

_____

Witness signature: _____ date: _____

◆ ◆ ◆
SUMMARY

Accident investigation is an important part of a safety program. The reasons for conducting an investigation are primarily to identify direct and contributing causes, and to ensure that the accident does not recur. Timing and severity are the important variables in investigations. The types of information collected can be grouped under human factors, situational factors, and environmental factors. The investigative methods include observations and walk-throughs, interviews, and re-enactments, all of which are complemented by investigative tools such as cameras and computers. Records also supply information that might be important in determining causes. The reporting of information collected is the last step in accident investigation.

E X E R C I S E

Accident Investigation Case

You are the president and largest stockholder of an original equipment manufacturer (OEM) that employs 300 workers. You have no safety specialist, but you do take a personal interest in accident prevention. Recently, you assigned general responsibility for safety to the day-shift superintendent as a minor part of her regular duties.

The plant has never been thoroughly analyzed for hazards, and you are aware that the operation is not as safe as it could be. Many of the operations require considerable ongoing maintenance by the workers to prevent accidents. Since the business has only been breaking even for several years, you have delayed making any improvements to plant and equipment. The superintendent and you have concentrated your

efforts on preventing unsafe acts by the employees. An elaborate system of worker reminders, instruction by supervisors, and posters have been used to make the workforce safety conscious. For the last few years, your performance with respect to medical aid and lost-time injuries has been average for your WCB rate group. Your company has escaped any lost-time injuries for the last two years, including the current year to date. The continuation of that record has become an important goal. Signs in the plant indicate the number of days that have passed without a lost-time injury.

Today at 15:30 hours, a container of nearly red-hot, upper-control-arm forgings was overturned. The hot forgings fell on a worker who was helping the drop forge machine operator. The man suffered third degree burns over 20 percent of his body and, while expected to recover, will lose most of his right arm, his right ear, and sight in his right eye.

Question

Describe the investigative methods and tools you would use to investigate this accident.

References

Laing, P., ed. 1992. *Accident Prevention Manual for Business and Industry: Administration and Programs,* 10th ed. Washington, D.C.: National Safety Council.

Ryan, T. 1991. "Accident Investigations: II Group Investigations." In F. Briggs, ed., *Guide to Health and Safety Management.* Don Mills, Ont.: Southam Business Publications.

7

Emergency Preparedness and Fire Prevention

◆ ◆ ◆

INTRODUCTION

Organizations must consider the possibility of a disaster, where the potential for loss is very high. No safety program is complete without a preplanned response to the threat of a disaster. One insurance company has estimated that losses in companies without an emergency plan exceeded those in companies with a good plan by a ratio of 15 to 1 (CCHOS, 1986).

What constitutes an emergency? An *emergency* can be defined as a sudden, generally unexpected occurrence or set of circumstances demanding immediate action. In the workplace, this would include an explosion or a fire out of control. There are several types of emergencies: fires and explosions, floods, hurricanes and tornadoes, earthquakes, sabotage, and war or civil strife.

Sometimes a work accident can lead to a disaster through a chain reaction. For example, a break in a chemical line that emits toxic vapours can cause a panic when the contaminated air enters the plant's ventilation system. This toxic release may even impact neighbouring plants or houses (Laing, 1992).

A disaster is measured by the degree of damage, loss, or destruction. Disasters can be caused by natural events such as a severe electrical storm with high winds. High-profile disasters have included:

◆ The crash of a Toronto subway car (probably caused by the failure of a train stop arm) in 1995, resulting in three deaths and the evacuation from smoke-filled tunnels of hundreds of passengers. The emergency response teams were working in 40°C temperatures;

◆ A train disaster in Mississauga, Ontario, where a freight train carrying propane and chlorine tank cars left the tracks and caught fire. The resulting evacuation of some 200,000 residents from the area made headlines.

While the general probability of any of these emergencies actually happening may be low, they *can* happen and a company (or the home) is remiss if it does not institute an emergency plan. Disasters may be prevented or mitigated by the effectiveness of the emergency plan.

A preplanned response to a disaster must consider the safety of employees and the public; the protection of the property, operations, and environment; and, ultimately, the restoration of the organizations' operations. Therefore, the goals of an emergency preparedness plan are to reduce and prevent injuries and fatalities; reduce damage to buildings, stock, and equipment; and rapidly restore normal operations.

Elements necessary in the management of emergencies include an emergency plan, an emergency manager, a fire plan, an evacuation plan, and a medical attention plan. In Canada, there are legal requirements for emergency preparedness, available through regulatory agencies. In general, these laws cover environment, pipelines, fire, oil, and gas, boilers and pressure vessels, dangerous goods, transportation, and occupational health and safety.

◆ ◆ ◆
EMERGENCY PLAN

The first thing that is required is a formal, rapid-response, workable, well-controlled emergency plan. The success of low levels of loss depends on this plan. The joint health and safety committees as well as the local government should be involved in developing the plan.

The basics are simple. An organization requires hazard evaluation, an emergency response plan, training, an evacuation plan, notification of authorities, supplies, and drills.

HAZARD EVALUATION Safety professionals (and the managers) must have evaluated the hazards that could generate an emergency (e.g., storage of flammable solvents near static electricity or ignition sources) as well as the hazards with the greatest risk and loss potential. They must also understand: how the emergency plans could be aborted or sidetracked if an emergency were to occur; the extent of possible damage and injuries or fatalities; and the possible financial loss of the total plant, its individual departments, and critical equipment or processes.

An emergency is a rare occurrence, and so knowledge of these hazards can be augmented by consulting Emergency Planning Canada, the Fire Commissioner of Canada, Environment Canada, as well as fire departments and insurance companies.

EMERGENCY RESPONSE PLAN A response plan for different types of emergencies must be created. These plans should be written, published, and posted. There must be good alarm facilities with emergency communication devices, and everyone in the plant must be familiar with their locations and use.

A list should be published of those people who are in charge of every aspect of any emergency activity. Accompanying the list should be information on the actual event, security and protection for the workers, protecting what is left, documenting damage and injuries, and liaison with bureaucrats, insurance, and media.

TRAINING Supervisors, workers, first-aid attendants, and others who will be dealing with the specific emergency need training in emergency response. The importance of this particular aspect of the plan cannot be overstated. The training and experience will pay major dividends. Training some workers in the control and handling of spilled or leaking hazardous wastes may be another component of emergency preparedness. Employers can assume, based on provisions in the Act, that a trained response team will go a long way to satisfy the due diligence requirements (Hosty, 1995).

EVACUATION PLAN Plans for evacuating employees and clients in the event of a major emergency or disaster are a key element in emergency preparedness. Every worker in the plant must know exactly where to congregate when the need arises, and be aware of at least two evacuation routes. There should be well-marked, unobstructed evacuation paths with well-lit exits. Notices about exit procedures should be posted, along with instructions about notifying appropriate personnel of the emergency. The evacuation of mentally and physically challenged personnel or clients needs careful consideration, because elevators are shut down in emergencies. Designated assembly areas and assigned assistance should be part of the plan.

A roll call (head count) should be done at the assembly site, and a list of missing employees should be given to the command centre. No one should be allowed to re-enter until all personnel are accounted for and debriefed.

NOTIFICATION OF AUTHORITIES Companies should be aware of any legislative requirements, such as the requirement to notify the Ministry of Labour, police, etc. In locations such as Toronto with the 911 emergency system, an industrial call for medical assistance will automatically bring police, ministry, and other associated specialists, along with medical assistance.

SUPPLIES Emergency first-line equipment such as fire extinguishers must be in well-defined, easily accessible locations. As noted above, designated workers must be trained in their use.

DRILLS Regular emergency drills, with the occasional unannounced drill to keep everyone current and knowledgeable, are a standard part of most plans. Rehearsals are an important part of training. Simulating disasters will help employees deal effectively with real emergencies. Fire drills are rehearsals that require employees to be aware of reporting requirements and the location of exits and fire extinguishers. Drills test the response capability of the organization. The results (evacuation times, etc.) are monitored and reported to management. A full-scale dress rehearsal involves simulated injuries and provides a measure of an organization's ability to respond.

◆ ◆ ◆
EMERGENCY MANAGER

In addition to the foregoing requirements, any emergency plan must have a senior person—generally the plant manager—who will be in charge of all of the emergency activities. This individual should speak for the organization and must be totally committed to the plan. If the emergency manager works a regular day shift and the plant is on multiple shifts, then there must be assistants on each of the other shifts with the authority and training to handle emergencies. The command centre, with a designated chain of command, is a critical component of the plan.

◆ ◆ ◆
FIRE PLAN

The fire plan will have the same characteristics as the main emergency plan, although some of the requirements dealing with major damage and fatalities may not be followed if the fire gets out of control and a full-blown emergency situation results. A group of workers must be trained in firefighting techniques and be part of the plant fire brigade. In small to mid-sized businesses where an in-house fire brigade is not economically feasible, workers should receive fire-extinguisher training and participate in ongoing practice sessions.

The local fire department is a good source of training for any in-house firefighting team that may be required. The fire department can also assist in fire hazard evaluations and regular inspections. Fire prevention and suppression is discussed in the final section of this chapter.

◆ ◆ ◆
EVACUATION REQUIREMENTS

The first function of any emergency plan is the safe and quick evacuation of all workers in the plant. Following are some basic requirements:

1. The plant must be divided into small, related areas. The workers in each of these areas must be identified and trained to recognize and remember workers who are not part of their section. This probably happens routinely during working hours, but the noted presence of these "outsiders" must become second nature. In case of a major emergency, all workers must be accounted for.

2. Outside the building and away from any roadways there should be assembly points that allow for the movement of emergency vehicles. The personnel from each work area noted above must be trained to quickly move to their respective assembly points and remain there until a head count is complete and missing workers are accounted for.

3. Once every employee has been accounted for and the extent of the emergency has been determined, employees can be instructed to return to work, or go home and report when called.

4. Any critical equipment or process that may increase the overall risk of the emergency should be addressed. For example, the supply sources of flammable materials such as gas must be shut off. These tasks should be undertaken only by maintenance personnel who are highly trained in emergency procedures.

5. The end of the emergency can be called only by the senior person responsible for the plant's emergency procedures.

6. A post-evacuation assessment must be done to identify problems in the evacuation plan. Remedial measures can then be taken.

The Canadian Standards Association has developed a standard for emergency response plans (ERP) that provides further information on evacuation requirements.

◆ ◆ ◆
FIRST AID AND MEDICAL ATTENTION

The various provincial regulations spell out in detail the requirements for first-aid and medical-aid facilities. Medical services run the gamut from a first-aid kit in a small firm to a full-blown hospital with doctors in very large firms. Degree of risk can be an additional factor in determining the extent of medical services. An insurance office with a staff of 4000 would not likely need the same facilities as an automobile manufacturer with the same number of workers.

Beyond conforming to legal requirements, every company should arrange to have at least one trained first-aid attendant present at each shift. All employees should be given the opportunity to take a cardiopulmonary resuscitation (CPR) course. A cost-benefit analysis may show the advantages of contracting with a local occupational health clinic for medical-aid services. These services can include pre- and post-employment medicals, exposure medical testing, and potential occupational illness identification.

Complete first-aid records must be kept and maintained. These records can be used to substantiate legitimate and bogus WCB claims should the need arise.

◆ ◆ ◆
FIRE PREVENTION AND SUPPRESSION

A *fire* is a chemical process in which fuel, oxygen, and heat are combined to create a disastrous condition. The products of fire are gases, flame, heat, and smoke.

The fire process can be graphically represented by means of the fire triangle. (see Figure 7.1). The new model is the fire tetrahedron. (See Figure 7.2). The triangular model shows that the three elements—fuel, oxygen, and heat—must come together for a fire to be sustained. The second model adds a fourth element—the chain reaction. Once a fire starts, it is perpetuated by the ongoing (or chain) reaction of the other three elements.

There are four stages of fire:

1. *The incipient stage.* At this stage, a source of ignition (a cigarette butt or a hot electrical wire connection) and fuel (papers or wood) come together. This stage can continue for hours until the resultant heat from the initial reaction becomes great enough to cause combustion. The air is filled with

FIGURE 7.1   Fire Tetrahedron

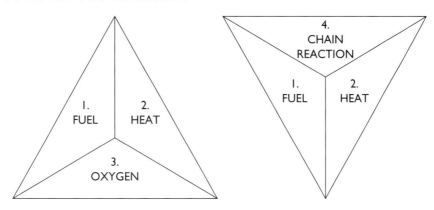

FIGURE 7.2   Fire Triangle

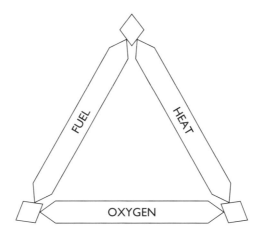

molecule-sized products of combustion. The airborne particulate can be detected with an ionizing (smoke) detector. In the case of an explosion, this stage (and the next) are very short.

2. *The smouldering stage.* The three elements are present and are causing the heat to rise through limited chain reaction. The area begins to fill with smoke, which increases in output as the process continues. With visible airborne particulate (smoke) now present, a photoelectric detector is effective. This stage is short and can be measured in minutes.

3. *The free-burning stage.* This is the stage at which flames first appear. The rate of energy release (heat) is increasing very rapidly and the surrounding combustible materials are beginning to burn. The free-burning stage is very short and can be measured in minutes or less. A rate-of-rise detector can be effective at this stage because it senses the rapid temperature increase. This detector works well in conjunction with a sprinkler system.

4. *The uncontrolled fire stage.* The fire is out of control and major property damage is under way. All personnel must be evacuated. This stage can be measured in fractions of a minute. The rate of reaction doubles every 10°C. No heat is lost during this reaction; rather it becomes cumulative.

The fire triangle or tetrahedron can serve to illustrate the requirements for extinguishment. By removing any one of the parts of these models, the fire cannot be sustained and will be put down. For instance, a carbon dioxide fire extinguisher will blanket the fire with a gas that will displace the oxygen, thereby smothering the fire. Similarly, water sprayed on the fire will cool the conditions or reduce the heat, also resulting in extinguishment.

There are four classes of fire based on the type of fuel or source of combustion.

1. *Class A.* Class A fires occur in combustible materials such as paper or wood. The preferred method of extinguishment is to use water to cool or remove the heat. A Class A extinguisher is identified by a green triangle containing the letter A.

2. *Class B.* Class B fires occur in flammable liquids such as oil, solvents, and gasoline. The preferred method of extinguishment is to smother with carbon dioxide or dry chemicals if the fire is small (e.g., a grease fire in a restaurant) or to cool with water if the fire is large (e.g., a petroleum tank farm fire). A Class B extinguisher is identified by a red square containing the letter B.

3. *Class C.* Class C fires occur in electrical equipment. Water cannot be used in this situation because of the possibility of electrocution. Carbon dioxide is the recommended medium for extinguishment. In some special cases such as computer rooms, halon may be used. A Class C extinguisher is identified by a blue circle containing the letter C.

4. *Class D.* Class D fires occur in combustible metals such as magnesium and some highly reactive flammable liquids such as picric acid. These

fires should be extinguished with a dense powder that will not react with any of the burning materials. A Class D extinguisher is identified by a yellow star containing the letter D.

Hazardous byproducts of fires besides heat and smoke include carbon monoxide, carbon dioxide, hydrogen sulphide, sulphur dioxide, hydrogen cyanide, and hydrogen chloride. These toxic materials come from the burning materials (fuel) when they break down into original chemicals under extreme heat and chain reactions.

When developing a fire-prevention and suppression program, the following should be considered.

1. *Structural design.* Standards for construction of buildings are detailed in the federal and provincial fire codes, as well as fire marshal and building codes and regulations.

2. *Barriers.* Walls and floors can be used to delay or prevent the spread of fire. Specially constructed fire barriers should be maintained.

3. *Detection and suppression.* Most buildings have a detection system, which senses heat and smoke. When triggered, sprinklers are activated to suppress the fire.

4. *Storage.* Combustible materials should be rated and stored in separate or isolated areas. They should *not* be stored near exits.

Many fires are triggered by unsafe acts (e.g., a person tries to weld a container containing flammable liquid residue without cleaning) and unsafe conditions, (e.g., faulty or improper equipment is installed near a potentially flammable process).

◆ ◆ ◆
SUMMARY

The goals of an emergency plan are to reduce injuries and property damages, and to restore the organization to its normal operations. Emergency preparedness consists of preparing an emergency response plan, designating and training those responsible for its implementation, and communicating it to employees. Developing an evacuation plan, establishing a fire-prevention and suppression program, and controlling fire hazards are other elements of emergency preparedness.

E X E R C I S E S

1. Determine if your workplace has an emergency response plan. Compare this plan with the one outlined in this chapter.
2. Prepare a fire prevention and suppression plan for your own home or apartment.
3. Decide what type of fire extinguisher would be most effective in the following fire situations:

a. a hair dryer engulfed in smoke
b. grease burning in a frying pan
c. rags smoking in the garage
d. a log that has rolled from the fireplace onto the living room floor
e. a coffee machine whose wires are shooting flames.

References

Canadian Centre for Occupational Health and Safety. 1986. *Emergency Planning* P86-10E. Hamilton, Ont.

Hosty, J.W. 1995. "Made in America: Guidelines for Emergency Response Training." *Accident Prevention* (March/April).

Laing, P., ed. 1992. *Accident Prevention Manual for Business and Industry: Administration and Programs*, 10th ed. Washington, D.C.: National Safety Council.

8

Chemical and Biological Agents

◆ ◆ ◆
INTRODUCTION

More than 65,000 different chemicals are currently in use in North America, and approximately 700 new ones are introduced every year. No toxicity data are available on about 80 percent of the chemicals that are used commercially (Adler, 1989). Increasingly, physicians are seeing patients who complain of sensitivity to low-level chemical exposures in the environment. These complaints have been variously labelled as multiple chemical sensitivity (MCS), 20th-century disease, total allergy syndrome, and environmental illness (Genesove, 1995). Certain industrial chemicals have been linked to cancer, lung disease, blood abnormalities, nervous-system disorders, birth defects, sterility, and skin problems. The specific effects of many chemicals are well documented, while others are still unknown (IAPA, 1988).

The term *chemical agents* is used to describe hazards that are created by any one of a very large number of chemical and/or physical reactions or actions. For example, vapours entering the atmosphere from solvents such as paint thinners are included in the chemical-reaction category. Airborne particulates (e.g., dust created by mechanical means such as sanding or grinding) are included in the physical-action category. These categories account for most of the health hazards found in industry and at home.

It has been estimated that 85 percent of all occupational illnesses are the result of chemical exposures (WCB, 1993). Health problems created by chemical exposures are more prevalent in the workplace than in any other location. Although for the sake of simplicity this chapter will discuss single chemical exposures, most of the exposures that take place in the workplace are more complex.

Biological agents or *biohazards* are natural organisms or products of organisms that present a risk to humans. Two of the better-known biological agents are legionnaires' disease (*Legionella pneumophilia*) and AIDS (HTLV-III/LAV). While exposure to biohazards is not as common as exposure to chemical agents, the results can be just as deadly.

◆ ◆ ◆
CHEMICAL AGENTS

To understand chemical agents, one must be familiar with the associated hazards each possesses. The hazard associated with a material is defined as the likelihood that it will cause injury in a given environment or situation. The potential degree of severity of the hazard is determined by its toxicity (i.e., its ability to cause injury to biological tissue) and/or its explosive properties, which are defined in terms of flammability and reactivity. The extent to which a potentially toxic substance is an actual health hazard will depend on other factors, such as the concentration of the chemical and the length of time the employee is exposed to it.

Chemicals exist in one of three states—solid, liquid, or gas. These states are separated by temperature and pressure conditions. This chapter assumes that the chemicals under discussion are at "standard pressure" or atmospheric pressure, thereby allowing for a simple examination by temperature.

All chemicals have different melting, freezing, and boiling points. In most situations, more than one of these states are present at the same time. Consider an open container of boiling water: the water is in the liquid state, while the steam is the water entering the gas state. Similarly, ice will feel hard (solid), be wet (liquid), and actually have evaporated water surrounding it (gas or vapour). The majority of chemical-related health problems result from contact with chemicals in the liquid and gas/vapour states. Most of the negative effects of exposure derive from airborne, respiratory contaminants known as *aerosols* (airborne particulate).

Listed below are seven basic types of contaminants (Olishifsky, 1988):

1. *Dust*: Solid particles generated by mechanical means such as grinding, crushing, or sanding. The heavier particles tend to settle out of the air under the influence of gravity. The lighter the particle, the longer it will take to settle out.

2. *Fume*: Airborne particulate formed by the evaporation of solid materials (e.g., metal fume emitted during welding where the parent metal will vaporize on application of weld-level heat and then condense upon contact with the cooler ambient air). Particle size is usually less than one micron or micrometre in diameter.

3. *Smoke*: Airborne particulate originating from the products of combustion, usually less than 0.1 micron in size. An example would be tobacco smoke.

4. *Mist*: Suspended liquid droplets in air generated by condensation from the gas state or by breaking up of a liquid into a dispersed state of finely divided droplets. Spray paint and hair spray are two sources of mist generation.

5. *Vapour*: The gaseous form of substances that are normally in the solid or liquid state at room temperature and pressure. Usually caused by evaporation. An example would be the airborne contaminant from any solvent.

6. *Gas*: One of the three states of matter created where the temperature is above the boiling point. Carbon dioxide and air are two examples.

7. *Liquid*: Chemicals are sometimes found in a liquid form that can come in contact with the skin or eyes when there is a splash or spill during manual mixing or pouring operations.

The workplace health hazard is posed by exposure to one or more of these airborne particulate. For instance, the white cloud that rises from a welding operation usually consists of fumes resulting from the condensation of the parent metal and the weld rod metal and coating; smoke resulting from the combustion of oil and other surface contamination; and vapours resulting from the evaporation of some of the oils and solvents on the metal surface.

◆ ◆ ◆
TOXICOLOGY: AN OVERVIEW

Toxicology is the scientific study of poisons. For the purposes of this chapter, toxicology will refer to the study of chemical-related occupational illnesses. (Of course, the risk of exposure to chemicals can be just as great in the home as it is in the workplace.)

Chemicals may enter the body by one of four routes. In order of risk, they are: respiration (inhalation), ingestion, skin absorption, and skin penetration (IAPA, 1988).

RESPIRATION (INHALATION) An average-sized human breathes approximately eight litres of air per minute while at rest (this quantity increases with any activity) (Williams and Burson, 1985). Most of the human exposure to chemicals comes from breathing airborne contaminants. The respiratory system, illustrated in Figure 8.1, does a very efficient job of distributing these contaminants throughout the body during the normal air exchange process.

FIGURE 8.1 The Respiratory System

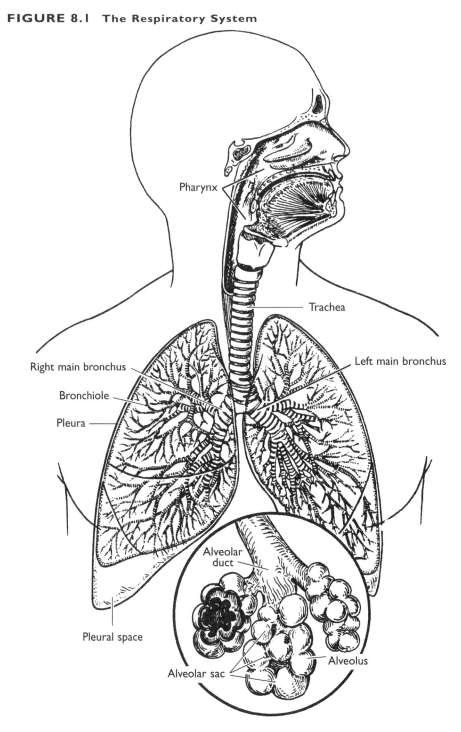

The first level of defence is the nose. The nose, or upper respiratory tract, is lined with hairs, or celia, that act as a coarse filter medium. The interior of the nasal passage is the second level of defence; here are found turbinates, which act as a humidification and heat exchange source. The third level of defence is further back in the throat where the hairs or celia are coated with a thick fluid called mucus. This mucus–celia system will entrap the finer particulate. The trapped contaminant is removed by blowing the nose and/or clearing the throat. (Everyone has experienced these conditions after cleaning the garage, dusting a room, or sanding wood for refinishing.) The fourth level of defence consists of myriad tiny air sacs, called alveoli, that are located at the ends of the lung's air passages. These sacs (which are the source of oxygen transfer from the lungs to the bloodstream) contain small cells called macrophages (Greek for "big eater") that dispose of any impurities via the lymph system.

Most of the airborne particulate that enters the respiratory system is trapped before it reaches the alveoli. Only airborne particulate that is in range of 3 to 5 microns will normally reach the alveoli. The term *respiratory particulate* refers to very fine airborne contaminants. Asbestos fibres and silica particulate can be examples of "respirable dust" when small enough to enter the alveoli and possibly cause asbestosis or mesothelioma and silicosis. A list of industrial air contaminants is provided in Table 8.1.

TABLE 8.1 INDUSTRIAL AIR CONTAMINANTS

Process Type	Contaminant Type	Examples of Chemical Contaminants
Bakeries	Dust	Flour, other vegetable dust, yeast, moulds
Can Manufacturing	Fumes	Metal fumes
	Vapours	Solvent vapours
Hospitals	Gas	Folmaldehyde, anesthetic gases, ethylene oxide
Water Supply and Treatment Plant	Gas	Chlorine, ammonia, hydrogen chloride, ozone
	Mist	Hydrochloric acid, sodium, hydroxide, calcium hydroxide

Source: *Industrial Hazards and Their Evaluation*, Workers' Compensation Board of British Columbia, Vancouver, 1994.

INGESTION For many solvents, entry through the mouth and digestive system is not as important as entry through the skin or the lungs. Poor personal hygiene can contribute to poisoning, as can eating, drinking, or smoking in an area where solvents are used. Ingestion of most solvents will cause damage to the lining of the digestive system. The ingested solvent may also be absorbed into the bloodstream and carried to target organs where it will produce toxic effects. Worse still, the ingested solvent may be aspirated into the lungs where it can destroy the surfactant layer, cause a chemical pneumonitis, and collapse the alveoli (Pilger, 1994).

SKIN ABSORPTION In many workplaces, chemical contact with the skin is a common occurrence. Many fat-soluble chemicals can be readily absorbed and most gases can pass through the skin very quickly. Chlorinated solvents such as carbon tetrachloride can pass through the skin into the blood, eventually reaching the liver where tissue damage may occur. Dimethyl sulfoxide is rapidly absorbed through the skin; in less than a minute following skin contact, most people can detect a garlic-like taste in the back of the throat.

The ability of a chemical to easily pass through the skin is often closely associated with its level of toxicity. For example, the toxicity of DDT is about the same for insects and humans when it is injected. However, it is much less toxic to a person when applied to the skin, because it is poorly absorbed through the skin. Other pesticides are much more rapidly absorbed through human skin. Many agricultural workers have died following skin absorption of pesticides, particularly the organophosphate insecticides.

Chemicals that are not rapidly absorbed through the skin may produce a localized irritation (dermatitis) at the point of contact through a process called defatting, which causes the skin to become more permeable to water vapour, leading to tissue water loss, skin drying, and cracking. Burns or blisters can result from contact with acids or alkalis (chemical action). Skin disorders can result from contact with certain plants (biological action). Skin damage can result from contact with radiation or heat (physical action).

PENETRATION (DIRECT CONTACT) Penetration occurs when the skin is cut or stabbed by any sharp object. The type of contamination will determine the illness. Cuts can occur when contact is made with sharp metal, glass materials, or other pointed instruments. Workers such as doctors, nurses, or veterinarians can easily be punctured by a hypodermic needle. The disorders range in severity from low-grade infections to HIV (human immunodeficiency virus).

BOX 8.1 TOXICITY TERMINOLOGY

- **Dose.** The degree of exposure and possible reaction with time. The dose is usually the basis for the values that are developed for threshold limit values (TLV), which are used as a control measure in the workplace. For example, the TLV for carbon dioxide is as 5000 parts per million (ppm), based on an eight-hour exposure time (ACGIH, 1994).

- **Acute toxicity.** Effect that manifests immediately following exposure or shortly thereafter. Burning one's hand on a hot surface, for example, results in immediate pain and discoloration.

- **Chronic toxicity.** Effect that manifests some time after the exposure (possibly months or even years). Some examples: cirrhosis of the liver from prolonged alcohol exposure; sensitization from isocyanates; occupational cancer, such as leukemia, from benzene exposure; or mesothelioma from asbestos exposure.

- **Local toxicity.** The effect of an exposure at the point of contact. Cleaning one's hands with a paint thinner will cause dry skin at the point of contact; this will be an immediate reaction.

- **Systemic toxicity.** Effect that occurs at some location remote from the point of contact. For example, inhaling a chlorinated solvent such as trichloroethylene can cause damage to the liver.

◆ ◆ ◆

CLASSIFICATION OF TOXIC SUBSTANCES

Toxic materials can be grouped under the following 12 classifications.

I IRRITANTS Irritants produce tissue or other damage at the point of contact. They are divided by route of entry into two groups:

(a) *Inhaled irritants.* Inhaled irritants refer to airborne contaminants or aerosols (including vapours, gases, and solid particulate). Aerosols that are inhaled into the lungs cause damage wherever they settle. Ammonia is dissolved into body fluids and absorbed by the mucous membranes of the upper airways, and can result in symptoms such as headache, nausea, salivation, and burning of the throat. Bronchitis may follow a very severe exposure, if the patient survives (Key et al., 1977).

(b) *Contact irritant.* A contact irritant is any material that causes some sort of irritation, such as a rash or itch, at the point of contact. In most cases, the effect will be localized to skin (dermatitis).

II ASPHYXIANTS Any material that interferes with the oxygen supply to the blood and body tissues is referred to as an asphyxiant. Normal air contains approximately 21 percent oxygen and 79 percent nitrogen. The average person uses about 3 percent of the oxygen in air. If the oxygen content falls below 15 percent, the body will be in trouble. There are two major types of asphyxiants:

(a) *Simple asphyxiants*. Any airborne chemical that reduces the quantity of oxygen in the inhaled air is referred to as a simple asphyxiant. Examples are methane, propane, and nitrogen.

(b) *Chemical asphyxiants*. If an airborne and inhaled chemical interferes either with the oxygen transport by the blood hemoglobin or with the ability of the body cells to use oxygen, it is called a chemical asphyxiant. Examples are carbon monoxide, which interferes with the ability of the hemoglobin to transport oxygen, and hydrogen sulfide (rotten gas), which can interfere with ability of the body cells to use oxygen (Key et al., 1977).

III ANESTHETICS AND NARCOTICS Any chemical that affects the central nervous system (CNS) can be considered to belong to this class. Most of these chemicals can, upon exposure, cause headaches, interfere with one's ability to concentrate, and act as a depressant. Examples include ethyl alcohol, acetylene, acetone, and toluene. In fact, all organic solvents can produce narcotic effects. Many of us have experienced some of these symptoms after consuming alcohol.

IV SYSTEMIC POISONS Systemic poisons can cause damage to one or more internal organs, as well as cell and neuron damage. Chlorinated materials such as DDT, chloroform, trichloroethylene, or endrin can cause damage to the liver and kidneys, usually as a result of chronic exposure. Benzene can cause damage to the blood-forming cells (the hemoeopathic system). Carbon disulphide is believed to damage the neurons. Other common systemic poisons: heavy metals such as lead, cadmium, and mercury; chemicals such as arsenic and fluoride.

V LIVER TOXICANTS This grouping includes any chemical that will cause direct damage to the liver. The toxic action may be chemical (caused by alcohol) or metabolite (caused by benzene). In most instances, slight damage can be repaired. Cirrhosis is the most common disease.

VI KIDNEY TOXICANTS Kidney toxicants, like liver toxicants, include chemicals that cause damage to the kidneys, usually through the process of metabolic transformation whereby harmless chemicals are rendered harmful or vice versa. Heavy metals such as lead, cadmium, and mercury, in addition to some solvents, can have this effect.

VII NEUROTOXINS As the name indicates, these are chemicals that can cause damage to the nerves in the body. Hexane, a component of gasoline, can produce a condition called peripheral neuropathy—a disease affecting the nerves of the extremities—which can result in numbness and loss of feeling. This condition is dose-related.

VIII SENSITIZERS Sensitizers, whether chemical or biological, cause the body's immune system to produce antibodies against the chemical. The end result is an allergy to the specific chemical. Workers thus affected may have to change jobs, if not employers. Although sensitization is usually a chronic process, a very large acute exposure can sometimes bring it on. Farmer's lung, humidifier fever, nickel itch, and nickel fume fever are some common examples of sensitization.

IX LUNG TOXICANTS Toxic chemicals that can affect the lungs include irritant gases such as hydrogen chloride and ammonia; vapours such as isocynates; and respirable solids such as asbestos, platinum, and silica. These materials can cause a variety of diseases from simple pneumoconiosis (dust in the lung) to cancer.

X MUTAGENS Chemicals that lead to changes or mutations in DNA are classed as mutagens. The actions of chemicals like lead, nickel, zinc, and manganese usually cause the death of cells, but may in some cases allow the distorted cell to multiply and create a potentially malignant tumour.

XI TERATOGENS Chemicals such as lead, DDT, and PCB can cause damage to germ cells or create defects in a developing fetus. Chemicals like thalidomide will cause gross abnormalities in the fetus.

XII CARCINOGENS Carcinogens are agents that cause or promote the formation of cancers. Well-known carcinogens include vinyl chloride, which can cause a liver cancer called angiosarcoma; benzene, which can result in leukemia; and asbestos, which can lead to mesothelioma. Following exposure to the carcinogenic chemical, there can be a latency period of five to fifteen or more years. Appendix A in ACGIH (1994) lists a number of known and suspected human carcinogens.

BOX 8.2 TARGET ORGAN CONCEPT

Many chemicals attack specific organs or become deposited in specific organs. Alcohol targets the liver; benzene targets the bone marrow; chromium attacks the nasal cavity; and lead is known to attack the kidneys. Detection is simplified by knowing the susceptibility of these target organs.

◆ ◆ ◆
SOLVENTS

Solvents were created, for the most part, by the science of organic chemistry, and are the most prevalent of products that we use both at work and at home. There are eight general characteristics or properties that make solvents effective but at the same time hazardous and toxic.

I LOW SURFACE TENSION This property allows a solvent to spread evenly and quickly and to provide excellent wetting of the contact surface. The wetting factor for mercury is 475; that for water is 72, and that for ether is 17. This characteristic allows material to flow more evenly and smoothly on any surface including skin. The wetting characteristic allows a spilled solvent to flow into cracks and joints and remain there, creating vapours that may be toxic.

II HIGH VAPOUR PRESSURE The fact that vapour pressure increases with temperature limits the amount or concentration of a generated vapour or gas. This solvent property allows efficient cleaning in processes such as de-greasing systems because of the high vapour generation at the high operating temperatures. It can, however, create an inhalation hazard, the risk of which increases with temperature. This is not considered a problem as long as the container is kept closed. In a fire situation, the pressure increase can cause an explosion.

III LOW BOILING POINT The lower the boiling point, the greater the rate of evaporation. This property is useful when cleaning or painting because the solvents will evaporate quickly allowing the article to dry or tack off. The lower the boiling point, the greater the health risk since more vapour can be generated at lower temperatures. Chemicals with boiling points close to room temperature or lower, such as ammonia (BP = -2°C) or hydrogen cyanide (BP = 25°C), can be a special problem since they can evaporate readily and are very toxic.

IV LOW HEAT OF VAPORIZATION This defines the amount of heat or energy that is required to change a liquid into a gas or vapour. The lower the amount of heat required, the less costly the process would be in an industrial environment. Similarly, the lower the amount of heat necessary, the greater the risk of exposure if the material is not properly controlled.

V HIGH VOLATILITY The main test of a solvent's effectiveness is the speed at which it will evaporate. The greater the volatility, the faster the evaporation—and the greater the health risk.

VI ABILITY TO DISSOLVE FATS The more effectively a solvent dissolves fat or oils, the more useful it can be. However, when solvents are applied to skin, the skin's surface oils are dissolved. The unprotected skin then becomes susceptible to infection and other trauma. Skin contact with solvents is one of the major causes of dermatitis.

VII FLAMMABILITY Flammability is one of the main hazards associated with solvent use. Care must be taken to ensure that there are no sources of ignition present during use. Chemical specifications usually list four characteristics that relate to flammability.

(a) *Flash point.* Defined as the lowest temperature at which a liquid gives off enough vapour to form an ignitable mixture with air and produce a flame with a source of ignition. If the flash point is close to room temperature, the danger of ignition can be very great.

(b) *Lower explosion limit* (LEL). Defined as the lower flammability limit or smallest fuel/air mixture that is ignitable, expressed as a percent. Carbon monoxide has an LEL of 12.5 percent by volume, which is equivalent to 125,000 parts per million (ppm). The upper exposure value for health exposure is 50 ppm, as shown in various standards. If the exposure to carbon monoxide in the workplace is maintained well below the health limit, there is no risk of ignition from that source.

(c) *Upper explosion limit* (UEL). Defined as the upper flammability limit or highest fuel/air mixture that is ignitable, expressed as a percent. Carbon monoxide has a UEL of 74 percent by volume. The LEL and UEL indicate that carbon monoxide can be ignited through a wide range of fuel/air mixtures, which can be an advantage if the gas is used for some heat application.

(d) *Auto ignition temperature.* Defined as the lowest temperature at which a flammable fuel/air mixture will ignite from its own heat source. This process is also known as spontaneous combustion.

VIII VAPORIZATION Most solvents will form very large volumes of vapour from a small amount of liquid. For instance, turpentine can form approximately 112 litres of vapour for each litre of liquid at standard temperature and pressure conditions.

INORGANIC SOLVENTS

Inorganic solvents fall into two classes—acids and bases. These are the simplest of chemical groups and are the oldest known forms. The difference between an acid and a base is expressed in terms of pH, a unit that notes the degree of acidity or alkalinity of a solution, having a scale of 1 to 14. A pH value of 7 is considered as neutral (i.e., neither acid nor base). A pH of 1 indicates extreme acidity, while a pH of 14 indicates extreme alkalinity or base.

ACIDS Materials such as hydrochloric acid (HCl), sulphuric acid (H_2SO_4), and chromic acid (H_2CrO_4) are some of the most common. All are very corrosive and are used for refining and processing metals. The plating process makes extensive use of these acids. The health effects are predominantly burns resulting from inhalation and skin contact. The eyes are the most susceptible body part. Chromic acid is a known carcinogen and a sensitizer. The most common sign of chromic acid exposure is the presence of chrome holes in the surface of the skin. These are ugly, black holes left when the skin has been corrosively attacked. Their size depends on the amount of exposure and personal hygiene practices.

BASES Sometimes referred to as alkalines, these chemicals include potassium hydroxide (KOH), sodium hydroxide (NaOH), and sodium chloride (NaCl) or table salt. Sodium chloride in its refined state is a requirement of a normal diet. In its less refined form, it is used to keep roads free of ice. The other two alkalines are used to etch or dissolve a variety of materials. All are toxic in the proper concentration.

ORGANIC SOLVENTS

Organic solvents, which are petrochemically based, are manufactured by combining the carbon atom with a great many other elements. These solvents can be identified by their molecular structure and can be grouped under the following 10 classifications.

I ALIPHATIC HYDROCARBONS This class, which derives from petroleum and natural gas, has three subgroups called alkanes, alkenes, and alkynes (synonyms for which are paraffins, olefins, and acetylenes respectively). These solvents are used for fuels, refrigerants, propellants, dry-cleaning agents, and lubricants. Aliphatic hydrocarbons are generally simple asphyxiants and central nervous system depressants. Methane and ethane, examples of simple asphyxiants, are highly flammable. Hexane has neurotoxic properties and can irritate skin and the upper respiratory tract. Benzene can appear as a contaminant in some products, and extreme care must be taken in use. Dermatitis is the most common health effect in this group.

II AROMATIC HYDROCARBONS Aromatics are manufactured from petroleum and coal tar bases. Their molecular structure is characterized by a hexagonal carbon ring. Benzene, toluene, and xylene are examples of this type of hydrocarbon.

The use of benzene has been restricted because this chemical is a dangerous carcinogen that can cause leukemia. Hydrocarbons that have been developed as substitutes—namely tolvene and xylene—possess most of the positive properties of benzene. Benzene can appear in each of these two substitutes as production impurities and should be controlled carefully. These chemicals are used in the manufacture of fuels, dyes, pharmaceuticals, plastics, and resins. The usual routes of entry are inhalation and skin absorption. All chemicals in this class are central nervous system depressants and can cause dermatitis.

III HALOGENATED HYDROCARBONS The term halogen is applied to five elements—astatine, bromine, chlorine, fluorine, and iodine. Thus any hydrocarbon containing a molecule of any of these halogens would fall in this class. Two of the more common chemicals are carbon tetrachloride—a possible carcinogen that acts acutely and chronically on the kidneys, liver, central nervous system, and GI tract—and trichloroethylene, which causes central nervous system depression and dermatitis, and has a synergistic reaction with alcohol. This class of solvent is not flammable, which is why carbon tetrachloride was widely used at one time as a fire extinguishment agent.

IV NITRO-HYDROCARBONS These compounds, which contain a NO_2 group, include such chemicals as picric acid, nitroglycerin, and nitrophenol. They are used in a variety of products related to explosives. Most are irritants and skin sensitizers, and result in headaches and nausea at low-level exposures.

V ESTERS Organic or inorganic acids combined with alcohol are the common sources of materials known as esters. Esters are used in the manufacture of plastics and resins, artificial flavours, soaps and perfumes, pharmaceuticals, and leathers. Typical examples are methyl acetate, pear oil, and banana oil. Although a few esters are physiologically inert, most can have anesthetic and primary irritant effects.

VI ETHERS This class of solvents is made by the combination of two similar alcohols. Ethers are good for dissolving fats, greases, and oils. Examples include ethyl ether, used for surgery in days gone by; chloromethyl methyl ether, used as an organic chemical synthesizer (and a known carcinogen); and ethylene oxide, used in the manufacture of ethylene glycol (antifreeze for automobiles). The materials in this class are serious primary irritants and anesthetics, and can cause nausea, headaches, and respiratory difficulties.

VII KETONES Acetone and methyl ethyl ketone (MEK) are two of the better-known compounds in this class. These chemicals, with their stability and high dilution ability for other compounds, are important in the manufacture of acetate rayon, vinyl resin coatings, artificial silk, and lubricating oils. They all have narcotic and primary irritant effects, and in combination with other chemicals like toluene may cause vertigo, nausea, or judgment impairment.

VIII ALCOHOLS Alcohols are widely used as solvents. Common names include ethyl alcohol (ethanol or grain alcohol); propyl alcohol or isopropyl alcohol; and methyl alcohol (methanol or wood alcohol). Most of us are familiar with ethyl alcohol as the basis of a good party. Isopropyl alcohol is used in rubbing liniments. Methyl alcohol is an industrial solvent used in inks and adhesives, embalming fluids, and paint and varnish removers. The health effects include headache, nausea, tremors, and fatigue (ethyl alcohol); potential narcotic (propyl alcohol); and dermatitis, optic nerve damage and blindness, loss of consciousness (methyl alcohol).

IX GLYCOLS ETHERS This class is toxic and can affect the blood, the brain, and the kidneys. Ethylene glycol, which is used extensively as an antifreeze because of its physical properties, may produce intoxication with chronic exposure. Occupational exposure is rare since ethylene glycol has to be heated in order to become highly toxic.

Ethylene glycol ethers such as cellosolve are used in the manufacture of lacquers, resins, perfume, liquid soaps, and cosmetics. Acute exposure can result in systemic effects such as narcosis, pulmonary edema, and severe kidney and liver damage.

X ALDEHYDES The common names in this class—aldehyde acrolein and formaldehyde—are highly volatile, and well known as skin and pulmonary sensitizers, as well as for their action on the central nervous system. Allergic responses are common.

◆ ◆ ◆
RESPIRABLE PARTICULATE

While solvents and their respirable vapours can be dangerous, other airborne materials such as dust and fumes can, under certain conditions, be just as toxic. These airborne solids, along with solvent vapours, are classed as aerosols.

Two of the most common and topical aerosols when respirable are *asbestos* and *silica*. While both are classed as silicates, they are quite different. Asbestos is a fibre whose size is measured by fibre length. Silica is a crystal whose size is measured by diameter. Both of these materials exhibit a physical or chemical reaction that takes place during the disposal process by the macrophages of the alveoli.

Asbestos fibres usually become trapped in the membrane of the alveoli. Over time, they may develop into a mass of trapped fibres, which can ultimately cause a fibrotic condition (asbestosis) or a cancer (mesothelioma). This carcinogenisis is manifested as a "welding" of the lung section to the pleura or the membrane surrounding the pleural cavity.

When crystals of silica are trapped in the alveoli, they form an acid when the macrophages attempt to cleanse the area. This acid kills the macrophage, thereby creating more contaminant for other macrophagal disposal. Eventually, this self-perpetuating cycle will fill the lung area with masses of dead cells, causing a fibrotic or hardening condition. Like that brought on by asbestos fibres, this fibrotic condition causes the lung to lose its flexibility, resulting in breathing problems.

It is important to remember that only respirable particulate will cause serious lung difficulties, not the mere presence of the material in the workplace. The diseases associated with these and other respirable contaminants can take many years to manifest themselves into recognizable symptoms.

As with solvents, other chemical exposures can aggravate the disease response. One of the most common causes of aggravation is tobacco smoke. Smoking, a lifestyle factor, can have a synergistic effect on some materials. An asbestos worker is four times more likely to develop lung cancer than a nonasbestos worker; the probability rises to 80–90 times if the asbestos worker smokes (Williams and Burson, 1985).

Many chemicals when exposed in combination in the human body have an additive effect. Others, like asbestos, have a synergistic effect. An additive effect model, in simple terms, can be expressed as 5+5=10; a synergistic model can be expressed as 5+5=30 (ibid).

Care must always be taken to ensure that worker exposures to any airborne aerosols are kept to an absolute minimum. The acronym ALARA (as low as reasonably attainable) describes this minimum level. Overall health and safety costs and worker well-being can be the end result. Quality management of the working environment is the most effective method of measurement of, and control of the acceptable level of health and safety.

◆ ◆ ◆
MEASUREMENT AND EVALUATION OF AIRBORNE CONTAMINANTS

The control of airborne contaminants requires a means of evaluation and the instrumentation for measurement. Airborne contaminants are measured using several methods; three of the more common are discussed here.

The easiest method involves the use of a direct reading, air-flow device of the Gastec, MSA, or Draeger type. These types use special direct reading colorimetric indicator tubes to measure the amount of contaminant in the air. Most of the chemicals to be evaluated have a tube for specific concentration ranges. When an air sample is drawn through the colorimetric tube, the contained reagent changes colour to indicate the presence of the measured chemical. The concentration is measured by reading the scale at the limit of the colour change, providing a direct value in ppm. The disadvantage of this kind of sampler is the accuracy, which could run ± 25%. The second disadvantage (which applies to the other two methods as well) is that the contaminant being sought must be known beforehand.

The second type of pump is a motor-driven, adjustable, constant flow unit. The air-flow rate can be adjusted to meet the specific analytical requirements of the sought-after chemical. This type of pump requires care and training to operate. Before using, the pump battery must be fully charged and the flow rate calibrated using a primary bubble-tube calibrator. (Note that the preparation procedures must be recorded before and after testing.) A sampling device such as a cassette, charcoal tube, or an impinger is used to collect an airborne sample of the contaminant. The collected sample must be analysed at a certified laboratory using very sophisticated instrumentation. Certified laboratories include those at University of Toronto, McMaster University, and the National Research Council.

The third type of instrument is the direct reading, real-time aerosol meter. This rather expensive piece of equipment will take a measured air sample and, using one of several methods, indicate the amount of air contaminant, the level of oxygen, or the flammability range depending on the particular instrument. This type of device is used widely in special applications such as confined space entry for monitoring carbon monoxide, carbon dioxide, or other known chemicals.

The accepted method of evaluation in industry uses the results from sampling instrumentation to determine an exposure value given to most chemicals. Threshold limit values (TLVs) have been developed over a number of years and published with annual updates by the American Conference of Governmental Industrial Hygienists (ACGIH). These values have been established through occupational exposure experience, scientific research, epidemiological studies, and international cooperation. Provinces like Ontario have adopted their own variations of these ACGIH guidelines. Ontario is currently enacting changes that will significantly lower the TLV for all workplaces. Provinces like Manitoba use the ACGIH values as issued. (It should be noted that the ACGIH values are only guidelines until legislated into law.)

The terminology used for evaluation is very specific. The following ACGIH definitions are generally accepted as a standard.

1. *Threshold limit value.* The TLV refers to the time-weighted concentration for a normal eight-hour workday and a 40-hour workweek, to which nearly all workers may be repeatedly exposed, day after day, without adverse effect. These values of permissible exposure are provided as a reference to which any actual workplace exposure can be compared.

2. *Time-weighted average.* The TWA refers to the actual measured and/or calculated exposures in the workplace. The TWA should not be confused, in

practice, with the TLV, which is considered to be a reference or guideline value.

3. *Short-term exposure limit.* The STEL refers to the concentration to which workers can be exposed continuously for a short period of time without suffering from irritation, chronic or irreversible tissue damage, or narcosis. A STEL exposure cannot exceed 15 minutes in duration, or occur more than four times a day; there should be at least 60 minutes between successive exposures.

4. *Threshold limit value – ceiling.* The TLV-C refers to the concentration that should not be exceeded during any part of the working exposure.

The above values are evaluated using two specific and related units— parts of the agent per million parts of air by volume (ppm) or milligrams of the agent per cubic metre of air (mg/m^3)—depending upon a variety of factors such as the physical state of the agent (ACGIH, 1994).

Suppose that a worker is exposed to an average concentration of carbon dioxide of 1500 ppm over his eight-hour shift. The range of exposure measurement was 950 to 2500 ppm with one brief exposure of 25,000 ppm for about 10 minutes. The TLV is 5000 ppm with a STEL of 30,000 ppm. A comparison of these numbers shows that the worker's exposure was within acceptable limits.

The mathematical model for a single airborne contaminant is

$$TWA = (C_1 \times t_1) + (C_2 \times t_2) + ... + (C_n \times t_n) \div (t_1 + t_2 + ... + t_n) \quad (1)$$

where C is the measured concentration in ppm or mg/m^3 and *t* is time duration of each sample in hours.

If a worker is exposed to measured levels of ammonia of 20 ppm for 3 hours, 26 ppm for 3 hours, and 25 ppm for 2 hours, then the TLV for ammonia is 25 ppm. Inserting these values into equation 1, we get

$$TWA = (20 \times 3) + (26 \times 3) + (25 \times 2) \div (3 + 3 + 2) = 23.5 \text{ ppm}$$

which is lower than the TLV and thus theoretically acceptable. If the 60% rule of thumb (described later) is used, then the acceptable TLV becomes

$$0.60 \times 25 = 15 \text{ ppm}$$

Because the exposure value of 23.5 ppm is greater than the 60% value, the exposure level is too high and therefore steps must be taken to reduce the occupational levels.

◆

The above example deals with an exposure to only one chemical agent. In reality, most exposures involve a combination of chemicals that can have additive or nonadditive results. In circumstances such as these, it is necessary to relate the actual airborne concentration to the TLV of each component.

For instance, if air contains 400 ppm of acetone (TLV=750 ppm), 200 ppm of isopropyl alcohol (TLV=400 ppm), and 5 ppm of ammonia (TLV=25 ppm), the TWA of the mixture is calculated using the relationship

$$TWA = (C_1 \div T_1) + (C_2 \div T_2) + ... \leq 1 \ (2)$$

where C is the measured concentration in ppm or mg/m^3 and T is the TLV of each component. In this case, the TWA = (400 ÷ 750) + (200 ÷ 400) + (5 ÷ 25) = 1.23 which is greater than 1. Therefore, this particular combination of chemical agents is not acceptable with respect to the health and well-being of the worker.

Although the actual measured exposure may be compromised by a number of factors, these values can be a cautious measure of actual worker exposure. As a "rule of thumb," the measured TWA should not be much higher than 60 percent of the TLV of a particular material. To sum up, the lower the TLV, the more toxic the agent. A chemical with a TLV of 5 ppm thus poses a greater risk than another agent with a TLV of 75 ppm.

The assessment of the airborne contaminant toxicity requires specialized training and equipment. The control methods are within the capabilities of any manager.

◆ ◆ ◆

BIOLOGICAL AGENTS

A biological agent or biohazard can be as subtle and as deadly as some chemical agents. The acute and chronic exposure effects described previously for chemical agents apply to biohazards as well, although the sources of exposure are different and the physiological reactions vary. The majority of exposures occur through inhalation.

Biological agents originate from plants and animals, or their byproducts, and may be infectious, toxic, or allergenic as a result of direct or indirect contact. The six biological agent groups and their main characteristics are presented in Table 8.2.

TABLE 8.2 BIOLOGICAL AGENTS

Agent Group	Agent	Source	Occupation
Bacterial	Anthrax (*bacillus anthracis*)	Direct contact with infected animals, hides, and wool	Veterinarians, farmers, butchers, wool workers
	Brucellosis (*brucella species*)	Exposure by ingestion or cuts, from excretions or secretions of infected animals	Livestock handlers, meat inspectors, farmers, microbiology lab workers
	Salmonellosis (*salmonella species*)	Oral exposure, usually from unsanitary food conditions (food poisoning).	Travellers, patient care workers, amateur chefs
	Staphylococcal food poisoning (*staphylococcus species*)	Ingestion of improperly stored or leftover food or food infected by workers	Food workers, health care workers, home storage
	Lyme disease (*borrelia burgdorferi*)	Tick bites	Outdoor workers
Chlamydiae	Psittacosis or ornithosis (*chlamydia psittaci*)	Inhalation or exposure to infected bird droppings	Zoo workers, taxidemists, pet owners
Rickettsia	Q fever (*coxiella burneth*)	Contact with sheep, cattle, goats, birth by-products, and contaminated dusts	Farmers, veterinarians, slaughterhouse workers, laboratory workers
	Rocky Mountain spotted fever (*rickettsia rickettsii*)	Tick bites	Outdoor workers - lumberjacks, ranchers
Viruses	Cat scratch disease	Breaks in skin, usually from animal scratch	Pet owners and breeders
	Serum hepatitis (hepatitis B virus – HBV)	Direct contact with infected material by puncture, abraded skin, or onto mucous membrane surfaces	Hemodialysis workers, surgeons, dentists, health-care workers
	Infectious hepatitis (hepatitis A virus – HAV)	Fecal – oral transmission (from contaminated water)	Travellers, primate handlers, dentists
Fungal	Dermatophytosis (*trichophyton species*)	Contact with people infected by soil, animals, or humans	Gardeners, military from showers (athletes foot), farm workers (cattle ring-worm, health care workers

TABLE 8.2 (continued)

Agent Group	Agent	Source	Occupation
	Histaplosmosis (*histoplasma capsulatum*)	Inhalation or ingestion of dust from areas that have been bird or bat habitats	Construction workers, chicken farm workers
	Farmers' lung (*aspergillus species*)	Inhalation or ingestion of dusts containing spores from mouldy hay or grain, or compost piles	Mushroom workers, brewery workers, bird hobbyists
	Humidifier lung (*penicillium species*)	Inhalation of airborne spores from sources of mould such as cheese, wood, HVAC system water	Cheese workers, HVAC (heating, ventilating and air-conditioning) workers, tree cutters

All biological agents are classified on the basis of their degree of risk to humans. The higher the class number, the greater the risk.

◆ *Class 1*: Agents of no or minimal hazard that can be handled safely without special apparatus or equipment, using techniques for nonpathogenic materials.

◆ *Class 2*: Agents of ordinary potential hazard that may produce diseases of varying degrees of seriousness through accidental skin penetration; can be easily controlled using standard laboratory practices.

◆ *Class 3*: Agents involving special hazards that require special conditions for containment.

◆ *Class 4*: Agents that are extremely hazardous to personnel; can cause serious epidemic disease and require stringent conditions for containment.

◆ *Class 5*: Foreign animal pathogens that are excluded from the country by law.

As Table 8.2 indicates, most biohazards encountered in the workplace fall into class 1. Viral agents such as hepatitis B would be included in class 2. People most at risk of exposure to biohazards are employed in unique or specialized jobs. In the case of salmonella food poisoning, however, members of the general public are also at risk.

◆ ◆ ◆
CONTROL OF EXPOSURES

The safe use and handling of chemical and biological agents can be ensured only through the active employment of a variety of control measures. Figure 8.2 outlines the various control measures used to ensure the safe handling of solvents. These controls are the subject of the sections that follow (IAPA, 1990).

ENGINEERING CONTROLS

One of the best ways to reduce the risks associated with handling solvents is to find alternatives. A thorough investigation should be conducted to ensure that the proposed substitute meets the intended purpose and at the same

FIGURE 8.2 Engineering, Work Practices, and Medical Control Measures

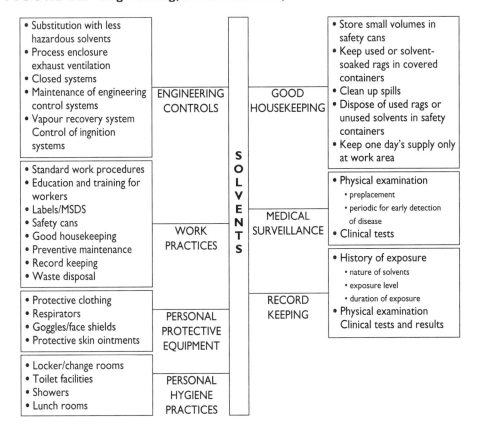

time does not contain dangerous properties. In addition, areas where solvents are being used should be properly enclosed to prevent or minimize the escape of vapours; an effective ventilation system should also be in place. Because some of the chemicals used may be a source of ignition, it is equally important to ensure that appropriate fire-extinguishing equipment is on hand, and that combustibles are isolated from sources of ignition.

WORK PRACTICES AND PROCEDURES

All employees must be properly trained in the identification and handling of dangerous substances. Senior management must ensure that policies and procedures are accompanied by an appropriate discipline system for dealing with those employees who willfully choose to neglect them. Standards must be communicated, in writing, to all employees.

Good housekeeping is essential when handling, storing, or using solvents. If containers are leaking, they must be transferred immediately to sound containers. Spills must be cleaned up properly, and employees who are exposed to solvents must wear protective equipment. Solvent-soaked rags should be disposed of in airtight all-metal containers and removed daily. Each municipality has its own guidelines for disposal of wastes, and employees must be familiar with those guidelines that apply to them.

Preventive maintenance must be conducted on a regular basis to ensure that no potential dangers exist. For example, air filters on ventilation equipment may become damaged or plugged, thus posing a potential danger in an enclosed area where solvents are used. Employees should understand the procedures for maintaining equipment and documenting all repairs.

Thorough recordkeeping is essential. Although provinces vary in terms of recordkeeping requirements, all demand that records be kept of employee exposure, workplace air monitoring, and equipment breakdowns and repairs.

Perhaps the single most important work practice is the education and training of all employees. Employees should receive training in safe operating and emergency procedures, in the use and care of personal protective equipment, and in the handling and control of solvents. Training must be conducted on an ongoing basis given the fact that new solvents are constantly entering the workplace. Finally, workers must be familiar with all aspects of the Workplace Hazardous Materials Information System (WHMIS) legislation, which was discussed at length in Chapter 2.

PERSONAL PROTECTIVE EQUIPMENT

Personal protective equipment (PPE) is specifically designed to protect workers from particular hazards. PPE should be used only when there is no feasible or practical way to enclose a process, provide local ventilation, or apply other control measures. It must not be used as an alternative to putting in the proper controls.

Because inhalation is the most common and hazardous route of entry, the most commonly used protection device is a respirator. Respiratory protection is more specialized for biohazards than it is for chemical agents, since a biological airborne contaminant can be much smaller in size than a chemical one. PPE for hands, face, and other body parts must be provided where necessary. No single protective device, such as a face mask, will adequately address all conditions for all workers. Each device must be matched to the chemical exposure and properly fitted to the individual.

PERSONAL HYGIENE PRACTICES

The ingestion of chemicals is often due to poor hygiene. Individuals who handle toxic chemicals without wearing proper protective gear such as gloves are at risk of food contamination. In other such instances, chemicals that are not adequately removed at the workplace can be transferred to the worker's home. To ensure that this and similar types of incidents do not occur, individuals who handle toxic substances must: remove outer protective clothing and clean their hands, arms, face, and nails before entering rest areas or lunchrooms; avoid touching lips, nose, and eyes with contaminated hands; wash hands before eating, drinking, or smoking; eat, drink, and smoke only in a designated clean area; and remove work clothes and wash or shower before leaving work.

MEDICAL SURVEILLANCE

Medical surveillance programs are implemented to ensure that employees who are exposed to solvents are not subjected to situations in which their health will be jeopardized. To be effective, pre-employment and pre-placement medical examinations should be conducted to establish a baseline of the employee's health, or exposure to solvents in previous workplaces. Follow-up medical examinations should be conducted periodically. Examinations may include chest X-ray, pulmonary function tests, and blood workups. Finally, recordkeeping is an important aspect of the medical surveillance program. The types of exposures employees face and their health records before and after exposure should be included in this process.

◆ ◆ ◆
SUMMARY

Chemical agents and, to a lesser extent, biological agents are the major causes of occupational diseases. Despite their associated risks, these agents are easily controlled if guidelines such as those provided in the WHMIS legislation are rigorously followed. This chapter has focused on the types, characteristics, measurement, and control of chemical and biological agents. All workers who are exposed to these agents should be knowledgeable about their potential health effects as well as trained in their proper use and handling.

EXERCISES

1. Choose a solvent (e.g., acetone, toluene) or a solid particulate (e.g., asbestos, lead, wood dust). Research the industrial applications of your chosen solvent or particulate, as well as the related occupational diseases.

2. A workplace has an air sample taken to determine the level of contamination of manangese dust in the grinding area. The TLV is 5 mg/m^3. The test results are as follows: 3.5 mg/m^3 for 2 hours; 4.0 mg/m^3 for 3 hours; 4.1 mg/m^3 for 1 hour; and 5.1 mg/m^3 for 2 hours. Calculate the occupational exposure and determine if it is acceptable. Discuss whether an employee working in this area would have grounds for exercising a work refusal under the Occupational Health and Safety Act.

References

ACGIH. 1994. *Threshold Values for Chemical Substances and Physical Agents in the Workplace*. Cincinnati, Ohio: American Conference of Governmental Industrial Hygienists.

Adler, T. 1989. "Experts Urge Control of Aerospace Toxics." *APA Monitor* (May).

Genesove, Leon, Dr. 1995. *Multiple Chemical Sensitivity Syndrome*, Toronto: Healthwise, Accident Prevention.

IAPA. 1988. *Chemical Control Program Guide*. Toronto: Industrial Accident Prevention Association.

IAPA. 1990. *Solvents in the Workplace*. Toronto: Industrial Accident Prevention Association.

Key, Marcus M., et al., eds. 1977. *Occupational Diseases: A Guide to Their Recognition*. Cincinnati, Ohio: U.S. Department of Health, Education, and Welfare.

Olishifsky, Julian B. 1988. "Overview of Industrial Hygiene." In Barbara A. Plog, ed., *Fundamentals of Industrial Hygiene* 3rd ed. Chicago, Ill.: National Safety Council.

Pilger, Charles W. 1994. *Toxic Solvents*. 23rd Intensive Workshop in Industrial Hygiene, Toronto.

Williams, Phillip L., and James L. Burson, ed.1985. *Industrial Toxicology— Safety and Health Applications in the Workplace*. New York: Van Nostrand Reinhold.

Workers' Compensation Board of Ontario. 1993. *Statistical Supplement to the 1993 Annual Report*. Toronto: WCB.

9

Physical Agents

The term *physical agents* refers to hazards whose origins can be explained by various principles of physics. This chapter will discuss four physical agents—noise, vibration, thermal stress, and radiation—in terms of their measurement and control. Most of the health effects associated with all four agents are chronic in nature; that is, the damage to the human body usually takes years to manifest itself.

◆◆◆
NOISE

Noise is popularly defined as "any unwanted sound." Technically, it refers to "the auditory sensation evoked by the oscillations in pressure in a medium with elasticity and viscosity" (Berger et al., 1988). When a sound occurs, the ear drum in the middle ear detects pressure variations in the air and transmits them into the inner ear. The inner ear, or cochlea, converts these mechanical pressure wave actions into electrical impulses. The brain, in turn, interprets these impulses as some specific sound that it has been trained to recognize.

The pressure waves that we recognize as noise are created when an energy source causes a vibratory action in a medium such as air. Think of a pebble being dropped into a body of water. A series of waves is created that radiate outward at some velocity until they finally disappear. This analogy aptly describes the propagation of sound in air. The pebble is the noise or energy source. The waves show the manner in which the sound pressure waves move outward from the source. The velocity with which these waves move is predicated on the strength of the energy at the source. The distance that the waves travel before disappearing or being dampened by the medium is dependent on a number of factors.

Noise propagates or moves through air in a wave pattern called a *sine wave*. This basic wave form that sound uses as it propagates can be illustrated

FIGURE 9.1 The Auditory System

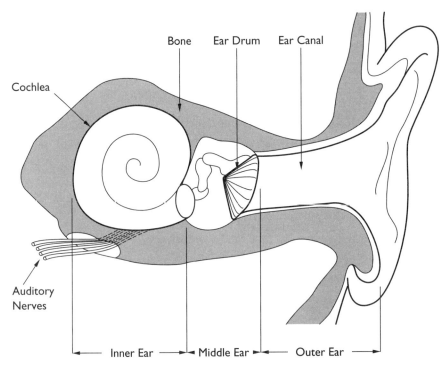

by a pure tone sine wave whose physical properties it shares. Sound has three basic properties: frequency, wavelength, and velocity in a specific medium.

Frequency is the number of times per second that a complete sine wave is repeated. It is expressed in units of Hertz (Hz), which is the same as the number of cycles per second. The lower the sound, the lower the frequency; conversely, the higher the sound, the higher the frequency. The range of frequency response exhibited by the human ear is approximately 20 to 20,000 Hz.

Wavelength is the distance that one complete sine wave cycle will travel.

Velocity, expressed in metres per second or m/s, explains how weather or ambient conditions can affect propagation. Mathematically, velocity of sound varies directly with the temperature of the medium and indirectly with the mass of the medium, as in

$$v = (\text{K T/m})^{1/2} \tag{1}$$

◆

where v is the velocity in m/s, K is a constant based on the gas laws, T is the temperature in °K, and m is the mass of the medium in kg/mole. What this tells us is (1) that sound travels faster, and thus farther, in hot weather (low mass) than in cold weather, and (2) that sound travels faster in dry weather (low mass) than in rainy or humid weather.

MEASURING NOISE LEVELS

Noise level is measured in units of decibels or dB. This is a unit of measure of sound pressure level (SPL), which is the technical name for noise level or the "amount" of noise that we hear. This relationship can be mathematically expressed as

$$dB = 20 \log (p/p_0) \tag{2}$$

where dB is the sound pressure level (SPL), p is the sound pressure, and p_0 is a reference pressure, usually 0.00002 Pascal (N/m^2) or 0.0002 micro-bars. A comparison of the relationship between sound pressure (SP) in Pascal and sound pressure level (SPL) in dB is shown in Figure 9.2.

While equation 2 has little practical application, other than identifying the basics of noise, a variation of it can assist us in noise-level evaluation. The variation is expressed as

$$\text{total dB} = 10 \log (10^{dB/10} + 10^{dB/10} + ... + 10^{dB/10}) \tag{3}$$

where the various dB values are for any number of machines or noise sources in an area. For example, one manufacturer had a machine with a noise level, or SPL, of 88 dB. The manufacturer decided to purchase an additional machine. The supplier insisted that the noise level of the new machine was 85 dB, below the current noise standard. However, when the values for each of these machines was entered into the relationship expressed in equation 3, the result was the total dB = $10 \log (10^{88/10} + 10^{85/10})$ = 89.8 or 90 dB which reached the current limit and could possibly create some hearing problems. Any other ambient noise in this workplace could cause the noise level to exceed the safety standards.

An easier way to make this same calculation is shown in Table 9.1. In our example, the difference in noise level between the two machines is 88 – 85, or 3 dB. Using the table, find the line that shows a difference of 3. The line where the difference ranges from 2.8 to 3.0 gives a factor of 1.8, which

FIGURE 9.2 **Relationship Between A-Weighted Sound Pressure and Sound Pressure in Nm^2**

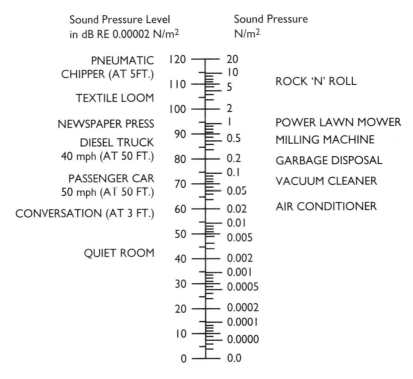

National Institute for Occupational Safety and Health, *The Industrial Environment: Its Evaluation and Control (DHHS/NIOSH 1973)*. Washington, D.C.: Government Printing Office, 1987, 301.

is to be added to the highest noise level. Thus, 88 + 1.8 gives a total of 89.8, or 90 dB, as before (Michael, 1988).

THRESHOLD OF HEARING One characteristic of the human ear and hearing is that we do not hear everything in a nice, neat way. If sound were measured electronically, the sound spectrum might appear more or less as a straight line. What the human ear hears or perceives is significantly different. As previously mentioned, the human hearing range of frequencies is approximately 20 to 20,000 Hz. Thus, a person can hear a bass note from a tuba or

TABLE 9.1 MEASURING NOISE LEVELS

Difference Between High and Low Noise Levels	Amount to be Added to Higher Noise Level	Difference Between High and Low Noise Levels	Amount to be Added to Higher Noise Level
0.0 to 0.1	3.0	3.7 to 4.0	1.5
0.2 to 0.3	2.9	4.1 to 4.3	1.4
0.4 to 0.5	2.8	4.4 to 4.7	1.3
0.6 to 0.7	2.7	4.8 to 5.1	1.2
0.8 to 0.9	2.6	5.2 to 5.6	1.1
1.0 to 1.2	2.5	5.7 to 6.1	1.0
1.3 to 1.4	2.4	6.2 to 6.6	0.9
1.5 to 1.6	2.3	6.7 to 7.2	0.8
1.7 to 1.9	2.2	7.3 to 7.9	0.7
2.0 to 2.1	2.1	8.0 to 8.6	0.6
2.2 to 2.4	2.0	8.7 to 9.6	0.5
2.5 to 2.7	1.9	9.7 to 10.7	0.4
2.8 to 3.0	1.8	10.8 to 12.2	0.3
3.1 to 3.3	1.6	12.3 to 14.5	0.2
3.4 to 3.6	1.5	14.6 to 19.3	0.1
		19.4 to ∞	0.0

a shrill note from a piccolo, but not a dog whistle. (This has direct implications for human hearing problems: Just because we cannot hear the sound does not mean that it is not present and possibly causing hearing damage.)

The response of the human ear is usually shown as a graph that represents the threshold of hearing (see figure 9.3). The term *threshold of hearing* refers to the envelope or range of sound that the human ear can perceive or hear. As noted, the standards for the measurement of noise use the unit of a decibel, or dB. When the human response is involved, the unit becomes dB(A) or A – weighted decibel. This response is built into the sound meters used for measuring noise exposure in the workplace.

FIGURE 9.3 Human Hearing Response Curve

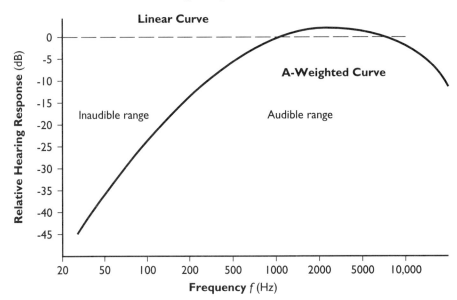

OCTAVE BANDS A further dimension of noise used for testing and evaluation is frequency. As noted previously, sound is not a pure tone but rather a "jumble" of frequencies. To test noise exposure properly, loudness and frequency must be examined independently. In order to do this, we use a sound meter that has provision for measuring octave bands. An *octave* is the interval between two sounds eight full tones apart, the higher having twice as many vibrations per second and double the energy as the lower. In music, an octave is the space between middle C and the C above middle C.

When sound is being evaluated using octaves, we employ a meter with settings that allow us to divide the noise being examined into specific bands of octaves. When one of the octave bands is activated, it permits the measure of sound pressure level in that band and excludes almost all sound from other frequency ranges. The accepted octave bands for measurement are 31.5, 63, 125, 250, 500, 1000, 2000, 4000, and 8000 Hz. These octave bands are illustrated in Figure 9.4, using a logarithmic base.

One of the reasons for using octave band measurement, as noted previously with reference to the dog whistle, is that noise that is beyond the range of human hearing may nevertheless be strong enough to cause hearing dam-

FIGURE 9.4 Octave Bands

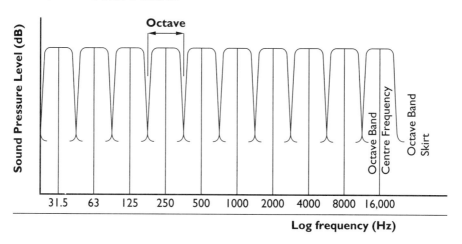

age. Additionally, octave band measurement is necessary to determine the proper type of hearing protection, which is usually frequency responsive.

TYPES OF HEARING LOSS

There are two basic types of hearing loss. The first is *conductive*, which restricts the transmission of sound to the cochlea or inner ear; the second is *sensorineural* (sometimes known as nerve deafness), which affects the cochlea itself and is almost always irreversible. Conductive hearing loss can be caused by wax buildup, infection, or trauma. From an industrial standpoint, it can be caused by nonhygienic application of hearing protectors or improper cleaning of the devices.

More prevalent in industry, however, is the sensorineural type of hearing loss. It is interesting to note that exposure to excessive noise first affects the speech range of frequencies, about 500 to 3000 Hz. Two indications of exposure to excessive noise levels at work are ringing in the ears when driving home (tinnitus) and cranking up the volume of the car radio to compensate for work-related, temporary hearing loss effects. Hearing loss is one of the most insidious of disabilities. It is not uncommon for major loss to occur gradually over a five-to-ten-year period, depending on the type of exposure.

Gradual hearing loss, known as temporary threshold shift (TTS), can sometimes be reversed by removal from the noise source. Permanent threshold shift (PTS) identifies a hearing disability that is permanent and may not be correctable. In many cases, a hearing aid can bring about some improvement. However, such a device is of little assistance when the hearing loss has been caused by noise exposure or "nerve deafness," because the hair cells in the cochlea have been destroyed.

To illustrate the destruction of the cochlea hair cells think of the grass that makes up your lawn. When you walk across the lawn, you will notice that the blades of grass where you walked are bent over. If you observe them a short time later, you will see that the bent blades are now standing erect as before. If you were to continue to traverse the same track continuously for a week or two, you would observe a brown path where the grass has been killed. This path would not likely regrow any grass if left alone. Thus it is with the hair cells in the cochlea or inner ear. The cells, which are the actual nerve sensors, have been destroyed by the "trampling" action of excessive sound pressure waves. Like the trampled grass, these destroyed cells will not regenerate, thus creating a permanent disability.

In the past, companies would sometimes hire workers with permanent hearing loss to work in high-noise areas since it was thought that the damage had already been done. However, it is now known that noise can cause extra-auditory effects including a startled response to a loud, unexpected noise; cardiovascular, neurologic, endocrine, and biochemical changes; and nausea, malaise, and headaches (Key et al., 1977). Laboratory and field studies have also demonstrated vasoconstriction, hyperreflexia, fluctuations in hormonal secretions, and disturbances in equilibrium and visual functions.

NOISE EXPOSURE STANDARDS

Noise exposure standards vary from province to province in terms of their relative stringency. The standards are based on worker exposure during a defined time frame. This relationship is referred to as *dose*, which describes the amount of noise absorbed by or impinged on an organ (the ear or the body) in a given unit of time. The noise standard or threshold limit value (TLV) in Ontario allows for an eight-hour exposure of 90 dBA without hearing protection. Most of the other provinces use a standard of 85 dBA for eight hours. The 5 dBA difference between the two standards represents a difference of twice the noise energy, the 90 dBA standard being greater. The official standard for Ontario is presented in Table 9.2. The 5 dB increments

TABLE 9.2 ONTARIO NOISE TLV, 1994
90 dBA exposure allowed for 8 hours in one day
95 dBA exposure allowed for 4 hours in one day
100 dBA exposure allowed for 2 hours in one day
105 dBA exposure allowed for 1 hour in one day
110 dBA exposure allowed for 1/2 hour in one day
115 dBA exposure allowed for 1/4 hour in one day
120 dBA exposure allowed for 1/8 hour in one day

noted in the table are referred to as a 5dB exchange rate. The exchange rate represents the doubling of the sound power, which in turn requires the halving of the exposure time.

By contrast, Saskatchewan uses 85 dBA for eight hours with a 3 dB exchange rate, while Nova Scotia uses 85 dBA for eight hours with a 5 dB exchange rate.

The above standards are based on continuous noise—an air compressor or machine running. Impact or impulse noise—a punch press operating with a more than one-second interval between strokes—has a totally different method of measurement based on the number of impacts per day.

Another widely applied or referenced set of standards is that established by the American Conference of Governmental Industrial Hygienists (ACGIH). ACGIH recommends a noise TLV of 85 dBA for eight hours. This organization's standards are updated annually.

Noise exposure tests can be done by an outside specialist or a trained person on staff.

NOISE CONTROL

Noise can be controlled by using logical methods. The process for control uses the health and safety professional's route of source–path–human. The first line of defence is to make the *source* of the noise lower or quieter. There are a number of possible approaches. One can make the machine generate less noise by adding sound-absorbing materials to the machine or placing

---

BOX 9.1 TESTING FOR NOISE EXPOSURE: A CHECKLIST

1. Calibrate the instrument.
2. Check the batteries and replace if in doubt.
3. Record full details of the test site, test methodology, and test subject(s).
4. Create diagrams or maps of the test area in order to support item 3.
5. Record all results.
6. Repeat the calibration and battery check after testing. Any deviation or change could invalidate the test results.
7. Draw conclusions from the actual test results, not from any preconceived notions about what those results should be.

---

vibration padding under it; by redesigning the operation so that the machine performs in a different manner; by isolating the machine in a separate room or sound-deadening enclosure; or by purchasing a new machine. All of these alternatives can be expensive and may not be too enthusiastically endorsed. However, a cost-benefit analysis, which takes into account such factors as noise-based illness, absenteeism, and WCB costs, may paint a more positive picture.

The second element—*path*—involves moving the worker to an operation station away from the source or erecting sound barriers between the noise and the worker, or both. Based on the physics of noise, as the distance from the sound source is doubled, the noise level will drop by a fixed amount. For example, a noise level of 90 dB is measured five metres away from a machine (a point source). If the distance is increased to ten metres, the noise level would be attenuated or lowered by 6 dB. This is what is called a "free field effect," which simply means that there is nothing around to reflect the sound back on the worker. In actual practice, such objects as the walls of the building and other machines will cause reflections that can reduce the amount of attenuation from this fixed amount. Nevertheless, the principle is still valid, and this process is usually less costly than the source approach.

The third element—*human*—involves the use of personal protective equipment. This approach is the least costly and the one that is most commonly used. It is not always the best, but many companies are not well enough informed to undertake other approaches. Some of these other approaches include job rotation, relocation, isolation, automation, rest periods, and the layout of the job or task site.

Whatever strategies are used to decrease noise exposure, personal protective devices may still be necessary. The two basic classes of hearing protection available are earplugs, which are inserted into the ears, and circumaural muffs or earmuffs, which are worn over the ears. A description of the various types of industrial hearing protection is provided in Table 9.3.

There are a number of factors to consider when deciding on the most effective kind of hearing protection for your specific application.

TABLE 9.3 TYPES OF INDUSTRIAL HEARING PROTECTION		
CLASS	TYPE	DESCRIPTION
EARPLUGS	A1	Preformed earplug, fitting of which should be done professionally.
	A2	User formable earplug, made of soft sponge-like materials that the user rolls between the fingers for insertion into the ear canal.
	B1	A stethoscope configuration with the spring headband holding earplugs in position in the ears. Easy to observe, and the band may be worn in several positions on the head.
CIRCUMAURAL	D1	An earmuff that surrounds the complete ear with a headband that sits only on the top of the head. Often best for comfort and optimum attenuation.
	D2	An earmuff similar to D1 but with a headband system that can be worn in many positions on the head. Attenuation may vary with headband position.
	D3	An ear muff attachment for a hard hat, which can be permanently attached or field applied. Usually used in construction settings.
NONLINEAR PROTECTORS	F1	A specialty device with an electronic amplifier system that allows only certain sound levels and frequencies to pass unimpeded.
	F2	A specialty device with a mechanical "ear valve" on each ear that responds to impact noise and causes attenuation.
COMBINATION		Many of the above types may be used in combination as necessary for attenuation of excessive noise levels.

1. *Comfort.* Earmuffs in particular can be hot in warm conditions. The spring band can generate a feeling of the head being squashed. Workers who are claustrophobic may experience feelings of confinement.

2. *Visibility.* This is mostly for the benefit of supervisors, who can see if the worker is wearing the protection in the required manner.

3. *Size.* People have heads of different sizes and shapes. It is imperative that hearing protective devices be fitted properly. Additional types of paraphernalia such as face shields must also be examined.

4. *Weight.* Generally, the lighter the protector, the greater the comfort.

5. *Ease of Donning.* A device that is easy to put on will gain more acceptance among workers.

6. *Cost.* The actual dollar cost will depend on the application and the required degree of attenuation.

7. *Effective Attenuation.* Most modern hearing protection devices use a noise reduction rating (NRR) system to indicate the degree of attenuation based on laboratory evaluation. This NRR value is usually accompanied by a chart showing attenuation by octave band frequencies. The higher the number, the greater the level of attenuation. A good rule-of-thumb relationship is expressed with the equation $NRR = L_{actual} - L_{standard} + 7$, where L_{actual} is the noise level measured in the workplace, and $L_{standard}$ is the noise standard for an eight-hour period. Thus, if a worksite has a noise level of 97 dBA and the standard is 90 dBA for eight hours, the required NRR for hearing protectors would be 97 – 90 + 7 or 14 dBA (Berger et al., 1988).

8. *Hygiene.* This requirement is the most critical and most abused. It is not uncommon to observe a hearing protection device hanging from a hook in a dirty environment. Care must be taken to keep the personal item cleaned and stored in a sanitary location.

9. *Useful Life.* Disposable inserts have a low useful life but excellent maintainability, while muffs have a longer useful life but require more maintenance and care.

10. *Maintenance.* All nondisposable hearing protection devices require ongoing maintenance and care. They must be cleaned regularly with soap and warm water, and checked periodically for wear. The foam seal pads on circumaural units must be regularly maintained because skin oils and

sweat will cause embrittlement and surface failure. Once the seal is damaged, the attenuation effectiveness is reduced.

Human hearing characteristics, and thus the possible effects of exposure to excessive levels of noise, are measured and evaluated using a device called an *audiometer*. The tests are carried out by a trained technician in a sound-proof enclosure. The hearing response is measured against loudness and frequency, and is plotted graphically. Both air conduction through the ear canal and bone conduction through the skull are measured. This measurement shows the cumulative effect of hearing loss due to excessive noise over a period of years.

◆ ◆ ◆
VIBRATION

Vibration refers to the oscillating motion of a particle or body about a reference position (Broch, 1980). Imagine a weight attached to the end of a string being spun in a vertical circle. The weight represents the particle and the repetitive motions of the spinning string represent the oscillation. If a person were to begin walking in some direction while spinning the weighted string, the path transcribed by the weight, or particle, would describe a sinusoidal path. A plot of this particle path would appear as a sine wave (see Figure 9.5), and appear the same as the wave form described in the previous section.

Vibration has a number of mechanical causes including the dynamic effects from machine tolerances, clearances, rolling or rubbing contact, and out-of-balance conditions with rotary or reciprocating parts. Vibration can be accidental (a car wheel that is out of balance) or intentional (a vibrating feeder on a dry bulk material conveyor).

Vibration is a health hazard for two reasons. First, the medium through which the vibration is transmitted will shake; second, the vibration is usually accompanied by noise that is usually excessive. As with noise, vibration is transmitted through a medium, although is this case the medium is solid (e.g., steel or brick). The health effects will vary depending on the frequency and amplitude of the vibration. At low frequencies, say up to 15 Hz, the body will experience what is known as *whole body vibration*. In this instance, the complete human body will "shake" with the source. We have all experienced this condition in an automobile or on board a ship—the

FIGURE 9.5 **Vibration Wave Characteristics**

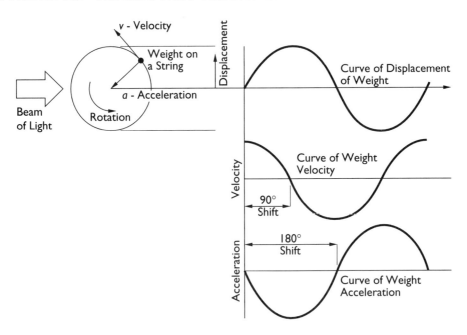

condition is called car or sea sickness. As the frequency of the vibration increases, parts of the body—not the whole body—will be affected by a process called *segmental vibration*.

One term that frequently comes up in discussions of vibration is *resonance*, which refers to the effect that occurs when a object reacts strongly to some particular frequency. If you sing in a tiled shower stall, you will occasionally hear a note that sounds louder than most—the space is resonant to that note. Parts of the human body can resonate when exposed to some lower frequencies. For instance, the head and shoulders can resonate at 20 to 30 Hz, while the eyeballs resonate at 60 to 90 Hz (Soule, 1973). If your vision becomes blurry when you have been working with a power tool such as a belt sander, you are experiencing minor levels of eyeball resonance, which is harmless unless prolonged.

Vibrating effects fall into two separate conditions. As noted, the first concerns low-frequency vibrations. The second deals with higher-frequency effects that happen too fast for the body to respond. When the higher frequencies occur, the effects of wave velocity and acceleration take precedence. To return to our example of the weight on the string, as the spinning goes faster, the physics concerned with rapid changes in direction of the particle along the sine wave result in rapid changes in acceleration and velocity. By definition, acceleration increases when an object changes position or velocity while moving (imagine the driver of a car increasing speed to pass another vehicle and the resulting change in velocity and position.) Vibratory effects are evaluated using measurements of velocity and acceleration caused by the source.

The health effects of whole body exposure include inhibition of muscular reflexes; impaired or blurred vision, and alterations of brain electrical activity. Segmental effects include sore neck and shoulder muscles and joints; Raynaud's phenomenon, or white fingers, caused by restricted blood circulation in the fingers; neuritis and degenerative alterations of the central nervous system; fragmentation, necrosis, and decalcification of the carpal bones; muscle atrophy and tenosynovitis.

The frequency response associated with vibrating systems is directly related to the mass of the system. In the simplest terms, if the mass or weight is increased, the effects of vibration can be lowered. This is one of the methods of control, to reduce the health effects.

Whole body effects can result from driving a motorcycle, truck, or tractor, or working near large machines such as air compressors or punch presses. Segmental effects are caused by using vibrating tools such as riveters, sanders, saws, air hammers, or hammer drills. The most serious segmental effects are those associated with hand–arm vibrations. Vibrating hand tools come with a catch-22. In order to properly control a vibrating hand tool, it is necessary to grip it securely; however, the tighter the hand grips the tool, the more severe the effects of segmental damage.

Some strategies for vibration control:

◆ Avoid the source by revising the task.

◆ Use equipment that produces lower vibrations.

◆ Add dampening devices to equipment to reduce vibrations.

◆ Decrease worker exposure time.

The human resource professional should also be aware that vibration has chronic effects that must be managed.

◆ ◆ ◆
THERMAL STRESS

The thermal condition involves extremes of cold and hot temperatures, usually coupled with high humidity. The human body can be seen as a machine that takes in chemical energy (food) and converts it to mechanical energy (muscles) and heat (see Figure 9.6). The balance of this heat generation, referred to as *homeostasis* is the basis for examination of the effects of heat and cold on the body. Simple thermodynamic theory shows that temperature, like water, flows from a high point or level to a low point or level. Thus, in cold climates, heat will flow from the body to the surrounding environment, thereby making the person feel cold. Similarly, in hot climates, heat will be absorbed by the body, making the person feel hot. Adding physical work to either of these situations will increase the body heat and change the thermal balance or imbalance. When these imbalances occur, the body is stressed thermally. This body thermal balance can be illustrated by the mathematical model (Hammer, 1989)

$$S = (M - W) \pm R \pm C \pm V - E$$

where S is the body heat storage or loss; M is the metabolic heat production of the body; W is the work output; R is the radiative heat gain or loss; C is the convective heat gain or loss; V is the respiratory heat gain or loss; and E is the evaporative heat loss.

FIGURE 9.6   The Body as a Machine System

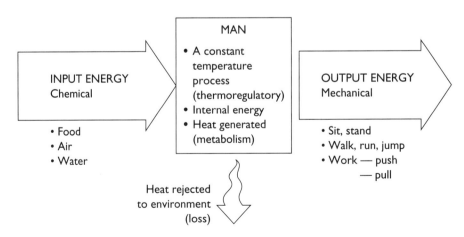

When there is heat production, (M - W), the body will gain heat if R, C, and V are positive; similarly, if there is heat lost, then R, and C, V, and E are negative. In medical terms, heat gain is referred to as hyperthermic; heat loss is referred to as hypothermic; and a condition of neither gain nor loss is known as balance. Referring once again to the mathematical model, hyperthermia occurs when $(+ R + C + V) > (- R - C - V - E)$; hypothermia occurs when $(+ R + C + V) < (- R - C - V - E)$; and balance occurs when $(+R + C+ V) = (- R - C - V - E)$ (Alpaugh, 1988).

There are three methods of heat transfer that apply to the body, as well as to any other thermal condition. The first method, *conduction*, occurs when two surfaces are in contact (e.g., the skin touches a hot stove, resulting a local burn). The second method, *convection*, occurs when one surface adds heat to the surroundings (e.g., the skin is close to air flow emanating from a flame or a heater). The third method, *radiation*, occurs when energy is transmitted by electromagnetic waves (e.g., the skin is exposed to sunlight).

The body has remarkable temperature control, with the blood system and the skin being the major players. As body heat increases, blood flow increases, the capillaries come closer to the surface of the skin (they actually open up), and sweating increases, thereby allowing increased heat exchange to the atmosphere. As body heat decreases, blood flow slows and the capillaries withdraw from the skin surface, thus reducing the amount of heat transferred to the atmosphere.

The health effects of heat and cold are well recognized by anyone who spends a lot of time outside in summer and winter. The focus of most thermal effect and control is the body core—from neck to groin and between the shoulders. The body core temperature range is 35 to 38.5°C, with "normal" at 37°C. When the core temperature goes outside this range, serious problems can result. Heat-related illnesses include heat stroke (the body loses control of its thermal balance), heat hyperpyrexia (the body temperature rises), heat syncope (heat-caused fainting), heat exhaustion, heat cramps, heat rash, and heat fatigue. Cold-related illnesses include chilblains, caused by reduced circulation in the extremities; trench foot, caused by cold, wet conditions; frostbite, caused by local freezing of tissue; and hypothermia, which occurs when cold causes the body's thermal regulation to fail.

Thermal stress adaptability depends on a number of physical factors, such as:

◆ Age (the younger the person, the greater the adaptability)

◆ Sex (females adapt better to cold, males to heat)

◆ Physical fitness (assists in rapid acclimatization)

◆ Mental attitude

◆ Physical and psychological demands of the job

The best way to prevent thermal stress is to provide for ongoing monitoring and control. Some strategies for heat stress control:

◆ Decrease physical effort by introducing work–rest regimens.

◆ Limit exposures through work rotation.

◆ Install fans or air conditioning.

◆ Promote intake of cool liquids such as water.

◆ Use protective clothing.

◆ Allow time for acclimatization.

◆ Screen new hires for heat tolerance and physical fitness.

The regular use of salt tablets may create more problems than it solves. Salt tablets can upset the body's electrolyte balance. Normal salt levels in food may be enough to satisfy sweat-induced loss (Hammer, 1989). Cold stress control measures include wearing protective clothing that is layered and allows for breathing of the skin, taking shelter from the wind, and taking regular rest periods.

Thermal stress is measured using the Wet Bulb Globe Temperature (WBGT) index. This index, which measures the effect of heat and humidity on a worker, is described in Table 9.4.

TABLE 9.4 WBGT HEAT STRESS INDEX RANGES	
WBGT °C	DESCRIPTION
< 27	No complaints of heat discomfort
27–29	Varying complaints
>29	Sedentary work for unacclimatized workers
>31	Continuous work suspended; work-rest schedules implemented
>38	Threshold limit value; no work without protection

◆◆◆
RADIATION

Radiation is divided into two distinct groups—ionizing and nonionizing. These two types of radiation are identified by wavelength and by their action on tissue.

IONIZING RADIATION

Ionizing radiation is any form of electromagnetic energy capable of producing ions through interaction with matter. Types of ionizing radiation include X-rays, gamma rays, alpha particles, beta particles, and neutrons. X-radiation is most commonly found in medical facilities. The other forms of ionizing radiation are commonly found in nuclear operations or research companies. All of these forms, except X-rays, occur naturally as well as in manufactured states. Natural radiation is found in ground-grown food, cosmic bombardment, building materials such as concrete, and fertilizers such as phosphorous. Most of these sources are measurable with very sensitive instruments but are insignificant from a health standpoint.

Radiation exposure or dosage is usually measured in a unit called a rem (*r*oentgen *e*quivalent *m*an). Natural radiation is approximately 125 mrem (millirem) per year. A dose of approximately 75 rem per year can cause serious health effects.

Manufactured ionizing radiation can be found in a number of products or operations other than nuclear energy. Most home smoke detectors use a source that emits alpha particles, which are harmless. In industry, ionizing radiation can be found in bulk-material measuring devices, high-voltage electronic devices, and medical equipment such as X-ray machines or scanners; none of these pose a health hazard to the general population.

The biological effects of equal amounts of different radiations depend on a number of factors, including whether the exposure is whole body or local, acute or chronic. Genetic effects can include cell mutation, burns, and radiation sickness. Control of exposure will include regular monitoring, shielding, job rotation, protective equipment, and extensive training.

NONIONIZING RADIATION

Nonionizing radiation refers to electromagnetic radiation that does not have energies great enough to ionize matter. Types of nonionizing radiation include ultraviolet radiation, visible radiation, infrared radiation, microwave radiation, and radio waves. The sun can be a source of all these radiations. The eye is the primary organ at risk from nonionizing radiation (See Figure 9.7).

FIGURE 9.7 Eye Effects of Radiation

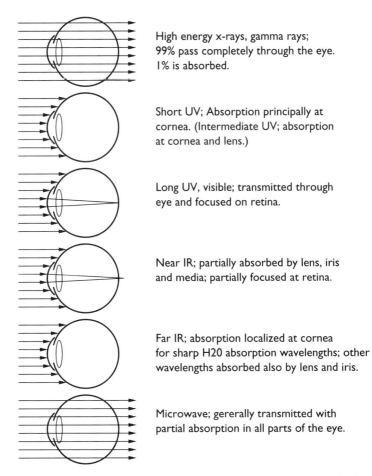

High energy x-rays, gamma rays; 99% pass completely through the eye. 1% is absorbed.

Short UV; Absorption principally at cornea. (Intermediate UV; absorption at cornea and lens.)

Long UV, visible; transmitted through eye and focused on retina.

Near IR; partially absorbed by lens, iris and media; partially focused at retina.

Far IR; absorption localized at cornea for sharp H20 absorption wavelengths; other wavelengths absorbed also by lens and iris.

Microwave; gererally transmitted with partial absorption in all parts of the eye.

General Absorbtion Properties of the Eye for Electromagnetic Radiation

National Institute for Occupational Safety and Health. *The Industrial Environment: Its Evaluation and Control (DHHS/NIOSH 1973)*. Washington D.C.: Government Printing Office, 1987, 376.

Specific health effects of nonionizing radiation forms can be itemized as follows:

1. *Ultraviolet radiation* (originating from mercury vapor lamps and fluorescent tubes): conjunctivitis and keratitis (inflammation of the cornea), reddening of the skin (sunburn), skin cancer.

2. *Infrared radiation* (originating from incandescent, fluorescent, and high-intensity discharge lights, and hot metals and glass): corneal and retinal burns, overheating of the iris, cataracts, skin burns.

3. *Microwave radiation* (originating from microwave ovens, radar, induction heating equipment, and diathermy equipment): deep tissue damage, surface skin rash, cataracts and eye lens opacities, biochemical changes and central nervous effects, pacemaker interference.

4. *Radio waves* (originating from radio and television broadcasting, most electronic devices—e.g., video-display terminals (VDTs)—and power-lines): a number of conditions, including tumours, none of which have been conclusively proven (Murray et al., 1981; Savage, 1993).

Control of nonionizing radiation exposures usually includes isolation or separation, protective equipment, and training. With respect to separation, a pregnant computer worker should be offered another job where she is not exposed to a VDT. Even though there is no hard evidence of fetal risk, and such a move may be impractical in a small firm, the company should not put itself in the position of subjecting one of its employees to a possible health risk.

◆ ◆ ◆
SUMMARY

This chapter has focused on four physical agents that are commonly encountered in industry—noise, vibration, thermal stress, and radiation. Industries in which agents like ionizing radiation are encountered have implemented extensive, specialized training programs and procedures. In most situations, however, simple prevention policies and programs are adequate for reducing and controlling worker exposure to physical agents.

EXERCISES

1. Workers in a manufacturing division have made a formal complaint that three machines are too noisy. Noise measurements are taken: the results are 83 dB, 87 dB, and 88 dB. Do the workers have a legitimate complaint?
2. "The exchange rate is 3 dB." Briefly explain what is meant by this statement.
3. One instrument that is used to measure noise is an octave band meter.

Briefly explain what specific information this meter provides.
4. Name three sources of UV radiation in an office. Then describe the health effects of UV radiation.
5. Briefly explain the term "dose" as it applies to physical agents such as noise and radiation.

References

Alpaugh, Edwin L. 1988. "Temperature Extremes." In Barbara A. Plog, ed., *Fundamentals of Industrial Hygiene*, 3rd ed. Chicago, Ill.: National Safety Council.

Berger, E.H., W.D. Ward, J.C. Morrill, and L.H. Royster, eds. 1988. *Noise and Hearing Conservation Manual*, 4th ed. Akron, Ohio: American Industrial Hygiene Association.

Broch, Jens Trampe. 1980. *Mechanical Vibration and Shock Measurements*, 2nd ed. Nærum, Denmark: Brüel and Kjær.

Hammer, Wille. 1989. *Occupational Safety Management and Engineering*, 4th ed. Englewood Cliffs, N.J.: Prentice Hall.

Key, Marcus M., et al., eds. 1977. *Occupational Diseases: A Guide to Their Recognition*, rev. ed. Cincinnati, Ohio: U.S. Department of Health, Education, and Welfare.

Michael, Paul L. (1988). "Physics of Sound. In *The Industrial Environment — Its Evaluation and Control*, 2nd ed. Cincinnati, Ohio: U.S. Department of Health, Education, and Welfare.

Murray, R.L., et al. 1981. *Potential Health Hazards of Video Display Terminals*. Cincinnati, Ohio: U.S. Department of Health, Education, and Welfare.

Savage, J.A. 1993. "Are Computer Terminals Zapping Workers' Health." *Business and Society Review* 84. (Winter): 41–43.

Soule, Robert D. 1973. "Vibration." In *The Industrial Environment—Its Evaluation and Control*. Cincinnati, Ohio: U.S. Department of Health, Education, and Welfare.

10

Controlling Physical Injuries Through Ergonomics

◆◆◆

INTRODUCTION

Ergonomics, or human factors engineering, is the study of the efficiency of persons in their working environment. This field of health and safety is essentially concerned with the interaction between humans and their total working environment. It encompasses multidisciplinary activities such as engineering sciences (biomechanics and mechanics), physical sciences (chemistry and physics), biological science (anatomy and physiology), and social and behavioural science (anthropometry, psychology, and sociology).

Ergonomics-related issues are becoming increasingly prominent. One-third of compensation claims in British Columbia over a five-year-period resulted from ergonomically related injuries, and WCB paid out over 400 million dollars for more than 100,000 ergonomics-related claims (MacDonald, 1995a). British Columbia was the first province to pass ergonomics legislation related to standards and regulations.

Studies have indicated that workplaces designed along ergonomic principles not only decrease the risk of physical injury but also increase productivity and efficiency. One airline company that introduced ergonomic changes, such as adjustable work surfaces, footrests and document holders, reported a 93 percent reduction in errors, a 50 percent decrease in musculoskeletal problems, a 33 percent drop in visual fatigue, with a 33 percent increase in efficiency (Dolan and Schuler, 1994). Others have reported 15 to 25 percent increases in production following the redesign of workstations (Purdie, 1990).

The goal of an ergonomics program is the design of a work system in which the work methods, machines, equipment, layout, and environment (noise, heat, light, and air quality) are matched or compatible with the physical and behavioural characteristics of the worker (Laing, 1992). Workplace design has traditionally focused on standardization—one size fits all—despite the wide variations in the physical characteristics of employees.

Anthropometric factors such as height, weight, reach, and strength, influence how the work is done, and the likelihood of achieving efficiency and safety. Inexperience and idiosyncratic ways of doing the work increase the probability of chronic injuries. Tasks have to be matched to the human capabilities to ensure optimal performance.

Furthermore, employers are legally required to accommodate the needs of physically challenged employees. Ergonomics has a role to play in adapting workstations to particular disabilities, and in making work accessible.

This chapter will focus on two categories of nontraumatic physical injuries (overexertion and back injuries, and repetitive-strain injuries) and discuss control of these injuries through ergonomics.

◆ ◆ ◆
OVEREXERTION AND LOWER-BACK INJURY

Materials handling (lifting and carrying) is a frequently performed operations in many organizations. Approximately 25 percent of all compensable injuries are a direct result of manual materials-handling activities (WCB, 1992). These injuries are the result of overexertion (primarily from lifting and lowering) and posture problems, both of which are the primary cause of lower-back pain. Back injuries—from stabbing pain to total disability—can have far-reaching effects on the worker, the worker's family, and the company.

CONTROLS

Following are some suggestions for administrative controls:

1. Train workers thoroughly for the job and the various high-risk components of it.

2. Hire job applicants based on validated criteria and measurable job specifications.

3. Encourage worker physical fitness and possibly provide physical-fitness equipment for that purpose.

4. Implement job rotation so that the worker does not become subjected to chronic exposure to injury potential.

With respect to engineering controls, materials handling can be mechanized through the use of conveyors and forklift trucks or other lifting devices of various configurations; or it can be automated through the use of automated guided vehicles (AGV)—which follow sensor lines on the floor, stopping as required to transfer their product—or computer-controlled inventory systems that allow computer-controlled machines to pick or stock inventory. Supports that force the back to remain straight but do not prevent the worker from lifting or handling heavier loads are used by some employees (Gross et al., 1984), although one study indicates that such supports do little or nothing to prevent back injuries (La Bar, 1994). Another option is to revise, substitute, or eliminate the stress-producing operation.

Listed below are 12 basic rules for proper lifting:

1. *Lift by gripping the load with both the fingers and the palms of the hand.* The more of the hand that is in contact with the object, the better the control and the more positive the application of the lifting force.

2. *Keep the back straight.* A straight back will reduce stresses on the spine and make the load distribution on each disc uniform.

3. *Maintain good balance.* If you are not steady on your feet, then an off-balance motion can impose significant stress on the discs.

4. *Size up the load and check the overall conditions.* Is the load being picked up in the open or is it surrounded by other boxes? Is it too large to grasp? How far does it have to be carried? How high does it have to be lifted? Is the floor dry or slippery?

5. *Choose the lifting position that feels the best.* There are several "correct" ways to lift a load. Figure 10.1 illustrates two of the more common ones: the straight back leg lift and the stoop lift.

6. *Check for slivers, nails, sharp edges, etc.* Sustaining a penetration injury while lifting is both painful and awkward.

7. *Avoid any unnecessary bending.* Do not place loads on the floor if they have to be picked up again later. Bend the knees, and do not stoop.

8. *Avoid unnecessary twisting.* No twisting is acceptable. Turn the feet, not the hips or shoulders.

9. *Avoid reaching out.* Keep all loads as close to the body as possible. The further away from the body centre, the greater the disc load and hence stress (see Figure 10.2).

FIGURE 10.1 Lift Positions

Straight back lift, straddle foot position
Lift with legs

Stoop lift, back straight
Lift with waist and legs

10. *Avoid excessive weight.* If the load is too heavy or too awkward, get help.
The definition of "excessive" will depend on the individual and his or her
physical condition and training.

FIGURE 10.2 Relationship Between Load Position and Lower-Back Stress

LOWER BACK STRESS = (A+B) C

where A = distance from front of body to rotation point of spine, approximately 20cm.
B = distance in front of body to load centre of mass.
C = load weight.

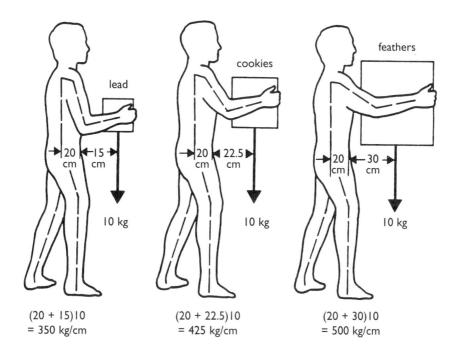

| (20 + 15)10 | (20 + 22.5)10 | (20 + 30)10 |
| = 350 kg/cm | = 425 kg/cm | = 500 kg/cm |

11. *Lift slowly and smoothly.* Use your body weight to start the load moving and then lift using your legs and arms.

12. *Keep in good physical shape.* The better your physical condition, the easier lifting will be and the lower the risk of sustaining a lower-back injury.

There are two formal ways of determining the load acceptability for lifting tasks. The first is an analytical technique developed by the National Institute of Occupational Safety and Health (NIOSH). This method, which can be done with little cost and effort, is described in the appendix at the end of this chapter. The second method—a video-scanning computer modelling tool developed by Vision 3000 and used by consultants such as Ergonomics Plus of Toronto—is very effective but costly.

Both methods examine the weight of the object to be lifted, the height of the lift, the distance between the load centre of gravity (or centre line) and the body (reach), and the origin of the load. The results are compared to epidemiological data developed from biomechanical experiments.

◆ ◆ ◆
REPETITIVE-STRAIN INJURIES

Repetitive-strain injury (RSI), cumulative trauma disorder (CTD), musculoskeletal injury (MSI), and overuse syndrome (OS) are injuries whose origins can be traced to continuous and repetitive actions that produce muscle and/or skeletal strain. Because the terms are basically interchangeable, this chapter will use the term RSI to refer to these conditions.

Any strain-producing body action that involves use of the fingers, wrists, arms, elbows, shoulders, neck, back (and, to a lesser extent, the lower body and legs), and that is repeated over a long period of time, can cause damage to joints and tissues. Tennis elbow, golfer's elbow, telephone operator's elbow, writer's cramp, and postal worker's shoulder are well-known examples of RSI. More recently named conditions include carpal tunnel syndrome, thoracic outlet syndrome, white fingers disease, or Raynaud's syndrome.

RSI is fast becoming the most common occupational disease. In 1993, in Ontario, RSI accounted for 6283 claims, a 25 percent increase from 1990 (Statistics Canada, 1994). A 1993 Union for Bell Operators Study revealed that 31 percent of operators were affected by repetitive-strain injury (Van Alphen, 1995).

There has been a great deal of debate on the question of whether RSI is, in fact, work-related. Two opposing arguments were presented at a symposium in Vancouver organized by the Environmental Health division at the University of British Columbia (Fournier, 1988). Dr. Peter Nathan of the Hand Surgery and Rehabilitation Centre in Portland, Oregon, stated that RSI cannot be proven to be occupationally related, and therefore compensation is not justified. Dr. Thomas Armstrong, an ergonomist at the University of Michigan, takes the position that RSI is work-related, particularly with respect to jobs characterized by high repetitiveness.

The origins of RSI can be traced to the following four general conditions:

1. *Unnatural joint position or posture*. Whenever a joint is forced to work in a position that is unnatural or stressed, the risk of RSI is increased. For instance, during keyboarding the wrists are forced out of axial alignment with the arm. The use of a hand tool such as a pair of pliers can force the wrist–arm axes out of line, creating a stress condition that could eventually cause joint irritation.

2. *Force application to hinge joints*. When these joints are forced to carry applied loading, particularly when flexed, the joint load distribution is uneven, causing excessive stress in a small area of the joint. The wrist is a good example of a hinge joint. When performing a task such as lifting while bent, this joint can begin to ache. Repetition of the activity can result in a loss of strength.

3. *Activity repetition*. Tasks such as keyboarding or using a hammer involve a repetitive flexing of the fingers and wrists. The action of typing applies low-load repetition to the fingers (touching the keys) and medium loading to the wrist (supporting the hand). The action of hammering applies a high-impact loading to the wrist, which is flexed into a nonaligned axis upon impact. The shock effect increases the potential risk of tissue damage.

4. *Pre-existing conditions* such as arthritis or circulation disorders can have a synergistic effect on RSI conditions. For example, arthritis is an inflammation condition of the joints that can be aggravated by the impact stress associated with hammering or keyboarding activity.

CONTROLS

The predominant method of control involves keeping joints in their natural position or aligned with the connecting limb. To illustrate the joint alignment argument, place your right hand flat on a table, thumb extended to the left. In the natural position, the hand and arm axes will be in line. Now, without moving your arm, flex your wrist to the left in the direction of the thumb. This position is known as "radial deviation." Flex your wrist in the opposite direction. This position is called "ulnar deviation." Raising your fingers off the table, while keeping your arm on the table, will create a position known as "dorsiflexior." If the hand and fingers are flexed downward, the resulting position is "palmar flexion." Each of these positions, if held for any length of time, will become uncomfortable. The radial deviation position and possibly the dorsiflexior position are associated with keyboarding.

DESIGN OF HAND TOOLS Virtually every activity we undertake that requires the use of our hands involves a tool of some sort. While a computer-controlled machining centre is not considered a hand tool in the same sense as a screwdriver or toothbrush, each of its individual pieces of production equipment poses its own RSI problems. Nevertheless, these items are rarely designed to fit the human hand. The common in-line screwdriver configuration, for example, requires that the hand and wrist be forced out of line. However, the T-bar handle in the ergonomic screwdriver allows the hand and arm to be kept in alignment by producing a lower wrist–arm angle (see Figure 10.3). The key to effective hand tool design is to maintain natural

FIGURE 10.3 Screwdriver Configurations

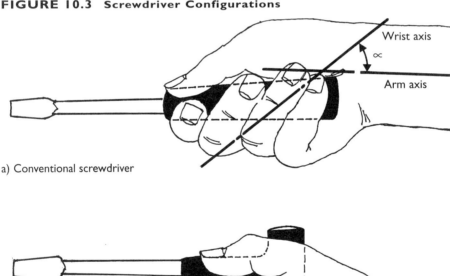

a) Conventional screwdriver

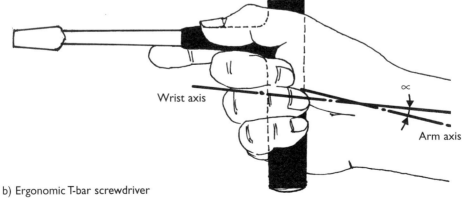

b) Ergonomic T-bar screwdriver

joint alignment such as that illustrated by the ergonomic hammer in Figure 10.4.

Ergonomically designed keyboards, which are available in some computer stores, are constructed to match the natural position of the hands at rest.

Hand-operated tools and devices must allow the hand–wrist–arm group to function in a neutral position (i.e., axes in line). Tools that are used in an assembly operation should be vertically suspended over the workstation on a balancer so that the worker can reach for and grasp the tool without twisting the arm–wrist–axis. The tool should be cycled with a hand grip, not a single finger trigger.

Tools should be designed so that excessive holding force to maintain proper control is not required. A vibrating tool can be hard to control

FIGURE 10.4 Hammer Configurations

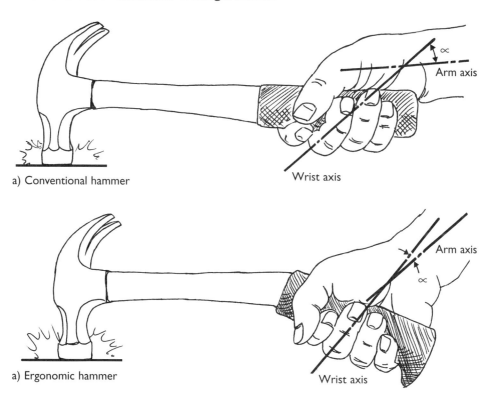

a) Conventional hammer

a) Ergonomic hammer

without maintaining a very tight and stressful hand hold or grip. Workers should move their arms more than their wrists and hands. Greater force can be exerted by the thumb and the middle finger than by the other fingers.

WORKSTATION DESIGN The four major components of workstation design are layout, control and display panels, seating, and lighting.

Layout. Design the workstation so that the arm is not used in an extended or reaching position. The further the hand is from the body, the less power it can exert and the smaller load it can handle. The arm can push and pull greater loads at a worktable if the action is to or from the body, than it can if pushing or pulling transversely.

Tasks should be designed so that the preferred hand (left or right) can do the most critical tasks. Foot motions can be used for minor operations, thereby relieving the hands from some repetitive actions. Avoid simultaneous hand-and-foot motions when the task requires close attention. Arm motions are faster and more accurate than foot motions. The hand and arm can be used for fine control or operation; the foot can be used to stop or start a cycle that involves no accuracy of placement.

Tasks that require frequent arm movements should be carried out with the elbows bent and close to the body. Arm movements should be smooth rather than jerky. The hand and arm can pull down with more strength than they can push up. The push power of the arm is greater when the hand is 50 cm in front of the body; the pull power of the arm is greater when the hand is 70 cm in front of the body (Grandjean, 1988). The greatest push power for the legs occurs when the angle at the knee is 140–165 degrees—close to standing. The greatest bending strength occurs when the angle of the elbow is 80–120 degrees—close to a right angle (Astrand and Rodahl, 1986). Pushing power is greater than pulling power.

Control and Display Panels. Controls and displays must exhibit the following four characteristics:

1. *Visibility*. The display must be within the worker's field of vision, with no obstructions. Characters should be of a readable size, with high contrast.

2. *Legibility*. Characters must be adequately spaced as well as distinguishable (a "3" should not look like an "8"). No more than one line or pointer should appear on each display.

3. *Interpretability*. The displays must be interpreted in the same way by all observers. Universal symbols help but can lead to misunderstandings. For

example, the red exit symbols may be confused with the red glow which means "stop." In Europe, exit symbols are green. As Box 10.1 illustrates, misinterpretation of display information can have tragic results.

4. *User-Friendliness.* Each control must be a different shape and have a different operating direction in order to be easily distinguished from adjacent controls. Picture the controls in your car: the radio volume rotates, while the station-change button is pushed; the most important controls— fuel volume and speedometer—are displayed most prominently.

Seating. Employees can spend long periods seated at their workstations. Poor sitting positions or posture can restrict blood circulation, increase blood pooling in the legs and feet, and add to the compressive load on the spine. Correct chair design will minimize the concentration of pressures under the thigh and the back of the knee. The most commonly recommended sitting posture is illustrated in Figure 10.5.

Work seating must be completely adjustable in all directions and planes. A forward-tilting seat may be preferred by employees who must lean over a workstation. (Interestingly, a study by Ontario Hydro revealed that only 5 percent of users adjust their furniture [McDonald, 1995b]). Seat cushions should have about a 2.5-centimetre compression, with minimal contouring to allow ease of position shift. Permeable fabrics allow ventilation and absorption of perspiration.

The backrest should be curved in the vertical and horizontal planes. It should also be vertically adjustable (so that the point of contact fits the small of the back in the lumbar region) as well as horizontally adjustable. Armrests are recommended unless a wide variety of arm movements are required. The chair base should provide stability and mobility. Five casters with a wide spread will prevent tipping (Canadian Standards Association, 1995).

Lighting. Lighting has two main purposes: to illuminate the tasks and to increase the safety and comfort of the worker. Bright overhead lighting can produce glare and annoying reflections on a computer screen resulting in eyestrain and headaches. Choosing the correct lighting for a workplace will involve consideration of the following factors:

♦ *Intensity:* the amount of light given off by a source.

♦ *Luminance*: the amount of light uniformly reflected or emitted from a surface.

FIGURE 10.5 Side View of Chair Dimensions

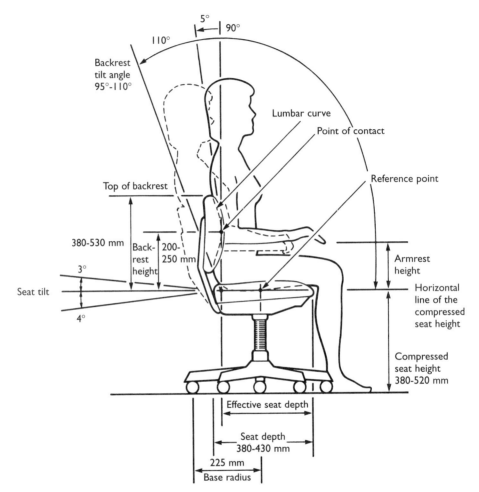

- *Reflectance*: the amount of light reflected from a surface (luminance) and the amount of light falling on the surface (illuminance). A dull black surface has 9 percent reflectance, while a shiny white surface has closer to 100 percent reflectance.

- *Luminaire*: a complete lighting device.

- *Contrast*: the relationship between the amount of light from a surface and the background.

◆ *Glare*: the reduction of visibility caused by brightness differences between an object and its background.

Both the *quantity* and *quality* of light must be considered. In the context of workstation design, quantity refers to the correct amount of light needed to perform a task. Quality is more complex and includes measures of distribution (or spread), glare, diffusion, shadows, contrast, and colour.

BOX 10.1 CONSEQUENCES OF DESIGN ERRORS

In February 1982, a giant oil rig, the *Ocean Ranger*, capsized and sank off the coast of Newfoundland, resulting in the loss of the entire crew of 84 men. A subsequent investigation revealed errors on the part of the crew in charge of ballast control. Part of their job was to assess the draft of the rig by looking out a port-hole in one of the legs of the rig, which was over eight metres above mean water level. To save time and energy, they left the porthole open. During a storm, water entered through the porthole and damaged the ballast control system. The problem was compounded when the crew misread the control manual and opened, instead of closed the ballast tanks. This case illustrates the importance of presenting display information in a way that will allow for error-free interpretation.

◆ ◆ ◆
SUMMARY

The increase in nontraumatic injuries such as back strain and RSI is costing employers in terms of lost production and compensation. Ergonomics, the design of the workplace to accommodate human characteristics and work methods, offers some solutions. The application of ergonomic principles to lifting, seating, tool design, and worksite design reduces the number of injuries, and increases productivity.

◆ ◆ ◆
APPENDIX: LIFTING CALCULATIONS USING THE NIOSH METHOD

The NIOSH method examines the weight of the object to be lifted, the height it is to be lifted, the distance from the body, and the location of the load at the start of the lift or pick. Two factors are calculated and compared to the weight of the lifted object. These factors are the Action Limit (AL) and the Maximum Permissible Limit (MPL).

The Action Limit is based on:

(a) Epidemiological data indicating that some workers would be at increased risk of injury on jobs exceeding the AL.

(b) Biomechanical studies indicating that lower-back, disc-compression forces created at the AL can be tolerated by most (not all) people.

(c) Physiological studies showing that the average metabolic

requirement for the AL would be 3.5 kcal/min.

(d) Psychophysical studies showing that over 75 percent of women and 99 percent of men could lift loads at the AL.

The Maximum Permissible Limit is based on:

(a) Epidemiological data indicating that musculoskeletal injury and severity rates are significantly higher for most workers placed on jobs exceeding the MPL.

(b) Biochmechanical studies indicating that lower-back, disc-compression forces created at the MPL cannot be tolerated in most workers.

(c) Physiological studies showing that the metabolic expenditure would be excessive for most workers frequently lifting loads at the MPL.

The equations for calculating the AL and the MPL are simple and straightforward and can be easily used on the job. Simply examine a specific lifting task and take a series of measurements. Then enter the data into the two equations and compare the results to the weight of the item being lifted. The equations are

$$\text{AL (kg)} = 40(15/H) \ (1{-}0.004 \ |V{-}75|) \ (0.7{+}7.5/D) \ (1{-}F/F_{max}) \ \text{for cm}$$

$$\text{AL (lb.)} = 90(6/H) \ (1{-}0.01 \ |V{-}30|) \ (0.7{+}3/D) \ (1{-}F/F_{max}) \ \text{for inches}$$

$$\text{MPL} = 3 \ (\text{AL})$$

where:

H is the horizontal distance (cm or in.) measured from the load centre of mass (usually where the hands grasp the load) to the midpoint between the ankles (the ankle bone) at the origin of the lift. H is between 15 cm (6 in.)

and 80 cm (32 in.). Objects cannot be closer than 15 cm without interfering with the body; objects further than 80 cm cannot be reached by most people.

V is the vertical distance (cm or in.) measured from the load origin or centre of mass (or to the hands if the object does not have handles to floor level at the origin of lift). V is assumed between 0 and 175 cm (70 in.) representing the upward-reach envelope of most people.

D is the vertical travel distance (cm or in.) of the object measured between the origin location and the destination location. D is assumed a minimum value of 25 cm (10 in.) and a maximum of 200-V cm (80-V in.). If the distance is less than 25 cm, then set $D = 25$ cm.

F is the average frequency of lifting (lifts/min.) with a minimum of 0.2 lifts/min., or once every five minutes as occasional lifting, to a maximum based on duration and operator posture as shown in Table 10A.1, for F_{max}.

TABLE 10A.1 F_{MAX} TABLE AVERAGE VERTICAL LOCATION OF LIFT		
DURATION	V>75 cm (30") (Standing)	V_ 75 cm (30") (Stooped)
1 HOUR	18	15
8 HOURS	15	1

When the AL and the MPL have been calculated, the results are compared to the three lifting regions to determine the acceptability of the lifting task and if controls will be necessary. Lifting tasks above the MPL are considered unacceptable and require engineering controls (e.g., redesign). Lifting tasks between the AL and the MPL require administrative controls (e.g., training, employer selection, and placement) or engineering controls. Lifting tasks below the AL represent a nominal risk to the workers.

To illustrate the analysis, assume a worker is lifting a 27-kg load from a skid onto a conveyor. The task is performed once each minute. The worker lifts for eight hours and is required to bend over. The job and lift dimensions, measured using a tape measure, are as follows:

W = 27 kg

D = 56 cm

H = 53 cm

V = 30 cm

F = 1 lift/min.

F_{max} = 12 from Table 10A.1

Solving the AL and MPL equations with these values:

$$AL = 40(15/53) (1\text{-}0.004 \, |30\text{-}75|) (0.7+7.5/56) (1\text{-}1/12)$$
$$= 40(0.28) (0.82) (0.83) (0.92)$$
$$= 7.0 \text{ kg (The term } |V\text{-}75| \text{ indicates an absolute value or a value that is always positive.)}$$

$$MPL - 3 \, AL = 3(7.0) - 21.0 \text{ kg}$$

The load weight of 27 kg is greater than the AL and the MPL; therefore, the task as noted is unacceptable and engineering controls will be necessary.

If the task is to be redesigned, an analysis of the lifting conditions shows the order of factors—from most to least effective—to be: *H*, *V*, *D*, and *F*. To improve the lifting task in the above example, the workstation can be redesigned by moving the worker closer to the load position (*H*); by presenting the load at a higher level (*V*); and by lifting the load a shorter distance (*D*).

If these revised values are

W = 27 kg

D = 25 cm

H = 30 cm

V = 80 cm

F = 1 lift/min.

F_{max} = 15 from Table 10A.1

then substituting these values into the lifting equations for AL and MPL shows:

$$AL = 40(15/30) (1\text{-}0.004|80\text{-}75|) (0.7 + 7.5/25) (1\text{-}1/15)$$
$$= 40(0.50) (0.98) (1.0) (0.94)$$
$$= 18.4 \text{ kg}$$

$$MPL = 3(18.4) = 55.2 \text{ kg}$$

Even with the redesign, the load weight is still greater than the AL but lower than the MPL. Some additional engineering controls may still be necessary (e.g., mechanical assists or reducing the load size). Administrative controls are also necessary (e.g., two-person lifting, work rotation, or weight training).

Previous studies (NIOSH, 1983) have shown that RSI frequency rates (injuries per hours on the job) and severity rates (hours lost per hours on the job) increase significantly when:

- Heavy objects are lifted (W is large).

- The object is bulky (H is large).

- Distances moved are large (D is large).

- Objects are lifted frequently (F is large).

Any control strategy should consider the variability and the effects of these factors. Lower-back discomfort and trauma are the usual results of improper lifting.

E X E R C I S E S

1. Select any lifting task at your workplace or simulate one at home. Using the NIOSH lifting equations (provided in the appendix), calculate the acceptability of the lift and recommend ways to make it less risky and more efficient.

2. A worker has to lift a package weighing approximately 16 kg onto a shelf that is 60 cm from where he is standing. He picks the load up from a point 30 cm from the floor; the final position on the shelf is 170 cm from the floor. The lift is repeated once each minute. Calculate the AL and the MPL, and determine the acceptability of the operation.

3. Determine the administrative controls available at your workplace for dealing with potential back problems or RSI.

4. Examine available literature and catalogues to determine how many methods and accessories are available to prevent Keyboard-related RSI. How many of these devices do you have in your own installation?

5. Using your study centre, draw a layout of the equipment and tools most often used. Then redesign the workstation using ergonomic principles.

References

Astrand, P.O., and K. Rodahl.1986. *Textbook in Work Psychology*, 3rd ed. New York: McGraw-Hill Book Company.

Canadian Standards Association. 1995. *Office Ergonomics* CSA Standard, CAN/CSA Z412-M89, section 5.

Dolan, S.L., and R.S. Schuler. 1994. *Human Resources Management: A Canadian Perspective*. Scarborough, Ont.: Nelson Canada.

Fournier, Suzanne.1988. "RSI and the Causality Issue. *At the Centre* (CCOSH) 11, no. 3: 8–9.

Grandjean, E. 1988. *Fitting the Task to the Man*, 4th ed. London, England: Taylor & Francis.

La Bar, G. 1994. "NIOSH Challenges Back Belt Use." *Occupational Hazards*. (September).

Laing, P., ed. 1992. *Accident Prevention Manual for Business and Industry: Engineering and Technology*. Washington, D.C.: National Safety Council.

Kroemer, K.H. 1988. "Ergonomics." In B.A. Plog, ed., *Fundamentals of Industrial Hygiene*, 3rd ed. Chicago, Ill.: National Safety Council.

McDonald H. 1995a. "To Regulate or Not to Regulate." *Accident Prevention* (January/February): 9–11.

McDonald, H. 1995b. "Know Thy Users." *Accident Prevention* (March/April):11–12.

National Institute of Occupational Safety and Health. 1983. *A Work Practices Guide for Manual Lifting: Technical Report 81–122*. Cincinnati, Ohio: U.S. Department of Health and Human Services.

Purdie, J. 1990. "Better Offices Means Greater Productivity." *The Financial Post*, November 26, 35.

Statistics Canada. 1994. *Work Injuries, 1990 to 1993*. (Ottawa: Labour Division, Statistics Canada, Minister of Supply and Services), Cat. No. 72-208.

Van Alphen, T. 1995. "New Epidemic in the Workplace—RSI: Pains, Strains and Computers." *The Toronto Star*, April 17, B1, B3.

Workers' Compensation Board of Ontario. 1992. Derived from the *Statistics Supplement to the 1992 Annual Report*, Toronto.

Occupational Stress

◆ ◆ ◆

11

INTRODUCTION

This chapter begins with a review of the concept of occupational stress and how it affects performance and health. It then examines sources of occupational stress and what organizations can do to minimize stress. The chapter concludes with discussions of burnout and trauma response and how organizations can deal with these problems.

◆ ◆ ◆

CONCEPTS AND DEFINITIONS

Health and safety issues related to occupational stress are probably the most difficult and complex issues facing employers, workers, and compensation boards. Provincial worker compensation boards, increasingly confronted with demands for compensation based on occupational stress, are beginning to develop policies for compensating workers' stress-related illnesses. The ramifications of this development are enormous, for occupational stress exists within every workplace and every job.

Occupational stress cannot be eliminated, but a major goal of industry should be to eradicate unwarranted occupational stress. Organizational stress that is ignored or improperly handled has serious health, safety, and "bottom line" consequences to workers and employers. Managers, health and safety professionals, and workers need to understand how occupational stress affects health and performance, and what can be done to avoid unnecessary problems.

Stress has many definitions, ranging from the simplistic and idiosyncratic to the complex and technical. The founder of stress research, Hans Selye, was able to define stress in terms of the following simple story:

> *A middle-aged man and woman walk down a dimly lit alleyway. A mugger jumps out of the shadows with a gun and says,*

---

*This chapter was written by Gerry Goldberg and Kim Ankers.

"Your money or your life." The man grabs his heart, gasps, and dies of a heart attack. [The woman subdues the assailant and calls the police.]

What kills the man is not the gun or the mugger (neither comes in physical contact with him) but rather the circumstances he finds himself in. We can start defining stress as a reaction to environmental demands, or "stressors."

◆ ◆ ◆
IDENTIFYING AND MANAGING STRESSORS

What is a stressor? Stressors range in complexity from simple biological stressors to psychological, interpersonal, and sociocultural stressors. All stressors are biological in that they evoke a general or nonspecific adaptive response of *fight or flight*. Simple *biological stressors* can include overly bright lighting, poor working postures, hot or cold environments, harmful gases, or noise. These stressors directly affect the biological function. *Psychological stressors* include fear, anger, boredom, anxiety, loneliness, isolation, loss of job, or insecurity.

Interpersonal stressors occur as a result of work, social, and/or family life. Some interpersonal stressors are also *sociocultural stressors*. These may come in two forms. The first is when a change in society results in wide-ranging cultural changes to which individuals must then adapt; the need for workers to adapt to new technologies is an example of this kind of stressor. The second form of sociocultural stressor results when an individual changes in relation to the rest of society. This may occur when an individual retires, is suddenly injured or disabled, gets married or divorced, or has a baby. Both forms of sociocultural stressors usually signal a broad range of other changes to which one must adapt on the sociocultural as well as interpersonal, psychological, and biological levels.

Hans Selye defines stress as "the non-specific response of the body to any demand placed upon it" (Selye, 1974). In other words, stress is the body's general response to any demand, be it biological, psychological, interpersonal or sociocultural. Selye rejected the view that stress is only a negative force. Stress, he stated, "is the spice of life." It results from the challenges of our everyday life, as well as the dangers.

The stress response is an adaptive response that enables us to meet the challenges of everyday life and to escape the dangers. Consider this example of the stress response in action. A mother sees that her young child is pinned by a heavy log. As a result of the stressor of danger to her child, her brain and hypothalamus send messages via nerve impulses to stimulate the sympathetic nerves and the pituitary. This causes a complex series of reactions that prepare the body for action. Adrenaline is released, blood flow increases (as does oxygen consumption), blood sugars are made available, the liver and spleen are activated, and the digestive system becomes inactive. All this occurs so that muscles can be maximally used to meet the challenge at hand. The mother is able to remove the log she would not previously have been able to lift.

Can we overadapt to stressors? While the stress response often is a very positive force in our lives, it can turn against the body. For the most part, the negative effects can be viewed as problems of overadaptation. Brady (1958) demonstrated how this might occur in a study known as "Ulcers in 'Executive' Monkeys."

The experiment involved placing eight pairs of monkeys under the influence of stressors. One pair at a time, the monkeys were confined to restraining chairs that allowed them to move their arms and legs but not to get out of the chair. Both received brief and mild but recurrent electrical shocks. One of the two monkeys, the "executive," had a lever that he had learned to press to avoid getting that shock. If that monkey pressed the lever very quickly, after a light went on, neither monkey would get the imminent shock. The control monkey had a lever in front of him but it was not connected.

After several days, the "executive" monkeys died of ulcers. The control monkeys had no signs of ulcers and appeared perfectly healthy at the completion of the study. (Unfortunately for them, autopsies were conducted to prove this point.) What killed the executive monkeys was not the shocks (the control monkeys had received identical shocks) but rather their own reaction, or overadaptation, to the situation. In other words, their adaptive responses led to their demise.

This study seems to indicate that responsibility or "executive responsibilities" may be the paramount harmful factor in the workplace. However, as will be discussed later in this chapter, it seems that responsibilities tend to be a major stressor only when there are insufficient means or "control" to meet them. The phenomenon of responsibility with insufficient control is more likely to occur with employees who are lower down on the organizational ladder.

How do we adapt to stressors? The ability to withstand stressors such as heavier workload or new technologies changes with time. When first confronted with a change or other new stressor, there might be some diminished ability to cope, but soon an *alarm* reaction occurs in which the body's coping skills and defensive forces are mobilized (i.e., the fight or flight reaction). This eventually evolves into the *resistance* stage in which coping skills and defensive forces are maximized to help the individual manage or adapt to the new stressors.

If the available coping mechanisms are sufficient to effectively meet the challenge of the new stressor, the person may eventually have little difficulty coping with the new situation. However, if his or her coping mechanisms are insufficient the stressors persist, eventually a stage of *exhaustion* is reached. As an individual progresses toward this last stage, performance and health are in increasing jeopardy.

This three-stage reaction to stressors is influenced by the amount and severity of the stressors, as well as by the number of coping skills and defensive forces one has available. In the case of the executive monkey versus the control, whatever the control monkey's early ability to resist, the executive's would be less, simply because there was the extra demand of responsibility placed upon it. The executive monkey would also achieve a lower level of resistance and more quickly become exhausted because of the extra load placed upon it.

In other words, managing stressors is very much like a juggling act. We are all engaged in juggling stressors or life demands. At any given time, an individual might be fighting with his or her spouse, taking on new social responsibilities, suffering from mild chronic back pain, planning a vacation, and adjusting to a new financial situation. Any individual, at any point in time, has the capacity to juggle a finite number of stressors. People need some stressors or challenges in their life in order to be happy and healthy, to get their "creative juices" going. But each individual's capacity to handle stressors varies depending on such factors as personality, age, years of experience, and health.

As well, an individual's capacity to cope may change over time. For each individual at a given point in time, there are a finite number of stressors that can be well handled. When that amount is exceeded—when, for example, one develops insomnia as a result of financial problems—then there is likely to be a strain on one's ability to cope.

Eventually this strain may result in "fumbling the balls" (e.g., allowing a minor difference of opinion to explode into a major argument). The strain may result in a breakdown in the juggling machine itself. An illness may occur or the lower-back ache that has existed for years may suddenly become too hard to deal with, so one calls in sick for work.

Can adapting to the workplace make us sick? The relationship between occupational stress and health complaints has been demonstrated in recent years. In the case of health complaints resulting from the introduction of video-display technologies, the evidence suggests that most health complaints (e.g., eyestrain, sore muscles, and emotional fatigue) are the result not just of using the technology but of experiencing its impact upon all aspects of the operator's life. New technologies bring change to both office and home. One study found only a .19 correlation between the number of hours of VDT use and health complaints of operators. This means that workers who use the new technology many hours per day have only slightly more health complaints than workers who rarely use it.

The relationship between health and the number and nature of life's demands was first studied by Holmes and Rahe (1967). They found that the more major changes or life events people experience within a given period, the greater the probability they will become ill. (Some theorists attribute this to the fact that such changes are disruptive to daily living routines.) The life events they examined included death of a spouse, retirement, change in financial state, planning a vacation, and minor violations of the law. While they that found some events were more predictive of future illness than others, none was sufficient by itself to lead to sickness.

It should be noted that stressors and changes don't have to be perceived as negative to have a negative effect. Christmas, vacations, marriage, and the introduction of new equipment into the office can all be viewed in positive terms but still add to the stress load.

In what ways can occupational stress affect health? How stress affects individuals will vary according to genetic predispositions and lifestyle, as well as social and cultural factors. A study involving more than 2000 management and professional people in a single Canadian organization identified five basic stress-symptom patterns experienced by workers under excessive stress (Howard, Cunningham, and Rechnitzer, 1978). Each of these patterns comprise a number of symptoms. *Emotional distress* may include insomnia, fatigue, loss of appetite, moodiness, and depression. *Medication use* includes taking anything to improve the negative internal feeling—tranquillizers, sleeping pills, diet pills, pain relievers, even vitamin pills. (Midnight nibbling and overeating also belong in this category.) *Cardiovascular symptoms* include high blood pressure and heart disease, while *gastrointestinal symptoms* include ulcers, colitis, diarrhea, and nausea. The last identified pattern, *allergy-respiratory symptoms*, includes allergies and hay fever.

Symptom patterns vary from population to population in a manner that demonstrates the role played by social and cultural influences on these stress outcomes. Some populations suffer more from gastrointestinal and cardiovascular disorders (possibly due to efforts to repress visible displays of symptoms), whereas others react to stress in more visible ways (e.g., emotional distress and medication use). Stress-related symptoms are thus at least partly determined by learned ways of adapting (or overadapting) to stressors. Stress can stimulate behaviours that are aimed at reducing stress but that are actually maladaptive (e.g., smoking, excessive drinking, abusive behaviour) and may only aggravate the condition.

◆ ◆ ◆
PREVENTION OF OCCUPATIONAL STRESS

The manifestation of stress-related symptoms can be determined by specific environmental and organizational stressors, as well as by biological and sociocultural disposition. The field of ergonomics has been developed to help identify stressors in the workplace and eliminate or minimize them where possible.

STRESS AND PERFORMANCE

Can there be too much or too little stress? The ergonomic approach to stress management involves asking the question, "Are you under the right amount of stress?" If you are under too little stress (i.e., don't have enough challenge in your job or life), you may be rusting out (Howard et al., 1979). According to a famous cartoonist, "The difference between a rut and the grave is only the depth." On the other hand, if there are too many challenges or aggravations in your life, you might find yourself heading into an exhaustion stage.

Is there an optimal level of stress? The relationship between levels of stress and performance is well documented. People vary in their ability and need to handle stress, and individuals vary at different points in their lives. However, studies of performance under increasing levels of stress consistently demonstrate an inverted U-shaped performance function. Performance tends to increase from low to moderate stress and then decrease as levels of stress continue to increase. Performance may refer to work, athletic, social or sexual performance, or performance in terms of maintaining health. While the point at which performance changes varies according to an individual's ability to cope and the task involved, the inverted U-shaped function tends to be demonstrated for nearly all measures of performance.

Under low stress, when one is understimulated and the creative juices are not flowing, boredom, fatigue, frustration, and dissatisfaction tend to be experienced. Performance can become sluggish; individuals may daydream or even doze off while on the job. There is time and energy available to notice little aches or pains, and to worry about them. Small issues such as interpersonal or procedural issues at work may take on extra significance in the mind of the understimulated worker.

It seems that when people don't have enough aggravation, they will seek it out or create it. An understimulated person not only performs poorly but notices every physical symptom, perhaps even inadvertently manifests symptoms in order to make life challenging. They are also likely to be involved in creating stress for others, hence office backstabbing. Captains of seafaring vessels knew this and created work to prevent crews from becoming mutinous.

Increasing stress or challenges, on or off the job, is often accompanied by increased performance and creativity as individuals reach optimum stimulation. With optimal stress, there is also better problem solving and greater self-satisfaction. Once this level is exceeded, however, and there are too many "balls to juggle" (i.e., too much stress), then performance declines. There is often irrational problem solving as one begins to "fumble the balls." Exhaustion, illness, and low self-esteem may appear as the individual becomes preoccupied with the decline in his or her performance.

A stress-management program would require the individual to examine the situation, not just the performance, and come up with a game plan to get things done effectively. This would include creating a list of items to be dealt with and then setting priorities. Prioritizing is simply saying, "I will put down some of the balls for now to move back into the optimum stimulation zone and get the most accomplished." One can then tackle the immediate challenges first and take on only the amount that will ensure effective or high performance.

Stress management is a means of obtaining the highest levels of performance and well-being. It is not necessarily a way to reduce workloads; rather its goals may be viewed as a means to maximizing performance, health, and safety. With these goals in mind, many workplaces have instituted regular performance evaluation programs in which supervisors and workers routinely review performance, identify problems and needs, and set mutually agreed-upon goals.

IDENTIFYING AND DEALING WITH SOURCES OF OCCUPATIONAL STRESS

Assessing the total stress or total number of stressors a worker confronts within the workplace calls for a systematic approach for identifying the sources of stress. C.L. Cooper and his co-workers were among the first to provide such a systematic approach by identifying and categorizing occupational stressors by general sources.

Occupational stressors can be classified as being either *intrinsic* or *extrinsic*. Intrinsic stressors are intrinsic to the job or job tasks, and can include work overload or underload, time pressures, a badly designed workstation, and noisy, hot, crowded, or isolated work environments. These stressors can reach substantial levels before they adversely affect behaviour or health. People appear to be more willing, or able, to adapt to intrinsic stressors or challenges than to most other common organizational stressors.

Extrinsic stressors are associated with a job but not a direct function of the job tasks. These stressors, which can very quickly lead to health, safety, and performance problems, have to do with an employee's role in the organization and career development, organizational structure and climate, relations within the organization and organizational interface with the outside (Cooper et al., 1983, Glowinkowski and Cooper, 1985). Workers' personality characteristics and behavioural patterns may also create a number of stressors, especially when there is a poor fit between the characteristics of a job and a worker.

The stressor of "responsibility with insufficient control" (discussed earlier in the chapter) underlies many other stressors. In the mid-1970s, the concept of "executive" responsibility as a cause of stress-related problems came under question. As stress-related problems like illnesses, absenteeism, and low morale within organizations came under greater scrutiny, it became apparent that these problems were more prevalent among lower-level employees.

An explanation for this phenomenon that has gained wide acceptance is that responsibility alone does not cause problems. Rather the problem is responsibility without sufficient control (i.e., authority, time, and resources) to do what is required. In the executive monkey study, the executive had the responsibility but at the same time very little control over the situation. By contrast, persons on the top of the organizational ladder have responsibility but also exercise substantial control. When executive responsibilities are delegated down the organizational ladder, there may be a failure to provide sufficient control in the form of information, time, equipment, and authority to enable lower-level employees meet these responsibilities. The probability and degree of insufficient control increases each time responsibilities are delegated.

SOURCES OF OCCUPATIONAL STRESS

Role in the organization. Much occupational stress derives from the fact that job responsibilities are not clearly defined or are in conflict with each other. Police and government inspectors, for example, are often faced with role conflict. When they are confronted with violations of laws and regulations, they must decide whether to act as an enforcer or as a resource person who provides appropriate information and services to ensure conformity in the future. Unions are arguing today that medical doctors, employed by an organization to conduct medical surveillance of hazardous substances, may find themselves in such conflict.

Lack of participation in the decision-making process is another major source of occupational stress. Failure to include the worker in decisions relating to how his or her job is to be done is not only stressful for the employee but is also a waste of a good source of information on how a job may be best designed. This problem is more likely to occur as organizations increase in size. The larger the organization, the more likely it is that the employee will not have contact with the designer of his or her job.

Within organizations that have adopted the Japanese style of management, workers are considered important sources of information regarding their jobs. They are consulted for their views as to what procedures, policies, and equipment should be included, changed, or eliminated to achieve more productive, healthier and safer, and less stressful work. This participation is often cited as a major factor in the growth of Japan's economy.

Career development. Lack of job security usually means that persons uncertain about their incomes are also uncertain about many other things like feeding their children or buying a new car. Each of these consequent uncertainties is a potential source of stress. Workers who do not get promoted may experience stress in the form of resentment and feel understimulated in their work. Those who are promoted may find themselves confronted with more demands than they can handle. They may also find that, as a result of the promotion, their social support system at work may no longer be available to them, particularly if they are supervising their former co-workers.

Relations within the organization. Poor relations with a supervisor, colleagues, or subordinates are generally accompanied by a breakdown in communication, formal as well as informal. This situation can shut off an employee's access to the kind of information he or she needs to stay on top of the job and its changing demands, resulting in responsibility with diminished control and consequent stress.

Organizational structure and climate. Organizational structure and climate can be the source of several occupational stressors. When workers are deprived of the opportunity to explore work-related (or nonwork-related) issues with others within the organization, their ability to develop practical skills for dealing with stress is compromised, and they experience the additional stressor of social isolation.

Stress is also created when workers perceive themselves to be unnecessarily restricted in their behaviour (e.g., restricted washroom times, ridgework procedures, dress codes). Energy-wasting emotions such as resentment are almost guaranteed under such circumstances. Office politics, backstabbing, and gossip may be the byproduct of this resentment.

Organizational interface with the outside. This refers to the degree to which a worker's employment and lifestyle, including family and social/personal life, are compatible. For example, devoting too much time and energy to work can lessen a worker's ability to meet family demands. Dual-career families can mean that spouses rarely see each other. Shift work can mean that a couple sleep in the same bed but rarely at the same time; especially when both partners are on rotational shift work.

Characteristics of workers and jobs. Another potential source of stress on the job is the workers themselves. Lifestyle, personality, and reactions to environmental stressors all influence a worker's level of stress. Not all individuals are suited to all jobs. Psychological tests are being increasingly used to ensure that the right worker is selected for the right job. Characteristics such as tolerance for ambiguity, motivation, and behavioural patterns may interact with work to create stressors. The Type "A" personality, for example, tries to do everything all at once, while maintaining a sense of hostility or cynicism. According to numerous studies, this sort of behaviour places an individual at greater risk of cardiovascular disease.

PROTECTING THE WORKER AND ORGANIZATION

Who's liable for stress on the job? Courts and tribunals are increasingly holding companies liable for stress on the job (Ivancevich, Matteson, and Richards, 1985). In 1994, the Prince Edward Island Supreme Court ruled that stress in the workplace should be considered an accident and thus covered by workers' compensation. The courts have increasingly been siding with workers against companies that fail to deal with occupational stress. By monitoring, diagnosing, and treating a stressful situation (and documenting these activities), companies and medical staff help ensure a healthy and safe workplace and at the same time protect themselves from liability.

Some observers contend that, to avoid stress, an employer need only ensure that the person hired for a job is well suited to it. While hiring the right person for the job is important, organizations have found that this is not enough. In the fight against occupational stress, workers and organizations benefit from diverse stress/wellness programs, employee assistance programs (EAPs), ergonomic programs, and programs designed to increase worker involvement and input.

Stress/wellness-management programs can include physical fitness routines, nutritional guidance, and teaching of specific stress-management techniques. Employee assistance programs deal with a broad range of work, personal, family, financial, and social problems (Berridge and Cooper, 1993; Goldberg et al., 1989; Goldberg and Klaas, 1992; Lawton, 1988). (See Chapter 14 for a discussion of these programs.)

Ergonomic programs focus on effective work place and job design as a means of reducing or eliminating unnecessary occupational stress. The stimulation of worker involvement and input is the goal of work life circles and performance evaluations.

◆ ◆ ◆
DEPRESSION AND BURNOUT

Depression is the most common psychological affliction of workers. Six to ten percent of any given workforce suffers from depression. Depression in the workplace costs the Canadian economy billions of dollars a year. Over 75 percent of the total costs of depression to society are not direct treatment costs but rather costs associated with lost productivity. In the United Kingdom, mental illnesses, including depression, account for 61 percent of work absences; further, the rate of job turnover is twice as high for employees affected by depression (Jansen, 1986).

Depression and the drugs used to treat it can result in increased accidents, illnesses, and suicides. When people are depressed, they are at high risk of accident and injury (U.S. National Safety Council, 1985). Symptoms of depression such as drowsiness and anxiety make workers susceptible to costly errors. Guidelines for supervisors have been developed in order to assist supervisors in identifying and managing depression (Goldberg, 1992).

Burnout can be defined as a depression-related syndrome characterized by emotional exhaustion, depersonalization, and reduced personal accomplishment. Pines (1993) describes burnout as the result of a failure in the existential search for meaning. Burnout most frequently occurs among individuals within the helping professions.

Burisch (1993) proposed six core symptoms of burnout: hyper- or hypoactivity; feelings of helplessness and exhaustion; inner unrest; reduced self-esteem and demoralization; deterioration of social relationships; and active striving to bring about a change. Certain personality characteristics predispose individuals to burnout (Cooper, Kirkcaldy, and Brown, 1994). Dentists who are anxiety-prone and emotionally unstable are among those individuals who are at greater risk of burnout (Cooper et al., 1988; Cooper, Mallinger, and Kahn, 1978).

Individuals who have emotionally taxing work, a client-centred orientation, and unusually high sensitivity to others are particularly susceptible to burnout. This condition has also been linked with specific work stressors like role ambiguity and role overload. One study of preschool teachers found burnout to be related to excessive numbers of students and too little structure. Reducing the teacher–student ratios and inducing management to impose more structure on daily operations brought about a decline in burnout. Other approaches to dealing with burnout include general stress-management techniques and cognitive training (e.g., helping workers to view burnout as a reaction to circumstances rather than a personal failure. Pines and Aronson (1981) have developed burnout workshops for a spectrum of workplaces. There are also specific programs for individual professions, such as the "Dentist-at-Risk Program" sponsored by the Ontario Dental Association.

◆ ◆ ◆
RESPONSE TO TRAUMA

Traumatic events are those events that will tend to overwhelm an individual's coping mechanisms. Physical assaults, threats of violence, disasters, serious accidents, near misses, robberies, and kidnapping are all examples of traumatic events. Less dramatic but also traumatic are layoffs, relocations, and reorganizations.

Traumatic events tend to shake people's feelings that they are in control of their fate. Often accompanying these events are vivid mental images that produce in the individual a (usually unjustified) sense that the event will occur again. These images, coupled with the loss of security, increase stress levels and can lead to a broad range of physical, emotional, cognitive, and behavioural reactions. These reactions can be similar to those that occur during the grieving process, where one might go through the emotional stages of denial, anger, depression, bargaining, and acceptance. Traumatic events may lead to severe short- and long-term effects including depression, suicide, substance abuse, family abuse, and post-traumatic stress disorder.

Many workplaces are either extending their employee assistance program to deal with trauma or hiring trauma-response professionals. Assistance may involve the development of organizational policies and plans, employee education and post-trauma debriefing and follow-up counselling (Choy and DeBosset, 1992). Policies and plans can include assignment of responsibilities, a checklist of duties for managers (including notification of the trauma-response professionals), and a designated safe meeting place for employees.

Both proactive education and post-traumatic counselling should provide staff with an understanding of organizational policies regarding trauma as well as an awareness of what constitutes normal and expected reactions (physical, emotional, cognitive, and behavioural) to trauma. Instructions for managing traumatic stress and a list of professionals to contact in emergencies should also be provided.

Organizations affected by downsizing, organizational reorganization, and job relocation can assist staff by providing counselling and practical help (Fame and Shehan, 1994). For example, the relocation may be facilitated by ensuring that the employee is fully informal about the new location, and by offering assistance in the selling and purchasing of a home.

◆ ◆ ◆
SUMMARY

This chapter has defined occupational stress and identified its major sources. Adapting to stress, both positive and negative, can have long-term health effects. As organizations attempt to determine optimum stress levels, individuals must understand the role of work factors in causing stress. Depression and burnout are conditions related to stress.

EXERCISES

1. Using the categories provided in this chapter, identify the various stressors facing students. What actions might be taken to alleviate these stressors?

2. People who are dissatisfied with their job or organization often state they would be less stressed if they quit and worked for themselves. Using the perspective provided in this chapter, explain why this is—or is not—a valid assumption.

3. Responsibility with insufficient control underlies many occupational stressors. List the many ways in which this phenomenon may occur within a workplace.

References

Berridge, J., and C.L. Cooper. 1993. "Stress and Coping in US Organizations: The Role of the Employee Assistance Programme." *Work and Stress* 7, no. 1: 89–102.

Brady, J.V. 1958. "Ulcers in 'Executive' Monkeys." *Scientific American* 199, no. 4.

Burisch, M. 1993. "In Search of Theory: Some Ruminations on the Nature and Etiology of Burnout." In W.B. Schaufeli et al., eds., *Professional Burnout: Recent Developments in Theory and Research.* Washington, D.C.: Taylor and Francis.

Choy, T., and F. DeBosset. 1992. "Post-traumatic Stress Disorder: An Overview." *Canadian Journal of Psychiatry* 37: 578–81.

Cooper, C.L., B.D. Kirkcaldy, and J. Brown. 1994. "A Model of Job Stress and Physical Health: The Role of Individual Differences." *Personality and Individual Differences* 16, no. 4: 653–55.

Cooper, C.L., M. Mallinger, and R. Kahn. 1978. "Identifying Sources of Occupational Stress among Dentists." *Journal of Occupational Psychology* 51: 227–37.

Cooper, C.L., J. Watts, A.J. Baglioni Jr., and M. Kelly. 1983. "Occupational Stress amongst General Practice Dentists." *Journal of Occupational Psychology* 61: 163–74.

Fame, M.W., and C.L. Shehan. 1994. "Work and Well-Being in the Two-Person Career: Relocation Stress and Coping among Clergy Husbands and Wives." *Family Relations* 43: 196–205.

Glowinkowski, S.P., and C.L. Cooper. 1985. "Current Issues in Organizational Stress Research. *Bulletin of the British Psychological Society* 38: 212–16.

Goldberg, G. 1992. "Identification and Management of Depression in the Workplace." *Occupational Health in Ontario*. Ontario Ministry of Labour, 13-1, 16–32.

Goldberg, G.E., S. Guirguis, D.L. Leong, and P.L. Pelmear. 1989. "Dealing with Alcohol and Drug Abuse within the Workplace. *Occupational Health in Ontario* 10, no. 2: 83–99.

Goldberg, G.E., and P. Klaas. 1992. "Identification and Management of Depression in the Workplace." *Occupational Health in Ontario* 13, no. 2: 16–32.

Holmes, T.H., and R.H. Rahe. 1967. "The Social Readjustment Rating Scale."

Journal of Psychosomatic Research 11: 213–18.

Howard, J., D. Cunningham, and P. Rechnitzer 1978. *Rusting Out, Burning Out, Bowing Out: Stress and Survival on the Job.* Toronto: Financial Post Books, Maclean-Hunter Ltd.

Ivancevich, J.M., T. Matteson, and E.P. Richards. 1985. "Who's Liable for Stress on the Job?" *Harvard Business Review,* March-April: 60–65.

Jansen, M.A. 1986. "Emotional Disorders and the Labour Force." *International Labour Review* 125, no. 4. (September–October).

Lawton, B. 1988. "The EAP and Workplace Psychiatric Injury."

Occupational Medicine: State of the Art Reviews, no. 4: 695–706.

Pines, A.M. 1993. "Burnout: An Existential Perspective." In W.B. Schaufeli et al., eds., *Professional Burnout: Recent Developments in Theory and Research.* Washington, D.C.: Taylor and Francis.

Selye, H. 1974. *Stress Without Distress.* Scarborough, Ont.: New American Library of Canada.

U.S. National Safety Council. 1985. "Depression Quietly Contributes to Industry Costs and Injuries." November–December, Chicago.

12

Sector Analysis

◆◆◆

INTRODUCTION

D ifferent industries and businesses exhibit different health and safety conditions and problems, although, of course, there is a fair degree of overlap. Before turning our attention to the hazards and control mechanisms associated with specific industry groups, we will examine some of the hazardous conditions to be found in the office environment.

◆◆◆

OFFICES

Since 1980, almost half of the employees in Canada and the United States have worked in an office environment (WCB, 1992). At the beginning of the Industrial Revolution, the office consisted of nothing more than a desk, a stool, poor lighting (possibly a candle or an oil lamp), a pen, and a clerk. The typewriter revolutionized the office by allowing a single person to create and record information in a shorter period of time. The introduction of the electric typewriter allowed for even greater efficiency, and individual skills became much improved. Today's computers enable workers to perform tasks even more efficiently.

Many of us do not consider the office to be a particularly hazardous environment. Nevertheless, the office is probably one of the more dangerous locations within an organization. Hazard identification and control is highly developed in work environments such as factories. Such is not the case with offices, which *appear* to be safe and hence not obvious candidates for intensive health and safety measures.

ERGONOMICS

The office workstation is the source of many health problems. Improper positioning of the visual-display terminal (VDT) and improper design of the desk and the rest of the workstation can lead to such problems as eyestrain, sore shoulders, lower-back pain, and wrist discomfort. Thus ergonomic considerations are critical when creating a healthy office environment (CSA, 1989). Figure 12.1 illustrates the various dimensional requirements for effective operator performance.

ILLUMINATION

Most high-rise offices have architecturally installed rows of fluorescent luminaires that usually provide too much general lighting (CSA, 1990). Task lighting, particularly for those working with computer terminals, is necessary. Task-specific lighting is designed to reduce or eliminate screen glare and reflections. Because the computer screen provides its own lights, only document illumination should be necessary. Computer terminals should not be located near windows, due to the same glare conditions.

AIR QUALITY

Heating, ventilating, and air-conditioning (HVAC) standards require that up to 40 percent fresh air be provided, and at least 40 percent relative humidity. Increased fresh air and humidification will, in fact, reduce heating costs in cold weather as well as improve the air quality. Most building managers don't believe this, however, and attempt to conserve energy by reducing fresh air and humidity. One way to determine if your office is in the "conserve energy" mode is to watch for dry, sore throats and the electric spark that occurs each time a metal door handle is touched.

One consequence of the "conserve energy" attitude is sick-building syndrome. This syndrome is created when the recirculation of indoor air causes the level of airborne contaminants to increase. Air contaminants can include ozone from copiers, formaldehyde from improperly cured resins used in furniture, carbon monoxide from smoking and vehicle exhaust, carbon dioxide from the workers, dust such as fibreglass, and organic chemicals found in solvents and cleaning fluids. The micro-organism known as *micropolyspora faeni* causes humidifier fever, a condition sometimes found in sick buildings. Figure 12.2 shows some pollutants typically found in offices.

CONTROL OF OFFICE HAZARDS

Organizations can control office hazards by providing properly designed furniture that fits the worker and the task; by maintaining good air circulation

FIGURE 12.1 VDT Work Station

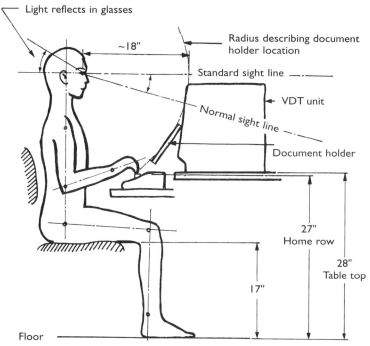

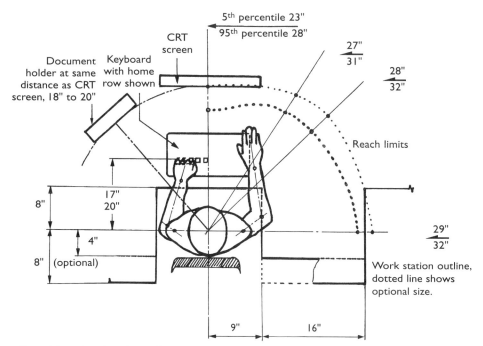

General dimensions based on anthropometric standard reach data for 5th and 95th percentiles (left hand opposite).

FIGURE 12.2 Air Pollution in the Office Building

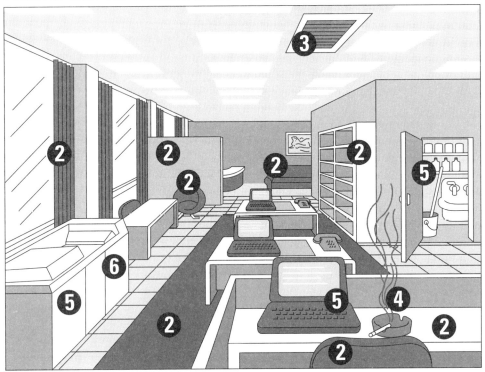

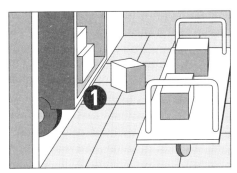

1. **CARBON MONOXIDE**
   Garages, motor vehicles, loading docks

2. **FORMALDEHYDE**
   Glues, partitions, carpet, drapery fabric, particleboard furniture, upholstery fabric

3. **BIOLOGICAL AGENTS**
   Humidifiers, air conditioners, dehumidifiers, washrooms, ventilation pipes and ducts

4. **TOBACCO SMOKE**
   Cigarettes, cigars, pipes

5. **VOLATILE ORGANIC COMPOUNDS**
   Felt-tip markers and pens, cleaning compounds, paint, copy machines, solvents

6. **OZONE**
   Copy machines

Source: Reprinted from "Indoor Air Pollution in the Office," copyright 1993, by the American Lung Association. Reproduced with permission.

and conditioning; by providing proper levels and types of lighting; and, finally, by installing exhaust systems that eliminate the toxic discharges from office machines.

◆ ◆ ◆
HOSPITALS

While some health and safety problems found in hospitals are unique (e.g., bacterial exposure), others are typical of all industries (e.g., lifting). The sections that follow will concentrate on the former types of problems.

CENTRAL SUPPLY

This department handles all of the materials coming into the hospital, and, in many cases, all of the materials leaving the facility. Dermatitis, infection, cuts, burns, and back strains are some of the hazards present.

TABLE 12.1 HAZARDS IN CENTRAL SUPPLY	
Ethylene oxide for sterilization	Noise
Flammable gases	Soaps and detergents
Infection	Mercury
Strains from lifting	Burns from steam
Cuts from equipment	

FOOD SERVICE

The food preparation sections of a hospital have many of the hazards found in most kitchens. Because cleanliness and sterility are paramount, a great deal of water and detergents are used on the floors. This can result in slippery walking surfaces.

Improper use of kitchen equipment can result in possible physical injuries. Electrical equipment such as mixers and slicers can cause shocks if they become defective through use, or if workers operate them in a wet environment. Fires from grease deposits and the chemical agents used to clean those deposits are two other potential hazards.

TABLE 12.2 HAZARDS IN FOOD SERVICES

Slips or falls on wet floors	Soaps, detergents
Tools, machinery	Caustic solutions
Sharp equipment	Oven cleaners
Noise	Ammonia
Microwave ovens	Solvents
Burns from stoves	Drain cleaners
Strains from lifting	Disinfectants
Heat stress	Pesticides
Electrical shock	Chlorinated cleaners

HOUSEKEEPING

The staff from this department circulate throughout the hospital. This means that they are exposed to all hazards that are present in the hospital.

TABLE 12.3 HAZARDS IN HOUSEKEEPING

Soaps and detergents	Climbing and lifting
Falls and slips	Cuts and punctures
Infection	Electrical shock, burns
Solvents	Cleaners and disinfectants

LAUNDRY

Laundry workers come in contact with a wide variety of infections and diseases. Sources of the contaminants include not only soiled fabrics but also needles, broken glass, or razor blades that may have been discarded with the laundry. Heat stress is a serious concern for workers in this area because of the high temperature and humidity created by the washing machines; this heat condition is aggravated in the summer.

TABLE 12.4 HAZARDS PRESENTS IN LAUNDRIES

Slips on wet floors	Detergents, bleaches, and soaps
Lifting	Noise
Heat stress	Cuts and punctures
Infections	

MAINTENANCE AND ENGINEERING

The specialists in this department keep the operational equipment running. These workers can come in indirect contact with many diseases and infections. Drain pipes from laboratories or treatment areas can contain dangerous levels of contaminant residue. The staff must be knowledgeable about the toxic properties of all of the materials used in the facility.

TABLE 12.5 HAZARDS IN MAINTENANCE AND ENGINEERING	
Lifting	Noise
Falls	Machinery
Welding fumes	Asbestos insulation
Drain cleaners	Solvents
Sewage	Ammonia
Pesticides	Flammable liquids

PATIENT-CARE AREAS

Nursing and medical services—the backbone of all health-care operations—fall into this category. The staff must take special care to avoid unnecessary exposure to infections or diseases. However, as discussed in Chapter 2 under the topic of work refused, a nurse is not permitted to refuse work that is "a normal condition" of his or her job.

An emerging issue (discussed at length in Chapter 15) is workplace violence. A survey by the Quebec Federation of Nurses revealed that 68 percent of its 45,000 members have been victims of physical violence in the workplace, ranging from a slaps to jaw-breaking punches (Picard, 1995). Nurses are particularly concerned with the insidious normalization that surrounds violence against nurses. This normalization hinges on the belief that it is "normal" for patients to take out their frustrations on nursing staff.

TABLE 12.6 HAZARDS IN PATIENT-CARE AREAS	
Lifting	Infection
Cuts and punctures	Slips and falls
Stress	Electrical shock and burns
Patient violence	

PHARMACY

This department is responsible for providing all of the drugs and dispensing devices (e.g., needles), and for disposing of broken glass (e.g., from mercury thermometers), and for providing the strict security that the presence of prescription drugs necessitate. Proper exhaust systems must be in place to remove any airborne toxic material.

TABLE 12.7 HAZARDS IN PHARMACIES	
Slips and falls	Pharmaceuticals
Mercury	Cuts and punctures

LABORATORIES AND RADIOLOGY

Hospital laboratories deal with more chemicals and infectious agents on a day-to-day basis than any one other department in the hospital. The toxic effects of various materials can be controlled easily with properly operating exhaust hoods, personal protective equipment, and security. (Security is required to keep unauthorized people out and to control dangerous drugs.) Food and drink must never be consumed within the laboratory proper.

CAT scan equipment and cobalt systems for radiation therapy are among the other potential hazards. Most of the radiation problems occur with ionizing radiation and scatter from equipment that may be old or improperly maintained.

TABLE 12.8 LABORATORIES AND RADIOLOGY	
Toxic chemicals	Toxic solvents
Cryogenic systems	Hazardous waste
Carcinogens	Infections and diseases
Cuts and punctures	Slips and falls
Electrical shock and burns	Lifting
Radiation (ionizing and nonionizing)	

SURGICAL FACILITIES

The operating theatres are restricted to authorized persons and must be maintained as sterile as possible. Compressed gases such as oxygen and anesthetic gas, which are delivered via lines from a central supply, are generally flammable and must be continually monitored for leaks. All of the electrical equipment in the theatre must be explosion-proof, and the floors must be made from electrically conductive material. Clothing must not produce a static charge. Segregated facilities must be provided for the disposal of general waste, sharps (needles), and biological waste.

TABLE 12.9 HAZARDS IN SURGICAL FACILITIES	
Antiseptics	Anesthetics and compressed gases
Infection	Sterilizing gases
Stress	Lifting
Electrical shock, burns, and fire	Sharps

◆ ◆ ◆
AUTOMOBILE MANUFACTURING

The automobile manufacturing industry uses virtually every manufacturing technique known in general industry. As the following sections will demonstrate, technological changes have introduced new hazards in this industry.

PARTS AND COMPONENTS

The engine and driveline components, wiring harness and accessories, trim, and wheels fall in this group. The materials involved include steel, plastics, aluminum, white metal, and rubber, the hazards of which are listed in Table 12.10.

TABLE 12.10 HAZARDS IN PARTS AND COMPONENTS	
Noise	Cuts and strains
Airborne contaminants	Burns
Toxic materials	Lifting
Heat	Amputations
Boredom	Traffic (fork trucks)
Stress	Dermatitis
RSI	Solvents and coatings
Welding and metal finish toxic materials (solder)	

BODY-IN-WHITE

The term "body-in-white" is used to describe the complete assembly of the auto body prior to painting. The processes involved include spot welding, arc welding, MIG or TIG, soldering, and metal finishing to produce a smooth and nondistorted surface for painting.

The complete assembly and spot welding of the body is now a completely automated process. Gigantic, rigid assembly jigs are used to align and weld the body. Dimensional accuracy is performed automatically using lasers and computer systems. Human access to any of these areas during operation is prevented by a series of lockouts that shut down the robot if they are tripped. Audible alarms work in conjunction with the lockouts.

TABLE 12.11 HAZARDS IN BODY-IN-WHITE

Cuts	Electrical shock and burns
Solder (lead)	Nonionizing radiation
Paint and solvents	Crushing
Muscle strains, RSI	Welding fumes
Dermatitis	Falls
Head, eye, and foot injuries	Bimetal barrier materials
Metal dust (including heavy metals)	

PAINTING

A multistage system for painting and finishing is used. Unlike the luxury European vehicles that boast hand-rubbed finishes, today's production cars are finished to eliminate rust potential and provide a bright, shiny appearance that will endure.

After the body is complete in white with bimetal protection, it goes through a series of immersion baths to clean and electrostatically prime all surfaces, both internally and externally. The trade refers to these baths as "the sheep dip." After the body emerges from the final prime application, it passes through a tunnel oven to dry prior to finish colour. The finish colour, or primary colour if the vehicle is to be two-colour, is sprayed onto the body in a long, water-wash paint booth. The paint spray guns are electrostatic (i.e., the car body carries a negative electric charge, while the spray gun and paint has a high positive voltage with insignificant current) so that the paint spray fan is attracted to the surface and is applied evenly over the complete body's exterior and interior. The water-wash booth removes any airborne contaminant that misses or oversprays the body by trapping it in a wall of cascading water.

After the finish coat is baked in a long tunnel oven using infrared heaters, the car body is sidetracked for masking (and the application of a second colour if required) and then allowed to proceed to the clear top-coat application, which gives the car its showroom appearance. The paint finish is inspected for imperfections that may require spot repair before continuing to final assembly.

TABLE 12.12 HAZARDS IN PAINTING	
Electrostatic equipment	Solvents
Paint mist	Infrared radiation
Burns	Heat stress
Cleaning acids	Toxic materials
Bumps and bruises	Cuts
Respiratory hazards	Eye injuries

FINAL ASSEMBLY

Often referred to as the trim line, chassis line, or final line, this area takes the auto body from the paint shop and adds all the bits and pieces (e.g., mouldings, engine and drive line, instrument panel, wiring and accessories, and wheels) needed to produce the final product.

Older plants that were more than one story high had many holes in the floors to allow the various assemblies to "drop," thereby facilitating their construction. Pits in the floors along some sections of the assembly line to permitted workers to perform tasks without bending over. Rarely were these pits in the right location. One could move assembly operations to suit the product, but one could not move a pit. This arrangement resulted in a number of workers falling or striking their heads on overhead car bodies.

Modern plants elevate the car body as required when work has to be done on the underside of the vehicle. Additionally, the total process is "staffed" by robots that do many of the repetitive tasks.

◆ ◆ ◆
CONSTRUCTION INDUSTRY

The construction industry is generally considered one of the most hazardous. It is commonplace to see construction workers forgo safety glasses when

TABLE 12.13 HAZARDS IN FINAL ASSEMBLY

Noise	Heat stress
Cuts and bruises	Toxic materials
Welding fumes	Flammable materials
Shocks and burns	Jammed between injuries
Falls	Back injuries
Head, eye, and hand injuries	

grinding or sawing, or hearing protection when engaged in high-noise operations such as those involving use of a jack hammer. WCB assessment rates reflect the level of risk and general performance associated with this industry group.

Construction projects run the gamut from a residential deck to a hydro dam to an office tower. Equipment needs can range from an electric saw to a backhoe to a 400-ton crane. With respect to injuries and hazards, a finger or hand is easily lost to a piece of moving machinery, and many toxic materials are present depending on the type of work. Sealers can cause allergic sensitivity; cement can produce cement dermatitis. Industry-related diseases include Raynaud's phenomenon, carpal tunnel syndrome, silicosis, asbestosis, and permanent threshold shift.

TABLE 12.14 HAZARDS IN CONSTRUCTION

Noise	Vibration
Falls	Crushing
Heat and cold stress	Electrocution
Falling objects	Carbon monoxide
Equipment rollover	Compressed air
Cuts and bruises	Cave-ins
Formaldehyde from resins	Oil mists
Burns	Lifting
Dermatitis	Power tools
Solder fumes	ABS adhesives
Sunlight UV and IR	Flammable materials
Solvents	Paint and coatings
Insulation (polyurethane foam with isocyanates, fibreglass)	

◆ ◆ ◆
MINING

The mining process comprises two basic types of operation—underground and open pit—both of which involve the removal of minerals from the ground. The next part of the process is the milling or refining of the ore into usable product. All mining involves the use of large, powerful, and specialized equipment.

An underground mine consists of one or two vertical shafts driven into the ground with a network of horizontal tunnels radiating out from these verticals. It is not uncommon to have these operating tunnels or drifts thousands of feet below the surface. Rooms or stopes are located on these various levels for maintenance and other work. The native rock, anchored with rockbolts driven into the rock, supports the mine structure.

Ore is removed by drilling a matrix of long holes into the rock face, charging the holes with explosives, and blasting the wall down. These charges are directional and timed with microsecond delays between each run or horizontal line of holes so that the face will collapse onto itself as the blast proceeds up the wall. The chunks of ore are transported to the hoists, or skips, which carry them to the surface for processing.

Dust is the major hazard during blasting; vibration, or shock, and the blast energy wave are secondary problems. Other hazards include radon gas, silica exposure, drilling into an undetonated charge in a misfired hole or a bootleg, noise, dust explosions, the explosives, and just the fact of being underground. Emergency teams are trained to deal with underground disasters.

An open pit mine is simply a very large and deep hole in the ground, tapered from top to bottom, usually at about 45° for ground stability. The ledges around the circumference are used for vehicle access for ore removal. Ore removal in an open pit mine is similar to that in underground. Drilling and blasting are usual. In instances where the material being removed is not dense and hard like rock, giant shovels and drag lines may be used.

Once the ore has been extracted, it is moved to the mill where it is crushed into small pieces for processing into a concentrated form. Depending on the minerals to be extracted, a number of refining processes can be used (e.g., milling, flotation, leaching, ion exchange, and precipitation). The refined product is pelletized under high temperature and shipped to a user.

TABLE 12.15 HAZARDS IN MINING

Falls into shafts or pits	Radon gas
Various mine gases	Roof or wall collapse
Toxic chemicals	Noise and vibration
Heat	Dust
Electrocution	Flammable materials
Exhaust gases	Explosives
Contact with moving machinery	Dust explosions
Confined space entry	Vehicle stability
Bootlegs	Blast waves
Removing deadheads (uncrushable rock) from crushers	

◆ ◆ ◆
PHARMACEUTICAL MANUFACTURE

The manufacture of drugs for the purpose of disease control presents its own health and safety problems. The major concern of manufacture is cleanliness, primarily to prevent contamination of the product. The requirement for cleanliness also helps prevent workers from being exposed to critical levels of the drugs, most of which are very potent. If these drugs are ingested accidentally through cuts or other routes of entry, the results can be serious and possibly life-threatening.

The manufacture of pharmaceuticals today takes place in "clean rooms" that are designed to restrict the materials to quarantined areas, and that boast very efficient exhaust systems and air-quality control. The workers wear disposable clothing.

TABLE 12.16 HAZARDS IN PHARMACEUTICAL MANUFACTURE

Toxic dust	Biological dust
Eye, hand, and foot injury	Noise
Moving machinery	Lifting and materials handling
Flammable chemicals	Solvents
Acids and alkalis	Dust explosion
Slips and falls	Cuts and punctures

◆ ◆ ◆
PLASTIC MANUFACTURE

There are more than 100 polymers (Greek for "many parts") in common use today (Burgess, 1981). The term "polymer" refers to the number of organic compounds that are chemically identical to another substance but have a different molecular structure. (The molecular structure of the polymer can be repeated many times, sometimes creating giant molecules.) For example, cotton, which is basically cellulose, and a simple, water-soluble sugar called glucosan have the same chemical formula ($C_6H_{10}O_5$), yet they are entirely different.

Polyvinyl chloride (PVC) can be formed in several ways to make products such as plastic bottles, plumbing pipes, tool boxes, and toys for children. PVC is a thermoplastic material, which means that it can be recycled and remoulded. (PVC should not be confused with vinyl chloride, which is a known human carcinogen.)

There are four main methods of producing plastic parts:

1. *Injection moulding.* A process in which liquid plastic is forced under pressure into a cavity in the shape of the part required.

2. *Extrusion moulding.* A process in which the liquid plastic is forced through a die in a continuous operation. The finished part is cut to length as required.

3. *Blow moulding.* A process in which the molten plastic is forced into a cavity, which is then injected with air to form the plastic to the shape of the cavity.

4. *Continuous casting.* A process in which the molten plastic is poured onto a moving conveyor and allowed to expand and cool in a controlled manner. Rigid foam is made using this method.

After the parts are formed, by whichever method, they have to be trimmed to remove any excess material (joints may also require smoothing). Then they are packaged for shipping.

TABLE 12.17 HAZARDS IN PLASTIC MANUFACTURE

Noise	Burns
Heat stress	Dust and fumes
Operating machinery	Flammable materials
Toxic chemicals	Spills
Lifting	Dermatitis
Residual material such as vinyl chloride	

◆ ◆ ◆

SUMMARY

This chapter has outlined a number of the health and safety hazards found in some of the major industrial sectors. The level of risk associated with these hazards will determine the types of control mechanisms adopted by the industry in question. Managers and employees must be constantly updated with respect to sector-related hazards.

EXERCISES

1. Identify some of the hazards that exist in your workplace or school. Using Chapter 5 as a reference, suggest corrective solutions.
2. Choose a particular hazard listed in this chapter and explore it in more depth by contacting the various industry health and safety professionals or the various sector safety associations for information. The Ministry of Labour library and the Canadian Centre (CCOHS) are potentially useful sources of information.

References

Burgess, William A. 1981. *Recognition of Health Hazards in Industry*. New York: John Wiley & Sons.

Canadian Standards Association. 1989. *Office Ergonomics—A National Standard of Canada*. CAN/CSA – Z412-M89, Toronto.

Canadian Standards Association. 1990. *Industrial Products—Lighting*. RPO-003-1990, Toronto.

Picard, A. 1995. "Abuse Suffered by Nurses Hurts Health Care." *The Globe and Mail*, October 24, A2.

Workers' Compensation Board of Ontario. 1992. Derived from the *Statistical Supplement to the 1992 Annual Report*, Toronto.

13

Management of Occupational Health and Safety Programs

*This chapter was written by Mary D. Smith, CRSP.

♦ ♦ ♦
INTRODUCTION

This chapter will examine the basic concepts underlying the successful occupational health and safety program. Components of the program and strategies for its the implementation will also be discussed. Underpinning every successful venture in occupational health and safety is management commitment to the reduction of accidents in the workplace. Sometimes it falls on the human resources department and the health and safety professional to convince senior management that such commitment is required. Chapter 14 examines health and safety programs that are based on social-psychological principles.

♦ ♦ ♦
OCCUPATIONAL HEALTH AND SAFETY PROGRAMS

Management decision-making is key to establishing preventative and corrective measures, and to monitoring and evaluating the OHS program. Successful OHS programs cannot be operated in isolation from the rest of the organization. The purpose of an OHS program is threefold: to protect workers, property, and the environment; to reduce and control accidents; and to increase the effectiveness or productivity of operations.

Each program should be designed to accommodate a particular industry, institution, plant, or location. Large, multi-location corporations may have corporate OHS departments that provide technical expertise and direction to each local plant official responsible for occupational health and safety. Small industries or institutions may not have the luxury of knowledgeable specialists on staff. Nevertheless, a successful program can be developed using the expertise of the broad range of health and safety professionals discussed in Chapter 10.

The standard that an employer strives to attain when developing a program will also be judged by those having jurisdiction to enforce the regulations. This is an additional area where employers should practice due diligence. To this end, the employer must do everything reasonable in the circumstances to ensure that the workforce is adequately informed and trained in the proper handling, usage, storage, and disposal of potentially hazardous products. Only then can the employer be assured that a due diligence defence has been achieved. To achieve this standard a successful training program needs to incorporate generic education with site-specific and product-specific training. As discussed in Chapter 5, many methods are available, and the choices depend on the complexity and number of controlled products, processes, and employees.

Smaller organizations tend to contract the training out to safety associations and consultants. It is extremely important to encourage internal responsibility for education and training. In order to accomplish this, the human resource practitioner should consult with the joint health and safety committee during both the development and post-delivery stages of the training program.

◆ ◆ ◆

ORGANIZING THE OHS PROGRAM

The following elements are common to any plan designed to accommodate all organizations, large or small, industrial or institutional.

I PROGRAM OBJECTIVES

The program objectives may be developed from input by joint health and safety committees, environmental committees, representatives from senior management, middle management, operations, maintenance, purchasing and engineering, and other employee representatives. The objectives should include the following criteria, which must be clearly communicated to all levels:

◆ To obtain and maintain support for the program at all levels of the organization, including employee groups and parties to collective agreements.

◆ To motivate, educate, and train all levels of management and employee groups in the recognition, reporting, and correction of hazards in the workplace, which will improve the level of understanding of all staff regarding the connection between safety, productivity, quality, mutual respect, and work satisfaction.

◆ To provide controls for worker exposure to potential hazards through the use of work practices, engineering controls, and personal protective equipment, and to plan for a program of inspection and preventative maintenance for machinery, equipment, tools, and facilities.

The objective of compliance with all environmental and OHS legislation, as well as with applicable codes and standards, will reduce the liability faced by all employers in the event of a catastrophic accident.

II POLICY

The second component of the plan is the creation and adoption of a formal policy. The policy should be written and signed by the chief executive officer/president of the organization and then made available to all employees.

Policy statements can range from simple, strong statements of the organization's commitment to occupational health and safety to long, detailed documents outlining the purpose of the program and defining the involvement and responsibilities of all employees. The Peel Board of Education policy statement reads as follows:

> *The Peel Board of Education will take every reasonable precaution to prevent injury or illness to students, employees, members and the public participating in board activities or performing their duties. This shall be accomplished by providing and maintaining a safe, healthy working environment and by providing the education and required training to perform these activities and duties safely.*
>
> *The Peel Board of Education will take every reasonable precaution to protect the environment within the board's area of responsibility. The board will assign appropriate resources to maintain an environmental program which complies with all federal and provincial environmental legislation. The board*

will include occupational health and safety performance in the evaluation of all principal/supervisory personnel.

The policy should be developed in consultation with employee groups. Once adopted, it should be widely publicized by means of meetings, newsletters, pamphlets, and so forth. The policy should be posted in management offices to serve as a constant reminder of the commitment and responsibility of the executive branch.

III ASSIGNMENT OF RESPONSIBILITY AND ACCOUNTABILITY

Ontario Hydro's corporate policy is an excellent example of corporate responsibility:

> *Ontario Hydro is committed to achieving sustained excellence in health and safety for its employees, and protecting the health and safety of the public where potential hazards exist related to the Corporation's operations and facilities.*
>
> *Ontario Hydro will meet and, where possible, exceed the letter and intent of all applicable legislation. Health and safety will be managed as a priority area in the Corporation with adequate resources and employee involvement in the development of programs. Objectives and standards will be established for health and safety programs, and performance will be measured. Both workplace and public hazards will be identified and eliminated or controlled. Where hazards cannot be eliminated, programs will be put into place to safeguard the health and safety of both employees and the public. Information necessary for the protection of employee and public health and safety will be maintained and communicated to those affected.*

The policy of the American Telephone and Telegraph Company, for example, states:

No job is so important and no service is so urgent, that we cannot take time to perform our work safely.

After the policy statement has been inaugurated, administrative regulations should be developed, outlining the responsibility for the program at various levels. The regulations should include accountability for program elements assigned to senior management and responsibility for occupational health and safety in performance evaluations at all levels of supervision. Employees should be held responsible for safe work practices, including the reporting of all observed unsafe practices, procedures, and hazards to the appropriate supervisor. All employees should be required to participate in OHS training and development programs.

A timetable for the review and evaluation of the policy and regulations by the chief executive officer/president/board should be outlined in the program, along with a procedure for budget development, monitoring, and control. The assignment of appropriate resources with responsibility and authority for the administration of the program should also be included. Finally, the administrative regulation should contain a mechanism for addressing and responding to recommendations from the joint health and safety committees within a specific length of time. Written responses to recommendations are legislated in many jurisdictions.

IV AUDITING THE PROGRAM

Auditing for the sake of regulatory compliance and for continuous improvement are the most cost-effective types of audits in the present environment of regulatory standards and enforcement. However, packaged audits that do little but create volumes of paper will not reveal how a program is functioning unless some direction is established. Besides ensuring that the audit has a purpose, management should decide if the results will be shared with the employees, the joint committee, or the general public.

The audit should be designed with a set of standards against which it will be measured. The scope of the audit should also be determined; does it encompass, for example, occupational health and safety, fire protection, emergency plans, and environmental controls? Selection of the audit team is also important. Are there knowledgeable, trained, and experienced staff in-house or is outside expertise required?

The protocol must be designed to provide a step-by-step procedure to assist the team in conducting a systematic review. It must lead the auditors to ask the right questions not only about the quality of compliance but also about the strength of the management systems to maintain the appropriate level of compliance. The audit may include a review of previous audits, a physical survey of the location, examination of administrative records, and interviews with management staff, workers, and the health and safety committee. All of these elements should be accurately documented and communicated to the appropriate levels in the organization. There must also be a comprehensive action plan in place to follow up on the documented findings of the audit. Responsible personnel and completion dates should accompany each action item.

There exists a common misconception that written procedures and audits raise the liability of the corporation in terms of regulatory compliance or in the event of an accident. In fact, many courts are basing the severity of civil and criminal penalties in part on the employer's ability to prove that they were duly diligent in auditing and correcting deficiencies in its own operation. If the corporation does not have written procedures and documented audits, how will it prove beyond a reasonable doubt that it has taken every reasonable precaution to ensure the health and safety of the worker and the environment?

In Canada, what was once the maximum fine for OHS violations—$25,000—is now routine. Corporations in some provinces can be fined up to $500,000 for each offence. Individuals can be fined up to $25,000 and sentenced to one year in jail.

V SAFETY COMMITTEES

Safety committees are a key component in the OHS programs. These committees, which may represent various constituencies within the organization or individual workplaces, are responsible for inspecting the workplace on a regular basis, identifying potential hazards, and recommending hazard-control measures. The safety committee may also recommend training and educational programs, investigate workplace accidents, and analyze accident and injury data.

The various statutes pertaining to health and safety across Canada clearly see joint labour/management committees as a means of achieving legislative objectives. However, this can happen only if the committee is appropriately staffed and given the authority to make decisions on behalf of the corporation. Decisions should be arrived at by consensus; when this is not possible, a dispute-resolution mechanism should be clearly articulated in the committee's written terms of reference. When safety joint committees operate in a cooperative fashion and share a commitment to safety, employees feel free to become actively involved and make positive contributions to the program.

VI ORIENTATION OF NEW OR TRANSFERRED STAFF

Orientation of new employees is a time-honoured tradition in business, whether it takes the form of an informal introduction to fellow workers, a formal group meeting, a plant tour, or a personnel sign-on procedure. A successful occupational health and safety program will include the provision of handouts outlining the OHS program and giving information on safety-related subjects including hazards on the job, good housekeeping practices, use of personal protective equipment, compliance with accident and injury reporting procedures, and evacaution procedures.

VII EDUCATION AND TRAINING

While all levels of management and supervision should receive education in occupational health and safety, it is not necessary that they be trained in the specific operations of the organization. Upper management should support the educational component of a successful program by providing the resources needed for professional-development workshops, in-house educational programs, and the like. If available, in-house health and safety professionals should provide educational material and information for all levels of the organization.

The trained worker is a safe worker. Training must be initiated before a new worker steps on the floor and approaches his or her workstation. Training includes all aspects of the assigned task, including quality control, safety, anticipated hazards, and workstation design. Well-trained and dedicated employees are the greatest deterrent to injuries, material damage, and health problems in the plant or institution. The reference to a "new" worker also includes a transferred worker who is not familiar with the task.

The chief health and safety responsibility of line supervisors is to train workers in safe work methods and techniques. The supervisor must be certain that the employee understands the potential hazards of the materials or equipment that he or she must handle, use, or store. While safety rules should be communicated in the context of education rather than discipline, if a supervisor feels that a worker is endangering his or her life or that of another worker, then prompt and firm disciplinary action is called for.

The program should include initial and follow-up training on all legislated components, which may include WHMIS, asbestos management, electrical lockout, and other issues relevant to each jurisdiction. A good program will also include initial and follow-up training on nonmandated subjects that may impact health or safety at work or at home.

VIII EMPLOYEE ASSISTANCE PROGRAMS/WELLNESS PROGRAMS

Employee assistance programs (EAPs) or wellness programs are cost-effective, humanitarian, job-based strategies designed to help employees identify problems and resolve them through confidential counselling, referrals to specialized services, education programs, and health-promotion activities. The EAP, which may be provided in-house or on a contract basis, may provide counselling to employees on psychological problems, financial or legal matters, and domestic concerns. Some EAPs offer health promotion and fitness programs that deal with weight control, nutrition, exercise, and smoking. EAPs do not intervene in the private lives of employees; rather they offer aid and referrals that can assist the employee in resolving problems that may be affecting job performance.

The EAP officer may report through the human resource department while maintaining an office off site. The organizational reporting line will be through HR, which is generally responsible for arranging for storing or maintaining confidential records.

IX PROCEDURES

In this era of increased litigation, a defence of due diligence can be achieved only by those organizations that are able to provide evidence of a documented and well-implemented OHS program. Written procedures are part of the successful OHS program.

General procedures must be provided for maintenance programs, accident reporting and investigation, workplace inspections, and training and education. Procedures for dealing with violence in the workplace may also be developed. General procedures should include standards for contractors and suppliers of equipment and general safety rules.

Specific procedures should be provided for higher-risk areas. These may include (but are not limited to) confined space entry, fork lift or elevated platforms, high-pressure gas regulators, and welding.

X PURCHASING

The OHS program should provide written safety standards to guide the purchasing department. The purchasing procedure should include a system for product review/approval and the application of standards and codes in purchasing. The purchasing department is vitally concerned with acquiring the best possible product at the best possible price. It is the responsibility of the buyer to base purchasing decisions on standards and codes as they relate to machinery, tools, equipment, and materials.

There should be a good communication between the OHS department/professional and the purchasing department. Purchasing departments can unwittingly acquire products that do not meet industry design standards. Goggles supplied to one group of workers were found to have imperfections in the lenses that caused eyestrain and headaches, leading to fatigue and accidents. The buyer should consult frequently with the safety department before making any purchases where safety is a factor.

XI OPERATING PROCEDURES

An operating procedure is an action taken by an employer to inform employees and clients about accepted business conduct. A sample operating procedure outline for occupational health and safety is provided in Box 13.1.

♦ ♦ ♦
COST-BENEFIT ANALYSIS

The practitioner can convince the executive branch that the costs of an OHS program are justified by developing a cost-benefit analysis that proves that occupational health and safety has a pricetag whether or not the corporation institutes a program.

The costs incurred by a corporation *without* an OHS program would include the following:

BOX 13.1 OPERATING PROCEDURES FOR OCCUPATIONAL HEALTH AND SAFETY

Section 1:		Legislative Policies
1.1.1		Program Objectives
1.1.2		Occupational Health and Safety Act
1.1.3		Environmental Protection Act
1.1.4		Occupational Health and Safety Policy and Administrative Regulations
1.1.5		Program Review and Evaluations
1.1.6		Emergency Plans Act
1.1.7		Transportation of Dangerous Goods Act
	1.2	Legal Responsibilities and Duties
1.2.1		Officers and Directors
1.2.2		Duties of Employers
1.2.3		Supervisory Staff
1.2.4		Employees
1.2.5		Contractors and Suppliers of Equipment
	1.3	Role of Standards and Procedures
1.3.1		Standards and Procedures in Occupational Health and Safety
1.3.2		Occupational Health and Safety Training and Education Requirements
	1.4	Joint Health and Safety Committees
1.4.1		Legal Authority and Composition
1.4.2		Functions, Rights, and Duties
1.4.3		Recommendations to Management
1.4.4		Orientation of New Committee Members
1.4.5		Right to Refuse Unsafe Work
1.4.6		Terms of Reference

(Ontario add Certification of Committee members, and Power to Stop Work)

	1.5	Implications of Legislation for Purchasing
1.5.1		Mission Statement
1.5.2		Health, Safety, and Environmental Impact on Purchasing
Section II:	Occupational Health and Safety Procedures	
	2.1	General Safety Rules
	2.2	Asbestos Management Program
	2.3	Workplace Hazardous Materials Information System (WHMIS)
	2.4	Electrical Safety Procedures
2.4.1		General
2.4.2		Electrical Lockout of Equipment
2.4.3		Audio Visual and Computer Equipment
	2.5	Confined Space Entry Procedure
	2.6	Workplace Inspection Procedure

BOX 13.1 (continued)

	2.7	Emergency Preparedness
2.7.1		Level I
2.7.2		Level II
2.7.3		Level III
2.7.4		Fire Safety
	2.8	Occupational Accident/Injury/Illness Reporting and Investigating
2.8.1		Staff
2.8.2		Property
2.8.3		First Aid
	2.9	Risk Management Procedure
	2.10	Construction/Building Modification Procedures
2.10.1		Building Renovations and Modifications
2.10.2		Project Management
2.10.3		General Standard Conditions
	2.11	Ergonomics
	2.12	Food Services Procedure
	2.13	Purchasing Procedures
2.13.1		Product Review/Approval Form
2.13.2		Application of CSA/CAN/ANSI Standards in Purchasing
2.13.3		Tender Documents
	2.14	Environmental Procedures
2.14.1		Reduce, Reuse, Recycle
2.14.2		Waste Reduction Plan
2.14.3		Chemical Waste Inventories, Removal
2.14.4		Underground Fuel Storage Tanks
2.14.5		Chemical Inventories
2.14.6		Chemical Spill Procedures
2.14.7		Incineration
2.14.8		Environmental Audit Protocol
2.14.9		Pesticide Licencing Protocol
2.14.10		Indoor Air Quality Protocol
	2.15	Communicable Disease
2.15.1		Common Communicable Diseases
2.15.2		HIV
2.15.3		Hepatitis
2.15.4		Universal Precautions
	2.16	Personal Safety
2.16.1		Assaults
2.16.2		Weapons
	2.17	Procedures Related to Specific Tasks and Equipment in Operations, etc.

1. Accidents resulting in injuries, workers' compensation costs, machine/material damage and associated costs, and damage to the facility and associated costs

2. Loss of production capability

3. Costs of retraining injured workers

4. Costs of training replacement workers

5. Health and safety costs resulting from noncompliance and associated fines

6. Environmental costs resulting from noncompliance and associated fines

7. Lost access to defence of due diligence

The costs incurred by a company *with* an OHS program would include the costs associated with the additional human resources personnel needed to administer the program, as well as a dedicated budget for training and communication. However, the benefits stemming from such a program would include:

1. Reduction in accidents and associated costs

2. Increased productivity

3. Improved labour-relations climate

4. Good defence of due diligence available

Work-related accidents fall into two categories: (1) those resulting in work injuries or illnesses, and (2) those causing property damage or loss of production. *Insured costs* of accidents are those costs covered by workers' compensation, private insurance, and medical expenses; these costs are definite and known. The *uninsured costs* of accidents are more difficult to identify and assess. A cost-benefit analysis would start with a pilot study to ascertain the approximate averages of uninsured costs. (The pilot study referred to in this section is taken from the *Accident Prevention Manual for Business and Industry*, National Safety Council.) In order to accomplish this, the National Safety Council model divides the most common incidents into four classes:

Class 1   Involving lost time at work.

Class 2   Medical treatment cases involving a medical professional at an office or hospital.

Class 3   Requiring first-aid treatment and minimal or no property damage.

Class 4   Accidents causing no injury or illness that result in property damage of $100 or more.

The pilot study revealed that the company had 20 Class 1 accidents, 30 Class 2 accidents, 50 Class 3 accidents, and 20 Class 4 accidents. Costs were determined and averages developed. No records were kept of the Class 4 accidents after the pilot study; instead a ratio was used of the number of Class 4 to Class 1 accidents found in the pilot study. This ratio was shown to be about 1:1.

Adjustments in annual costs must be made to reflect inflationary trends, which can quickly render the results obsolete. In addition, wage-related cost elements must be kept up to date. The pilot study should be repeated at least every five years to establish new benchmarks. Following are some assumed figures that have been applied to the four uninsured classes.

Class of Accident	Number of Accidents Reported	Average Uninsured Cost
Class I	20	$300.00
Class II	30	$100.00
Class III	50	$ 20.00
Class IV	20	$500.00

In a pilot study it is important to include a sufficient number of cases to make the analysis significant. At least 20 accidents should be investigated. The following items are subject to reasonably reliable measurement (less tangible are the effects of accidents on public relations or employee morale):

1. Cost of wages paid to workers who were not injured but who lost time as a result of the accident.
2. Cost of damage to property or material.
3. Cost of extra overtime work needed to make up for time lost as a result of the accident.
4. Cost of wages paid to supervisors investigating the causes of the accident.
5. Cost of the replacement worker in terms of training and lost production.
6. Cost of clerical staff processing workers' compensation claims.
7. Cost of work and rehabilitation arrangements provided for the injured worker.
8. Cost of professional in-house staff investigation.
9. Miscellaneous costs (insurance claims, equipment rental, losses due to cancelled contracts, etc.).

The above analysis related best to the Class I, II, and IV accidents. Class III accidents are common first-aid cases, where the injury is slight and no significant property damage occurs. These cases are of short duration but may occur frequently. The pilot study should investigate at least 20 first-aid cases, taking into consideration loss of working time per trip to the first-aid station or dispensary, average cost of materials per visit, and average lost time of supervisor per incident.

To all uninsured costs the investigator must add the costs of workers' compensation and insured medical expenses. For self-insured companies, this figure will be the total amount paid out in settlement of the claim, plus all expenses incurred in administering the insurance, plus an administration fee paid to the Workers' Compensation Board.

The cost-benefit analysis sends a powerful message to senior management, because accident costs represent lost profit. The general method for recouping lost profit is increased sales. For publicly funded institutions, the equation is harder to prove; the loss is one of service, not profit, and the public is the loser.

◆ ◆ ◆

SUMMARY

This chapter examined the various components and strategies that are needed to develop and implement a successful OHS program. To help the human resource practioner convince management of the benefits resulting from such a program, strategies for developing a cost-benefit analysis were also provided. Besides being cost-effective, the OHS program will ultimately reduce the organization's liability with to health, safety, and environmental issues.

E X E R C I S E S

1. Using the following figures assigned for each accident class, create a cost-benefit analysis to demonstrate the uninsured accident costs for Company XYZ, based on one year's accident experience. Class I, $485 (38 accidents); Class II, $125 (185 accidents); Class III, $21 (3800 accidents); and Class IV, $735 (4 accidents).

2. Using the sample operating procedure outline supplied, list the resources that may be needed to develop and deliver training courses in-house. Identify the health and safety professionals who should be in charge of the program's technical components. What role should the supervisor play?

14

Social Psychological Approaches to Occupational Health and Safety

INTRODUCTION

This chapter will draw upon social psychological principles in examining strategies for achieving worker health and safety. The chapter begins with an overview of four strategies for establishing an organizational culture in which health and safety are expected, valued, and rewarded by management, workers, and the surrounding community. Attention is then focused on four programs that demonstrate the value of these strategies.

◆ ◆ ◆

STRATEGIES FOR INFLUENCING HEALTH AND SAFETY BEHAVIOUR

LAW- AND RULE-BASED STRATEGIES

While respect for authority is basic to most societies, laws and rules need to reflect a consensus of those governed. They require surveillance and a system of penalties and/or rewards in order to be effective. The first health and safety laws in North America were strongly worded but had little influence as there was very little surveillance or compliance (Bird and Germain, 1990).

Another problem with law-based strategies is that people may feel safety is being forced upon them or that their freedom is being restricted. This view often breeds resistance and hostility. More recently developed strategies tend to focus on creating laws and rules that reflect a social consensus (e.g., seat-belt and drinking-and-driving laws).

EDUCATIONAL/MOTIVATIONAL STRATEGIES

Educational/motivational appeals, unless embedded within broader programs, tend to yield short-term results that may not transfer to work situations. Effects of these messages may be quickly overturned by the everyday cues within the workplace that trigger old habits and/or unsafe work

---

*This chapter was written by Gerry Goldberg and Kim Ankers.

practices. These strategies are useful, but only when used as a component of a larger social-influence program. For example, Workplace Hazardous Material Information System (WHMIS) training is conducted only within the context of a broader WHMIS program that includes appropriate labelling and material safety data sheets (MSDS).

In Canada, ParticipACTION attempts to influence lifestyle through presentations to groups and use of various media. They also initiate activities to stimulate public participation and focus attention on health. Their messages, like the programs in which they are embedded, are created in light of social marketing techniques.

SOCIAL MARKETING

Social marketing strategies are used to promote behavioural changes by linking them to the needs, interests, and lifestyles of the target group (Altman, 1986; Goldberg, 1990a; Simpson, 1987). The methods used are often based on product marketing techniques.

Social marketing involves the study of a particular group (target group) that is to be the target of a campaign to change some aspect of lifestyle or behaviour (this would include safety-related behaviours). Social and demographic factors such as age, sex, and cultural background are examined, and interviews, focus groups, and surveys are among the means used to gain an understanding of the needs, interests, goals, and values of the target group.

INDIVIDUAL AND COMMUNITY PARTICIPATION

Another way of to stimulate interest in health and safety is to encourage individual and community participation. Programs can be developed using the insights gained from social marketing studies. Safety issues can be directly linked to the activities or social functions associated with a particular target group (Weyant, 1986; Goldberg, 1990a). Personal participation can be fostered with the help of individuals, groups, or organizations within the workplace or community. Involving a broad range of people in safety programs may enhance community perceptions and norms regarding safety, risks, and safety-related behaviour.

Involvement and social consensus are the basis of modern laws regulating health and safety. When considering occupational health and safety in Canada, these laws commonly require some form of internal responsibility system (IRS) that places responsibility for health and safety on all stakeholders within the workplace. Generally, the centrepiece of the IRS is a joint worker–management health and safety committee mandated to identify and deal with workplace health and safety issues by consensus.

◆ ◆ ◆
BEHAVIOUR-BASED SAFETY PROGRAMS
I BEHAVIOUR MODIFICATION

Behaviour modification as an approach to safety has become popular in recent years (Goldberg, 1991; Krause and Finley, 1993; Krause and Hidley, 1992; Peterson, 1993). Behaviour modification programs aimed at occupational health and safety attempt to understand and control environmental or situational factors that influence related behaviours. This involves identifying situational conditions that encourage both safe and unsafe behaviours, and then using this information to alter working conditions.

Rather than "explain" unsafe acts in terms of a person's tendency to carelessness or inattentiveness, behaviour modification focuses attention on the situational factors that promote unsafe acts. Situational factors can become triggers or prompts for behaviours. They do this by indicating that, if specific behaviours occur, certain results or consequences will follow. This is the basis of what is known as *learning by consequence*, or *operant learning*.

One easy way to remember the fundamentals of learning by consequence is to think about the "ABCs" of learning: "A" refers to the antecedents, or the conditions, that trigger a behaviour; "B" refers to a behaviour or action; and "C" refers to the consequences (rewards and punishments) that follow from the behaviour.

DEVELOPING THE PROGRAM The first step in developing a behaviour modification program is to gain the interest and involvement of both labour and management, and to form a working committee consisting of representatives from both groups. The committee's first task is to draw up a list of critical behaviours, which comprise both desired safety behaviours (use of personal protective equipment) and undesired behaviours (standing in a pressure valve's line of fire). The committee must then identify and deal with the environmental influences on these behaviours (i.e., both antecedents and consequences).

The next step is to measure the rate of compliance by observing the worker on the job. This can be done in a nonthreatening manner by having trained co-workers or trusted others randomly observe workers. After recording the observed behaviour, the observer provides the worker with feedback and attempts to engage the worker in identifying the specific factors that may have contributed to each failure to conform to the expected behaviour. Information concerning each worker's behaviour is kept confidential and is not used to discipline. The focus is on promoting worker involvement in creating a healthier and safer workplace.

II INTERNAL RESPONSIBILITY SYSTEM

An internal responsibility system depends for its success upon everyone responding to workplace hazards and emergencies in an appropriate manner. As the following two cases demonstrate, failure to do so can have tragic consequences.

> In 1989, 22 people were killed in an Air Ontario crash near Dryden, Ontario. The crash, which occurred shortly after take-off, was caused by ice build-up on the wings. Among the survivors were a flight attendant and an off-duty Air Ontario pilot who worked the same route. This pilot was travelling with his wife and two small children. Both individuals noticed the ice build-up on the wings and were very concerned. But they did not advise the pilot of their concerns. When asked why, the flight attendant said she had made a similar comment on a previous flight and had been told by the pilot to mind her own business. The passenger pilot indicated that he had not wanted to question the competence of the pilot.

> At a major Ontario company, three highly skilled employees were working together in a room. Although all three employees were trained in resuscitation techniques, when one of them suddenly suffered a heart attack, the other two did not offer help. Even though there was an emergency telephone located in the room, 15 minutes went by before they called for help. The employee was dead by the time help arrived. Later, during

questioning, fear of liability was raised as a possible motivation, but neither man could really explain his inaction.

Stimulating workers to notify appropriate agents of workplace hazards, to offer safety advice and warnings, and to help co-workers in emergencies is critical to the success of an internal responsibility system.

HELPING SITUATIONS Helping situations have certain characteristics that may frustrate intervention on the part of bystanders. Emergencies are *exceptional* or unique in that they are rare and unusual events. What is happening and what should be done may not be immediately obvious. For example, when you notice someone lying on the ground, you can't be sure whether the person is there as a result of an accident, illness, or personal choice. Emergencies also tend to be *sudden*, at least from the bystander's point of view. Finally, emergencies are *urgent* and *demanding* in that they may require an immediate response in often dangerous circumstances.

Potential helping situations usually produce anxiety that can interfere a person's ability to make appropriate helping decisions. While battling a fire, one firefighter may hear a cry for help and act in a seemingly heroic manner, while another may notice only the falling debris, and be compelled to leave the area. Each firefighter takes in a different aspect of the situation and acts accordingly. People who have performed heroic deeds often acknowledge they were unaware of the dangers associated with their actions.

COSTS AND BENEFITS OF HELPING BEHAVIOUR Helping behaviour can be improved by attending to the physical factors that interfere with the helping process, as to the costs and benefits associated with offering help, and to the social-psychological environment. Prompts, hints, or signals that encourage the helping decision come from the physical, task, organizational, and psychosocial environments. Social prompts can be as obvious and simple as a request for help. Physical prompts are things we see, hear, smell, taste, or touch. Although helping responses tend to increase as more physical prompts become available, factors such as noise can interfere with a bystander's ability to react appropriately.

Costs, whether social (embarrassment, humiliation) or physical (injury, violence), can have a powerful effect on helping behaviour (Goldberg 1988). One study demonstrated the influence of time pressure on helping behaviour. Student priests late for their own presentations on "The Good Samaritan" failed to heed the message they were about to give. In their rush to avoid an embarrassing late entrance, they ignored the groans of a man slumped in a doorway (Darley and Batson 1973).

Financial or material rewards may stimulate helping, but not always. The promise of a reward may, in fact, detract from the act of helping. For example, a worker may enjoy training a new employee; however, if the reward for helping is contingent upon the new employee attaining a certain level of competence, failure of that employee to progress as required may sour the relationship.

A positive organizational culture and productive workplace practices can be instrumental in stimulating helping behaviour. Knowledgeable and confident employees are more likely than insecure and unhappy ones to express safety concerns and/or warnings and to provide emergency assistance.

III RISK COMMUNICATION

Good labour relations are essential to the establishment of an organizational health and safety culture. Risk communications and risk management provides an opportunity for management to respond to the needs and concerns of workers and involve them in promoting safety awareness. Unfortunately, communication and management of risk can sometimes lead to a breakdown in labour–management relations (Goldberg, 1992). While employers, safety professionals, and scientific specialists within industry and public agencies are responsible for apprising workers of potential risks, it is not uncommon for these individuals to find that their efforts to reassure and calm workers and communities have failed or even backfired.

Worker and community outrage over work-related risks is a growing phenomenon. Experts within industry and government must adjust to this phenomenon by dealing with risks from more than just a technical and scientific perspective. It is essential that workers and communities are invited to become active in the risk-management process. Whatever costs are associated with achieving this participation are outweighed by the costs associated with worker and community outrage.

PATTERNS OF RISK COMMUNICATION While some stakeholders communicate within the domain of "technical risk" (government and industry experts), and others communicate within the domain of "perceived risk" (the workers or community, media, interest groups) (Covello et al., 1987; Krewski, 1989). Those within the former domain use a technical language, whereas those in the perceived-risk domain use the language of politics and persuasion. Government bridges the two domains, and so must speak both languages. According to Krewski's (1989) model, most risk-communication problems arise between the expert and the public sphere. When workers and/or communities appear to disregard the technical evidence, the expert may come to see these groups as irrational and attempt to influence the "opposition" by distorting information to achieve a more persuasive effect. This will tend to exacerbate mistrust of experts as well as outrage.

MAINTAINING TRUST AND AVOIDING OUTRAGE Those who have had frustrating experiences after communicating information about risks to workers or communities commonly believe that "if it were not for the media or advocacy groups/leaders there would be no outrage." While media and advocacy groups or leaders can play a role in focusing and directing worker and public outrage, it is the perceived attributes of the risks themselves that are central to the creation of outrage. In fact, it has been found that certain attributes of risks make the risks seem more serious, if they are perceived as involuntary, unfamiliar, uncontrollable, controlled by others, unfair, memorable, dreadful, acute, focused (time, space), fatal, delayed, artificial, undetectable, and/or if individual mitigation seems impossible (Sandman, 1986). These are not distortions of risk; they are part of what is meant by the term.

OUTRAGE FACTORS Outrage factors refer to those characteristics of risk that have been found to trigger worker and/or community outrage. For example, people are outraged when risks are perceived as being involuntary, government/industry controlled versus individually controlled; unfair; involving ethically objectionable issues; artificial versus natural; exotic versus familiar; associated with memorable events, high dread, or poorly understood and undetectable (Hance, Chess and Sandman, 1988). Outrage is also created when sources of information about the risk are viewed as untrustworthy.

It appears that risks that are perceived as naturally occurring are more acceptable than risks that are the result of human actions. Thus while people may actively intervene to prevent the establishment of toxic-waste dumps hundreds of kilometres from their home, they may ignore the naturally occurring radon gas seeping into their homes. Although the residential radon gas poses far greater health risks than the distant toxic-waste dump, there is less concern about it because it is perceived to be "a part of nature."

CULTIVATING TRUST Workers and communities view experts and agencies with trust when they appear competent, caring, honourable and honest, and supportive of meaningful worker or public involvement (Hance, Chess, and Sandman, 1988). Experts and agencies appear competent by demonstrating a knowledge of the facts; coordinating information that meets people's needs and takes into account outrage factors by listening to various groups and by attending to feelings and values as well as reasons. They appear honourable and honest when they explain agency processes, avoid mixed messages (eg., say a location is safe but send in inspectors who are wearing what appear to be "space suits"), keep promises, and avoid closed meetings. Encouraging meaningful worker or public involvement means involving the public early, following up and getting back to people, and enlisting the help of organizations that have credibility with workers or the public.

IV DEALING WITH MASS PSYCHOGENIC ILLNESS

Concern regarding exposures to diverse health risks seems to be increasing. Health and safety professionals regularly find themselves confronted by workers and media reports about "sick-building syndrome" and indoor air quality (IAQ). There are many situations in which environmental problems need to be addressed. Outbreaks of symptoms that lack an identifiable biological, chemical, or physical agent are referred to as mass psychogenic illnesses (MPI).

Such situations are often very frustrating for health and safety professionals as well as management, and tend to reflect a failure both to maintain the trust of workers by attending to their needs and interests and to involve them in risk assessment and management decisions.

Manitoba telephone operators who were experiencing symptoms of illness and discomfort became the focus of a study when no physical agent could be found to explain the symptoms. It was noted that management and health and safety professionals had trivialized and ignored the role of occupational stress and psychosocial factors in contributing to these symptoms. Many studies point out that central to the prevention of MPI are good labour relations in which workers' trust managers and occupational health professionals to respect and attend to their health and safety concerns (Lees-Haley, 1993). However, research on cases of MPI have brought about a better understanding of how to apply the principles of risk communication and other behaviour methods to the these phenomena.

Within the workplace, an outbreak of MPI was recorded as early as 1787 (Heckler cited in Brodsky, 1988). Although there is no identifiable causative agent in most cases, this does not mean that those affected are malingerers. Symptoms are real, can be quite severe and may include vomiting and fainting.

Investigations indicate that outbreaks follow a common pattern and are associated with a number of workplace factors (Brodsky, 1988; Kerckhoff, 1982; Singer et al., 1982; Watson et al., 1984). General antecedent conditions, such as poor labour relations and increased workload, usually set the scene. Specific triggers have run the gamut from foul odours to insects in shipping crates or carpeting. Under these circumstances, those workers who are not in regular or casual communication with co-workers (i.e., social isolates, private or withdrawn individuals, etc.) become dramatially ill. Co-workers note the illness, compare their own stress-induced feelings, and conclude without further verification that these are symptoms of a disease. Symptons then spread through a social network with friends "catching it" from each other. Persons with relatively few social contacts at work tend to be affected before those with more social contacts.

Outbreaks have also been associated with job dissatisfaction, stress and anxiety (both on and off the job), social isolation at work, poor worker–management relations, role or status incongruities, and financial pressures. More specific triggers include poor lighting, extreme temperatures, overcrowding, loud noises, and fear of chemical intoxication.

Goldberg (1990b) suggests numerous strategies for preventing outbreaks. One approach managers and health and safety professionals may take is to involve workers in developing programs that deal with both general and specific triggers. Stress-management courses may prevent stress-induced outbreaks, while WHMIS training shed light on hazardous materials that are potential triggers. Workers can also be made aware of the types of sensations (soreness, fatigue, drowsiness, etc.) they experience as a result of doing their jobs.

When concerns are raised over an unusual occurrence, such as a unexplained smell, managers and health professionals should assure workers that their concerns are being taken seriously and then take immediate action to identify and deal with the potential problem.

◆ ◆ ◆
SUMMARY

This chapter began with a review of both traditional and modern strategies for promoting worker awareness of health and safety issues and appropriate workplace behaviours. These strategies were then examined in the context of behaviour-based safety programs, which included behaviour modification, internal responsibility system, and risk communication.

EXERCISES

1. Think of a health or safety media presentation that influenced you. What made it effective?
2. Describe an occasion in which you or someone you know responded with an appropriate helping behaviour.
3. Examine some of your favourite activities or hobbies. Are there any hazards associated with them? Would these hazards be as acceptable if they were part of your work environment?
4. Describe an environment that was of particular concern to you, your friends, or your community. What made this risk unacceptable?

References

Altman, D.G. 1986. "A Framework for Evaluating Community-based Heart Disease Prevention Programs." *Soc. Sci. Med* 22: 479–87.

Bradley, G.L. 1989. "The Forgotten Role of Environmental Control: Some Thoughts on the Psychology of Safety." *J. Occupational Health and Safety—Aust NZ, 5(6)*, 501–508.

Bird, F.E., Jr., and Germain, G.L. 1990. *Practical Loss Control Leadership: The Conservation of People, Property, Process and Profits*, rev. ed., Loganville, Ga.: Publishing Division of International Loss Control Institute.

Brodsky, C.M. 1988. "The Psychiatric Epidemic in the American Workplace."

Occupational Medicine: State of the Art Reviews 3:653–62.

Covello, V., D. von Winterfeldt, and P. Slovic. 1987. "Risk Communication: A Review of the Literature." *Risk Abstracts* 171–82.

Darley, J.M., and C.D. Batson. 1973. "From Jerusalem to Jericho: A Study of Situational and Dispositional Variables in Helping Behaviour." *Journal of Personality and Social Psychology* 27: 100–108.

Goldberg, G.E. 1988. "Preventing and Dealing with Emergency Situations: A Guide to Helping in the Workplace." *Occupational Health in Ontario* 9, no. 2: 86–95.

Goldberg, G.E. 1990a. " Miners and the Social Marketing of Safety Attitudes." *Occupational Health in Ontario* 11, no. 3: 106–23.

Goldberg, G.E. 1990b. "Preventing and Dealing with Mass Psychogenic Illness." *Occupational Health in Ontario* 11, no. 1: 21–27.

Goldberg, G.E. 1991. "Behaviour Modification: Mind over Matter." *Occupational Health and Safety Canada* 7, no. 2: 56–63.

Goldberg, G.E. 1992. "In the Face of Fear." *Occupational Health and Safety Canada* 8, no. 2: 34–46.

Hance, B.J., C. Chess, and P.M. Sandman. 1988. *Improving Dialogue with Communities: A Risk Communication Manual for Government*. Submitted to New Jersey Department of Environmental Protection Division of Science and Research.

Kerckhoff, A.C. 1982. "A Social Psychological View of Mass Psychogenic Illness." In M.J. Colligan et al., eds., *Mass Psychogenic Illness: A Social Psychological Analysis*. Hillsdale, N.J.: Lawrence Erlbaum Associates.

Krause, T.R., and R.M. Finley. 1993. "Safety and Continuous Improvement: Two Sides of the Same Coin." *The Safety and Health Practitioner* (September): 19–22.

Krause, T.R., and J.H. Hidley. 1992. "On Their Best Behaviour: The Behaviour-based Process Focuses Attention on Those Critical Behaviours That Immmediately Precede Accidents." *Accident Prevention* 39, no. 5: 10–14.

Krewski, D. 1989. *Current Issues in Risk Management: Risk Communication, Risk Perception and Pharmacokinetics*. Discussion paper for Federal–Provincial Advisory Committee on Environmental and Occupational Health.

Lees-Haley, P.R. 1993. "When Sick Building Complaints Arise…" *Occupational Health and Safety*, 51–54.

Peterson, D. 1993. "Establishing Good 'Safety Culture' Helps Mitigate Workplace Dangers." *Occupational Health and Safety*, Vol. 62, No.7 (July), 20–24.

Singer, J.E., C.S. Baum, A. Baum, and B.D. Thew. 1982. "Mass Psychogenic Illness: The Case for Social Comparison." In M.J. Colligan et al., eds., *Mass Psychogenic Illness: A Social Psychological Analysis*. Hillsdale, N.J.: Lawrence Erlbaum Associates.

Simpson, H.M. 1987. "Community-based Approaches to Highway Safety: Health Promotion and Drinking-Driving." *Drug and Alcohol Dependence*, 20: 27–37.

Watson, D.L., G. deBortali-Tregerthan, and J. Frank. 1984. *Social Psychology: Science and Application*. Glenview, Ill.: Scott, Foresman and Company.

Weyant, J.M. 1986. *Applied Social Psychology*. Oxford: Oxford University Press.

15

Trends in Occupational Health and Safety

◆ ◆ ◆
INTRODUCTION

The field of occupational health and safety is dynamic and complex. As some safety issues decline in importance due to regulations and training, others, such as carpal tunnel syndrome, emerge. This chapter looks at four of these issues: workplace violence, indoor air quality, communicable diseases, and commitment to health and safety.

◆ ◆ ◆
VIOLENCE IN THE WORKPLACE

The threat of violence has become an unwelcome part of Canadian life, even in the workplace. The extent of the problem is difficult to estimate because employers usually call the police, not the health and safety department. However, one employee assistance firm reported that 52 percent of the traumas handled in 1993 involved violence, as compared to 30 percent in 1990 (Hancock, 1995).

Work usually requires close interaction with people, particularly for those employed in the retail, hospitality, transportation, health-care, and education sectors. One study of 45,000 nurses reported that 68 percent had suffered physical violence, ranging from slaps to jaw-breaking punches (Picard, 1995). When a police officer is touched, the suspect is automatically charged with assault or resisting arrest. When a nurse, who is far more vulnerable and victimized, is attacked it is seen as part of the job.

Employees are increasingly concerned about aggressive clients and violent patients. Violence has been consistently identified by workers in the service sector as a growing problem. Aggression is no longer considered acceptable as an inherent part of the job, and workers across the continent are increasingly reporting acts of violence in the workplace.

---

*This chapter was written by Mary D. Smith, CRSP. Portions were contributed by Gerry Goldberg and Kim Ankers.

WHAT ACTION HAS BEEN TAKEN?

Although most provinces have heard from stakeholders in health care and residential facilities about the need for a specific regulation to govern safety in that sector, only two provinces have addressed the issue. Saskatchewan has enacted legislation as part of the Occupational Health and Safety Act.

However, British Columbia's regulatory language may become a template for other jurisdictions as the demands for action increase. The regulation defines violence as:

> *the attempted or actual exercise by a person, other than a worker, of any physical force so as to cause injury to a worker, and includes any threatening statement or behaviour which gives a worker reasonable cause to believe that the worker is at risk of injury (s.8.88).*

The legislation, which applies to any place of employment, requires that a risk assessment be performed and that is include previous experiences with violence in the workplace. Policies and procedures must be developed to eliminate or minimize the risk. Procedures are to include reporting, investigating, and documenting violent incidents, in the same manner in which accident reporting is handled. All information must be provided to the joint health and safety committee (if one exists) or posted in the workplace.

The employer is required to educate workers and to inform them of persons who have a history of violence; to inform a worker of the nature of the risks the worker is likely to encounter; to provide training in appropriate response to a violent incident; and to control or minimize the risk of violence. The legislation applies only to violence exhibited by a party outside the workforce. Violence between workers is still viewed as a criminal matter.

COSTS OF WORKPLACE VIOLENCE

Violence is costly. Functional capabilities are affected by the fear, anxiety, and insecurity associated with potential or actual exposure to violence. The reactions of staff who are confronted or injured by acts of violence range from short-term psychological trauma to post-traumatic stress disorder. When the attacker is a student/patient/resident for whom the employee is responsible, common reactions include anger, depression, shock, disbelief, apathy, self-blame, fears of returning to work, compassion for the aggressive person, and a change in relationships with co-workers.

VIOLENCE PREVENTION AND CONTROL

If employers in the service sector are not responsive to the impending crisis, workers will rely increasingly on the compensation system. In the past, many violent acts causing injuries were treated as part of the job. Now, workers are encouraged by the publicity surrounding the issue to report violence-related injuries to the workers' compensation system. (Many of these workers are members of limited or restricted professions—e.g., hospital and nursing-home staff, ambulance attendants, and classroom teachers—where the right of refusal is denied.) The increased cost of doing business may force the employers to take a more proactive stance against violence in the workplace.

Some workplace violence can be prevented by designing facilities, such as barriers between workers and the public, that reduce the incidence of violence. Well-lit corridors and clear aisles provide good sight lines. Video cameras and signs announcing their use have proven effective.

Some organizations have even established policies of zero tolerance; the Ontario Ministry of Education and Training requires all school boards to institute policies of violence-free educational institutions.

Others have trained employees to identify and report violence, and protect themselves. Sears Canada provides its employees with a booklet outlining reporting procedures. Shoppers Drug Mart trains employees what to do in the event of a robbery. Others have trauma counsellors on standby; Home Depot has a crisis management team that arrives within one hour of the incident.

♦ ♦ ♦
INDOOR AIR QUALITY

Concerns about indoor air quality started to surface in the 1970s and have continued to rise since then. At first, these concerns coincided with energy-conservation efforts. Designers and building owners intent on saving precious energy dollars were determined to improve building insulation and sealing techniques. So successful were their efforts that the occupants of buildings were soon breathing a greater proportion of recycled air and a reduced amount of outdoor air.

Another concern had to do with the increasing use of chemicals in synthetic building materials. The slow release of these chemicals into the indoor environment has been associated with *sick-building syndrome* and its attendant complaints, which include headaches, dizziness, fatigue, disorientation, and eye, ear, and throat irritation (Mansdorf, 1993).

Indoor-air-quality concerns centre on office buildings. The ventilation standards that exist in most jurisdictions for industrial and mining settings do not extend to residential, office, or institutional buildings. White-collar employees are becoming increasingly vocal about their concerns. In Ontario, local public health units and various ministry inspectors investigated over 2000 indoor-air-quality complaints between 1976 and 1988 (Rajhans, 1989). These investigations do not begin to represent the total picture. One large organization, employing health and safety professionals, investigated over 200 complaints in a single year (Smith, 1988). These complaints are not reflected in the government numbers.

CONTROL MECHANISMS

Four methods exist for controlling sick-building syndrome: (1) elimination of tobacco smoke; (2) provision of adequate ventilation; (3) maintainance of the ventilation system; and (4) removal of sources of pollution.

Building codes in most provinces provide legislated criteria for all new buildings. There is increasing demand for air-quality standards and a normalized protocol for the investigation of air-quality concerns (Kendall, 1994). The control and reduction of chemical emissions from building materials, furnishings, and consumer products may have to be regulated. Further research into the effect of indoor air contaminants on humans is needed. In the meantime, management can refer to the *Canadian Standards Association Guideline for Managing Indoor Air Quality in Office Buildings* (Z204), which focuses on design, operation, and preventative maintenance.

The occupational safety and hygiene department at one municipal corporation had a traditional indoor-air-quality program in place for five years. The surveys and literature research done as part of this program failed to show any connections between the concerns registered and the measured problems. Looking for a way to solve this dilemma, the hygiene staff embarked on a program of risk management A target group of 200 employees received training in techniques and concepts of indoor air quality. The operational units were given detailed information about the mechanical ventilation systems in their buildings. Preliminary results indicate a reduction in indoor-air-quality concerns. (James, 1994)

◆ ◆ ◆
COMMUNICABLE DISEASE IN THE WORKPLACE

The issue of communicable disease in the workplace is a controversial one. Public health legislation in the various jurisdictions is constantly changing to reflect advances in science. Diseases that in the past necessitated home isolation for long periods now require only short isolation periods during which the disease is considered infectious. Immunization by inoculation is available for many serious communicable diseases. Less serious communicable diseases include athlete's foot, giardia lamblia (diarrhea), herpes simplex (cold sores), impetigo, and influenza. There is no reference in health and safety legislation to communicable disease.

WORKER RIGHTS

The issue of communicable disease in the workplace has been raised primarily in the area of work refusals. (The right to refuse unsafe work was discussed in Chapter 2.) Workers have invoked this legislated right with varying degrees of success. In New Brunswick, a worker refused to work beside another worker who had a transmissible skin infection (*McLean v. Humpty Foods*, 1994). The court found in favour of the plaintiff, who had been laid off as a result of the refusal.

A slightly different case occurred in a workplace governed by federal legislation (*Fontain v. Canadian Pacific Ltd.*, 1989). The Canadian Human Rights Tribunal ruled that discrimination on the basis of a physical disability under Section 7(a) of the Canadian Human Rights Act would include a person who had human immunodeficiency virus (HIV). The tribunal found that the complainant had been constructively dismissed (i.e., the inhospitable workplace climate had left him no reasonable option but to depart). Under public health and human rights laws, employers are required to give reasonable accommodation to the person through job restructuring and modified work schedules.

The Canada Labour Relations Board recently ruled on an appeal of a Labour Canada inspector's decision that no danger existed when a correctional officer refused to work with inmates who had contracted HIV or hepatitis B (HBV). The board found that there was no evidence that ordinary contact could lead to HIV infection. Under the Canada Labour Code, the mere suspicion that there is a hazard is not sufficient to allow a refusal to work. The board dealt with the HBV evidence by ordering the employer to vaccinate correctional officers and provide the necessary safety education.

HIV AND HBV

Should HIV and HBV be occupational concerns? Statistical data would suggest that occupational factors play a minimal role in the transmission of HIV (Bertollini, 1992). Both HIV and HBV are transmitted through blood or body fluids. HIV is fragile and cannot survive for long outside the body environment. HBV, on the other hand, is extremely hardy and can remain stable for days or weeks. The number of HBV cases rose from 5 in 100,000 to 11.3 in 100,000 in 1990 (Baxter, 1992). Although a vaccine is available, its efficiency life has yet to be determined.

To protect those in high-risk occupations (e.g., health-care, laboratory, and dental workers), Health and Welfare Canada and the U.S. Department of Health and Human Services have developed a protocol called "universal precautions." In lay terms, universal precautions means assuming that all blood and body fluid may contain infectious material. Precautions include washing hands, wearing protective clothing or equipment, and immediately disposing of materials (e.g., needles) that may be contaminated with blood or body fluids. These precautions should be practised by all workers at all times.

◆ ◆ ◆
COMMITMENT TO OCCUPATIONAL HEALTH AND SAFETY

For many decades, occupational health and safety issues in Canada have been taking on increasing prominence. Tolerance for occupational risks that were once accepted continues to decline. Media attention on wellness issues, increasing OHS legislation, union and consumer activism, and new discoveries made through research are among the factors that have contributed to this decline. Community standards have changed and illnesses and shorter lives are no longer acceptable within the Canadian mining industry.

One reason for a decreasing tolerance of occupational risks is that concern for personal health and safety (on and off the job) seems to be growing. Government, educational institutions, and mass media are responding with programs that reflect this interest and increased awareness of factors that influence wellness.

In the mid-eighties, factors cited as central to the evolution of safety activism included union activist, consumerism, attitudes of the courts, medical research, escalating equipment costs, and increasing legislation (Bird and Germain, 1990). During the last ten years, issues relating to provincial worker's compensation boards have emerged to keep health and safety an important workplace issue. Increasing costs of compensation are seriously threatening most provincial systems of compensation and adding to the costs of Canadian goods and services. Some jurisdictions are increasing the employers' responsibility to get injured workers back to work by making them more liable for compensation of lost earnings. Not only does this increase the financial burden for employers, but it also requires them to address wider issues. Compensation boards are also recognizing broader definitions of occupational illness.

In response to the challenges posed by escalating compensation costs, health and safety professionals need to demonstrate both the cost-effectiveness of specific health and safety programs and their overall relationship to productivity. Many organizations have already reaped the rewards of cost-benefit analysis. For example, one program that dealt with emotional disorders among airline personnel yielded a return of $16.35 for every dollar invested; Firestone Tire and Rubber realized savings of $1.7 million or $2350 per person involved in their program (Jensen, 1986). The benefits of fitness programs have become so compelling that many organizations are considering making them mandatory or providing bonuses to those who use them.

The cost-effectiveness of health and safety initiatives, combined with growing public interest in wellness issues, bodes well for future commitment to occupational health and safety.

◆ ◆ ◆
SUMMARY

The phenomenon of workplace violence appears to be growing, particularly in the service sector. Prevention and reduction strategies include incorporating safety principles in the workplace design, training employees in self-protection and reporting, and introducing a zero-tolerance policy.

Indoor-air-quality complaints have increased in recent years. The proliferation of chemicals in sealed buildings has given rise to the sick-building syndrome. Installation and maintenance of ventilation systems, elimination of tobacco smoke, and the removal of pollutants are all effective control strategies.

Communicable disease in the workplace is a controversial issue. Workers who believe that their health and safety may be jeopardized by working with someone believed to have a communicable disease are invoking the right to refuse unsafe work. Education, personal hygiene, and universal precautions are among the protective measures that should be adopted by workers in high-risk occupations.

Commitment to occupational health and safety is growing, driven by such factors as cost-benefit analysis, worker/public interest in health and safety issues, and declining tolerance for occupational risks.

E X E R C I S E S

1. The next time you visit a retail store (preferably one that is part of a large chain), observe the safety measures that have been adopted to protect employees against workplace violence. Ask the employees if the store has an anti-violence policy, and if they know what to do if a customer becomes abusive or if the store is robbed.

2. Describe at least five ways to reduce the number of complaints about the quality of indoor air.

3. Explain how you, as manager of the human resource department, would handle a work refusal by employees who declared that their health was being placed at risk by the presence of a co-worker with a communicable disease.

4. Describe any efforts recently undertaken by your organization or school that would indicate an increasing awareness of, and commitment to, occupational health and safety.

References

Baxter, J.A. *Hepatitis B: A Summary of the Occupational Health Concern*, P86-14E. Hamilton, Ont.: Canadian Centre for Occupational Health and Safety (CCOHS).

Bertolloni, R. 1992. *Acquired Immune Deficiency Syndrome (AIDS): A Summary of the Occupational Health Concern*, P86-8E. Hamilton, Ont.: Canadian Centre for Occupational Health and Safety (CCOHS).

Hancock, M. 1995. "Violence in the Retail Workplace." *Accident Prevention* (May/June): 15–21.

James, K. 1994. "A Fresh Approach to Air Quality Complaints." *Occupational Health and Safety Canada* 10, no. 3, (June): 48–55.

Jensen, M.A. 1986 "Emotional Disorders and the Labour Force." *International Labour Review* 125, no. 5 (September/October).

Kendall, P.R.W. 1994 (September). *Indoor Air Quality: Issues and Concerns.* Toronto: Department of Public Health.

Mansdorf, Z. 1993. "Indoor Air Quality: A Modern-Day Dilemma." *Occupational Hazards* 55, no. 3 (March): 11–14.

Picard, A. 1995. "Abuse Suffered by Nurses Hurts Health Care." *The Globe and Mail*, October 24, A2.

Rajhans, G.S. 1989. *Draft Report on the Interministerial Committee on Indoor Air Quality (Ontario)*. Presented at the ASHRAE/SOEH Conference, IAQ, April 17–20.

Smith, M.D. 1988. "A School Daze." *Occupational Health and Safety Canada*, 4, no. 6 (November/December): 34–35.

Appendix I

◆ ◆ ◆
LIST OF OCCUPATIONAL HEALTH AND SAFETY ORGANIZATIONS

This appendix identifies significant organizations and their general roles. For a more comprehensive listing, please consult the "Canadian Handbook of Health and Safety Training" (Templegate Information Services: Toronto, 1992).

GOVERNMENT RESOURCES

Human Resource and Development Canada
    Occupational Health & Safety
    Hull, PQ   K1A 0J2
    Support for federal government departments across the country.

Alberta Occupational Health and Safety
    10709 Jasper Ave, Edmonton, AB   T5J 3N3
    Provides a number of services that can help employers and committee members establish relevant training programs.

British Columbia Occupational Safety and Health
    Educational Services, Worker's Compensation Board of BC
    6951 Westminster Highway, Richmond, BC   V7C 1C6
    Responsibility for promoting development of safety and health education programs in industries.

Manitoba Government
    Education Branch, Workplace Safety and Health
    1000–330 St. Mary Ave, Winnipeg, MB   R3C 3Z5
    Responsible for administering the provincial OHS legislation. Provides education, materials, and consultants.

New Brunswick Government
  Occupational Health and Safety Commission, Department of Labour and Human Relations
  PO Box 6000, Fredericton, NB   E3B 5H1
  Coordination of provincial activities including education and training.

Newfoundland Government
  Occupational Health and Safety, Department of Labour
  PO Box 4750, St. John's, NFLD   A1C 5T7
  Under provincial legislation, the department is obligated to provide education and training.

Nova Scotia Government
  Occupational Health and Safety Division, Department of Labour
  PO Box 697, Halifax, NS   B3J 2T8
  Coordination of training and educational services.

Ontario Ministry of Labour, Workplace Health and Safety Agency
  121 Bloor St. E, 9th floor, Toronto, ON   M4W 3M5
  Oversees the work of safety associations to deliver curriculum of training for certified members of health and safety committees. Associations work independently to deliver programs, products, and consulting services.

Prince Edward Island Government
  Occupational Health and Safety Division, Ministry of Labour
  PO Box 2000, Charlottetown, PEI,   C1A 7N8
  Primarily involved in inspections and consulting services.

Quebec Government
  Commission de la santé et de la securité du travail (CSST)
  1199 rue de Bleury, PO Box 6056, Station A, Montreal, PQ
  Administered by both management and labour, it covers the functions of the government safety branch and the workers' compensation board. Services include training, materials, and programs.

Saskatchewan Government

Occupational Health and Safety, Ministry of Labour and Employment
1870 Albert Street, Regina, SK   S4P 3V7
Provides a number of services related to information, education, and consulting.

Appendix 2

OCCUPATIONAL HEALTH AND SAFETY ACCREDITATION ORGANIZATIONS

Organizations to which Canadian health and safety professionals may apply for accreditation, or for active membership in support of certification programs, are listed herein. Specific information may be obtained from the registering agency.

PROFESSIONAL ASSOCIATIONS

American Industrial Hygiene Association (AIHA)
Continuing Education Department, PO Box 8390, 345 White Pond Drive, Akron, OH   44320
Offers chapters and professional hygiene courses and continuing education credits to members.

Association of Canadian Registered Safety Professionals (ACRSP)
6519–B Mississauga Rd., Mississauga, ON   L5T 1M5
Designates general safety professionals (CRSP) who have completed a 6-part registration program and examination.

Canadian Board of Occupational Medicine
1040 Riverside Dr., Suite 46, London, ON   N6H 5C8
Certifies physicians who have achieved an acceptable standard of competence in the practice of occupational medicine.

Canadian Council for Occupational Health Nurses Inc.
260 Hearst Way, Suite 240, Kanata, ON   K2L 3H1
Establishes criteria and standards required for nurses who wish to qualify as a CCOHN (Canadian Certified Occupational Health Nurse).

Canadian Institute for Radiation Safety (CAIRS)
555 Richmond St. W, Ste 1106, Toronto, ON   M5V 3B1
An independent, not-for-profit national institute dedicated to radiation safety.

Canadian Registration Board of Occupational Hygienists
c/o Occupational and Environment Health Unit, University of Toronto, 150 College St., Toronto, ON   M5S 1A8
Provides a formal examination process for the designation Registered Occupational Hygienist (ROH), a combination of academic and work-related experience.

Canadian Society of Safety Engineering (CSSE)
330 Bay St. Suite 602, Toronto, ON   M5H 2S8
Association of health, safety, and environmental professionals dedicated to loss prevention; provides preparatory exam for CRSPs, oversees Canadian Occupational Health and Safety Week, Educational Trust Fund and Awards.

Certified Health & Safety Consultants (CHSC)
330 Bay St. Suite 602, Toronto, ON   M5H 2S8
Accreditation for consultants in OHS (CHSC). Formal certification process involving prerequisites and training courses at postsecondary level.

Occupational Hygiene Association of Ontario
6519-B Mississauga Road, Mississauga, ON
Supports accreditation process for occupational hygienists.

Ontario Occupational Health Nurses Association (OOHNA)
302 The East Mall, Etobicoke, ON
Provides annual conference for members.

ASSOCIATIONS, SOCIETIES, AND LABOUR ORGANIZATIONS

Alliance of Health & Safety Professionals of Ontario
6519-B Mississauga Rd., Mississauga, ON   L5T 1M5
Group of several regional safety associations who serve to lobby provincial government regarding OHS issues.

American Industrial Hygiene Association (AIHA)
Continuing Education Department, PO Box 8390, 345 White Pond Drive, Akron, OH   44320
Offers chapters and professional hygiene courses and continuing education credits to members.

Association of Canadian Registered Safety Professionals (ACRSP)
6519–B Mississauga Rd., Mississauga, ON   L5T 1M5
Certifies general safety professionals (CRSP) who have completed a 6-part registration program and examination. No courses are endorsed, but a preparatory course is available from the Canadian Society of Safety Engineering.

Association de securité des pates et papiers du Québec
1200 Germain-des-pres Ave., Bureau 102, St. Foy, PQ   G1V 3M7
Offers guidance and training courses to members regarding WHMIS and other health and safety matters.

Association paritaires
Various, *see* CSST Quebec
A variety of associations under the auspices of the Commission de la santé et de la securité du travail du Québec.

BC Construction Industry Health and Safety Council
4336 Dominion St, Burnaby, BC   V5G 4M7
Assists member firms to develop comprehensive health and safety programs and delivers information and training courses.

Canada Safety Council
  6–2750 Stevenage Dr., Ottawa, ON   K1G 3N2
  A nongovernment, not-for-profit organization that operates in conjunction with provincial councils. Offers courses in traffic safety, defensive driving, and driving improvement.

Canadian Board of Occupational Medicine
  1040 Riverside Dr., Suite 46, London, ON   N6H 5C8
  Certifies physicians who have achieved an acceptable standard of competence in the practice of occupational medicine.

Canadian Centre for Occupational Health and Safety
  250 Main St. E, Hamilton ON
  Established in 1980s. Provider of reliable information on hazardous chemicals and other hazards. Plays role in supporting and facilitating training.

Canadian Council for Occupational Health Nurses Inc.
  260 Hearst Way, Suite 240, Kanata, ON   K2L 3H1
  Establishes criteria and standards required of nurses who wish to qualify as a CCOHN (Canadian Certified Occupational Health Nurse).

Canadian Institute for Radiation Safety (CAIRS)
  555 Richmond St. W, Ste 1106, Toronto, ON   M5V 3B1
  An independent, not-for-profit national institute dedicated to radiation safety.

Canadian Labour Congress
  2841 Riverside Dr., Ottawa ON K1V 8X7
  Collates information and provides safety seminars.

Canadian Registration Board of Occupational Hygienists
  c/o Occupational & Environment Health Unit, University of Toronto
  150 College St., Toronto, ON   M5S 1A8
  Provides a formal examination process for the designation registered occupational hygienist (ROH), obtained through a combination of academic and work-related experience.

Canadian Society of Safety Engineering (CSSE)
> 330 Bay St., Suite 602, Toronto, ON   M5H 2S8
> Association of health, safety, and environmental professionals dedicated to loss prevention; establishes National Training Standards, and certifies OHS consultants (CHSC). Also oversees Canadian Occupational Health and Safety Week, Educational Trust Fund and Awards.

Certified Health & Safety Consultants (CHSC)
> 330 Bay St., Suite 602, Toronto, ON   M5H 2S8
> Accreditation for consultants in OHS. Formal certification process involving prerequisites and training courses at postsecondary level.

Mines Accident Prevention Association of Manitoba
> 700–305 Broadway, Winnipeg, MB   R3C 3J7
> Provides services to members.

Occupational Hygiene Association of Ontario
> 6519-B Mississauga Road, Mississauga, ON
> Supports accreditation process for occupational hygienists.

Ontario Occupational Health Nurses Association (OOHNA)
> 302 The East Mall, Etobicoke, ON
> Provides annual conference for members.

Ontario Health and Safety Associations
> Various.
> Under the Ministry of Labour (Workplace Health and Safety Agency), sectoral associations providing training, materials, and consultants. Includes the following: Construction Safety, Electrical Utilities (Municipal and Transport) Safety Associations; Farm Safety Association; Industrial Accident Prevention (and Tourism) Association; Ontario Natural Resource Safety Association; Workers' Health and Safety Centre.

Petroleum Industry Training Service
> 2115–275h Avenue NE, Calgary, AB   T2E 7E4
> Provides members with specialized training.

Quebec Metal Mining Association
704–2 Place Quebec, PQ   G1R 2B5
Health and safety courses for members.

Saskatchewan Construction Association
1939 Elphinstone St, Regina, SK   S4T 3N3
Seminars and information for employees in construction industry.

Saskatchewan Trucking Association
Professional Driver's Safety Council, 1335 Wallace St.,
Regina, SK   S4N 3Z5
Administration of professional driver courses.

Welding Institute of Canada
391 Burnhamthorpe Road E, Oakville, ON   L6J 6C6
A nonprofit organization providing technical assistance, research,
training, and education services to members of welding industry.

Index

◆

To the owner of this book

We hope that you have enjoyed *Occupational Health and Safety,* and we would like to know as much about your experiences with this text as you would care to offer. Only through your comments and those of others can we learn how to make this a better text for future readers.

School _____ Your instructor's name _____

Course _____ Was the text required? _____ Recommended? _____

1. What did you like the most about *Occupational Health and Safety?*

_____
_____
_____

2. How useful was this text for your course?

_____
_____
_____

3. Do you have any recommendations for ways to improve the next edition of this text?

_____
_____
_____

4. In the space below or in a separate letter, please write any other comments you have about the book. (For example, please feel free to comment on reading level, writing style, terminology, design features, and learning aids.)

_____
_____
_____
_____

Optional

Your name _____ Date _____

May Nelson Canada quote you, either in promotion for *Occupational Health and Safety* or in future publishing ventures?

Yes _____ No _____

Thanks!

PLEASE TAPE SHUT. DO NOT STAPLE.

TAPE SHUT

TAPE SHUT

FOLD HERE

Nelson

MAIL ⇒ POSTE
Canada Post Corporation
Société canadienne des postes
Postage paid   Port payé
if mailed in Canada si posté au Canada
Business Reply   Réponse d'affaires
0066102399   01

0066102399-M1K5G4-BR01

TAPE SHUT

TAPE SHUT

NELSON CANADA
MARKET AND PRODUCT DEVELOPMENT
PO BOX 60225 STN BRM B
TORONTO ON M7Y 2H1